Aluminium in Changing Communities

Aluminium
in Changing Communities

H. D. Huggins

ANDRE DEUTSCH

in association with
INSTITUTE OF SOCIAL & ECONOMIC RESEARCH
UNIVERSITY OF THE WEST INDIES

FIRST PUBLISHED 1965 BY
ANDRE DEUTSCH LIMITED
105 GREAT RUSSELL STREET
LONDON WC1
COPYRIGHT © 1965 BY H. D. HUGGINS
ALL RIGHTS RESERVED
PRINTED IN GREAT BRITAIN BY
TONBRIDGE PRINTERS LTD

Flow-Chart: BAUXITE to ALUMINIUM

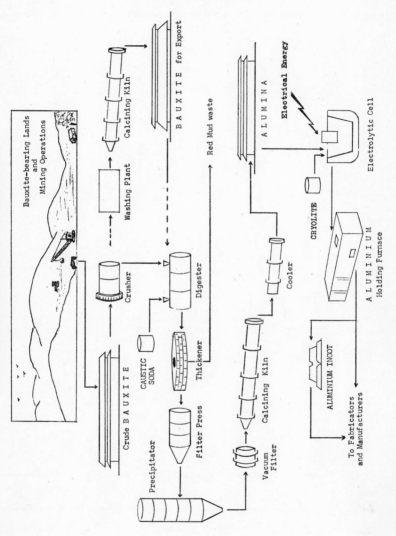

Flow-Sheet: BAUXITE to ALUMINIUM

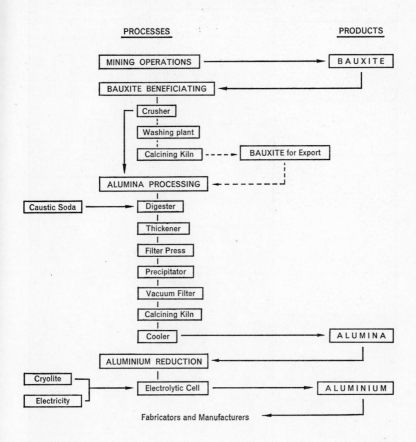

The flow sheet indicates the stages through which the ore (bauxite) passes to become the metal aluminium which ultimately passes into the hands of the fabricators and manufacturers.

Under BAUXITE BENEFICIATING the flow, indicated by broken lines, refers to the process normally in use when bauxite is shipped as bauxite. The other flow, refers to the process usually in use when the bauxite is converted locally into alumina.

Diagram of Western World Production, 1961

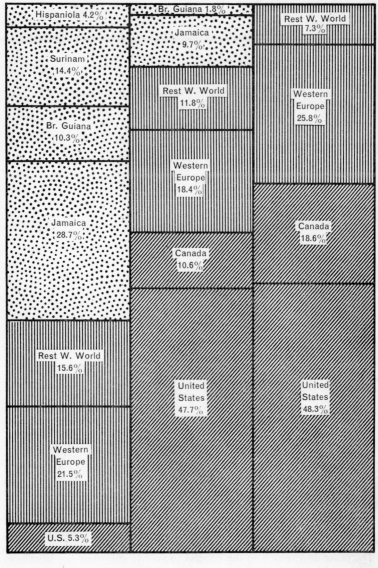

Bauxite   Alumina   Aluminium

Preface

The present study has its origins partly in the circumstance that I have found the economics of the aluminium industry interesting, particularly interesting in those aspects which appear to influence the policy of location of the manufacture of alumina. In addition to being interesting in its own right, the aluminium industry is of much significance to the Caribbean.

The Caribbean is also of much significance to the industry. Until quite recently the deposits of the ore in Jamaica were the greatest known to be in any one country, territory or island. In 1960 the North American producers in the industry secured 81 per cent of their requirements of the raw product from the Caribbean (including Surinam and British Guiana) and in that year North America and Western Europe secured 56 per cent of their combined requirements of the raw product from the Caribbean.

The history of how this study came to be undertaken begins with the circumstance that a Guggenheim Fellowship and a Visiting Research Professorship at Yale University made it possible for me to spend the academic year 1957–58 in the United States. Shortly after I took up residence there the Director of the International Bank's Economic Development Institute in Washington, Mr Michael Hoffman, invited me to give a lecture to his group on the aluminium industry. I discovered that my knowledge of the industry was indeed slight. Reading and discussions which followed convinced me that there were few people (outside of the staffs of the several aluminium enterprises) whose knowledge of the economics of the industry was not also slight. It was at this time that the 'episodes' which I refer to in Chapter II attracted so much public attention and that the Canadian protest against alleged dumping made the aluminium industry a much discussed subject. This in some ways marked the beginning of a new era in the history of the aluminium industry in general, and particularly in the history of the North American producers. Caught up in the rigours of administration and committee work I did little on the study for about three years. Then I spent the summer of 1962 in the United Kingdom, in Germany, in France and in Brussels studying the ramifications of the industry in Western Europe and learning in discussion much that can be learnt in no other way. I found it rewarding to hold discussions with people in the Aluminium Federation in the United Kingdom, with others in Aluminium Zentrale in Düsseldorf, in Vereingte Aluminium Werke in Bonn, in Metallgesellschaft in Frankfurt, in Giulini in Ludwigshafen, in L'Aluminium Francais in Paris, in the European Economic Community in Brussels, and with representatives of companies in New York, in Montreal and in Jamaica, in British Guiana and Surinam.

The name which I have given to the study is *Aluminium in Changing Communities*. The word 'communities' is used in two senses. One is the normal and usual meaning of a people of a particular region. Here the 'particular region' refers to the Caribbean. Like so many comparable communities the Caribbean has undergone great change in the post-war era of the 1940s to the 1960s; the attitudes of peoples within this and similar communities have changed and the attitudes of the world at large have changed to these communities. There has been and continues to be an interplay of social change with economic development. In some of these communities there are certain export enterprises which are financed by external capital, which are directed to export markets and which have a dominant role in domestic economies – enterprises like sugar, oil, tin, bauxite. One of the fields in which there has been notable and needed change is in the attitudes of those who make policy in such export-oriented enterprises. Much of this study concerns itself with the policy of one of these export enterprises (bauxite-alumina) in a very changing community (the Caribbean).

The second sense in which 'communities' is used in the name of the study refers to certain economic communities in and to which the end products of the aluminium industry are significant. One such tightly-knit aluminium economic community is North America together with the United Kingdom (the greatest consumer of aluminium in Western Europe). It was an aluminium economic community in which trade was free, and up to the later 1950s expansion and relationships were orderly. And then there came about vast changes in relationships in the North America-United Kingdom aluminium Community. In the 1950s also new economic communities came into being in Western Europe – the European Free Trade Association and the European Economic Community – which promised to have marked effect on policy relating to production and marketing of aluminium. It is mainly with some of these changes that this study has concerned itself. In 1963 Britain was refused admission to the European Economic Community. I argue that, as far as the Caribbean aluminium enterprises are concerned, this refusal to admit the United Kingdom to the European Economic Community is not as significant as one might at first think.

Anyone who wishes to understand the working of the aluminium industry will find it helpful to remember that there are three main products involved in the three stages of aluminium production:

THE ORE   (mostly bauxite, mechanical process involved)
ALUMINA   (white powder, chemical process involved)
ALUMINIUM (the metal, electrolytic process involved).

These stages are given in rather more detail in Diagrams 1 and 2 (pages 5 and 7). This division of processing operations into three enterprises – bauxite, alumina and aluminium – forms the motif on the dust-jacket, and is the central theme of the study. There are three vertical bars on the dust-jacket. The one at the top left depicts the suppliers of bauxite by countries in 1961; that in the middle, suppliers of alumina; that at the right, suppliers of aluminium. In each diagram blue represents the Caribbean; dark grey, North America; silver, the rest of the Western World. These three bars encompass what the study is about: The Caribbean supplied some 58 per cent of the Western world's supplies of bauxite in 1961, but only 12 per cent of alumina and no aluminium. The 1961 output of bauxite in the Western world is valued at some £60 millon and in this the Caribbean (used throughout the study to include British Guiana and Surinam) has a dominant role. The value added for the manufacture of alumina from this bauxite is some £150 million or nearly three times the value of the output of bauxite. In the second stage the Caribbean participates only to a modest extent (12 per cent of alumina compared with some 58 per cent of bauxite). The value added in the third phase – production of aluminium – is some £470 million in which the Caribbean does not participate at all. To these relationships there are two footnotes: one is that Surinam has a scheme under way for the production of aluminium; the other is that because the reduction of alumina to aluminium is so dependent on electric power, it is not feasible to produce aluminium in Jamaica, despite its large deposits of bauxite, unless or until a cheap source of power becomes available. This explains why the study has in consequence concerned itself mostly with the story told by the vertical bar in the middle (alumina); less with the vertical bar at the left (bauxite); and with the vertical bar at the right (aluminium) only to the extent that aluminium policy affects bauxite and alumina. Should at some future time someone embark on the production of hydro-electric power in British Guiana or should nuclear energy become competitive in price for the production of electricity, examination of possible implications of the third stage of the process (aluminium) would doubtless receive more attention than is the case in this study.

Acknowledgements

I have to make acknowledgement to two groups and each has contributed in a different way. One group consists of bodies which made this study possible:

a. The Institute of Social and Economic Research, University of the West Indies, out of whose budget the cost of much of this study has been met, as well as the whole of the cost of the visit to the United Kingdom and Europe in 1962;

b. The Guggenheim Foundation which, in awarding a Fellowship, was primarily responsible for making this study possible;

c. The Economics Department of Yale University for having invited me to spend the academic year 1957–58 as a Visiting Research Professor at the University;

d. The International Bank's Institute for Economic Development which invited me in 1957 to give a lecture on the aluminium industry and which thus started me on work on this study;

e. Aluminium Federation (London), Aluminium Limited (Canada) and Aluminium Zentrale (Düsseldorf) whose libraries helped me track down many items of information.

The second group to which I must make acknowledgement consists of individuals who have influenced this study. Of this group Mr Dennis McFarlane and Dr A. Kundu and Mrs Norah Mailer gave me much guidance in the breakdown of the national account figures. Without their help (guidance would be the better word) I could not have attempted the breakdown and analysis on which Chapter V is based. Mr S. M. Chhangur has worked closely with me in the collection and computing of the statistics. While these individuals have helped in the directions which I indicate, the interpretation is mine alone and no one else should be held responsible for the interpretation which I have put upon the figures. There are others whose views I have received either in correspondence or in discussion, who have to some extent influenced my thinking but who also cannot in any way be held responsible for the conclusions at which I have arrived. Among these are:

a. my colleagues in the Institute of Social and Economic Research and in the Department of Economics who helped in seminar discussion and/or in criticizing the manuscript, including: Professor Charles Kennedy, Dr George Cumper, Dr David Edwards, Mr Alistair McIntyre, Mr Clive Thomas, Mr Roy Chang, Dr George Eaton, Mr Michael Faber;

b. people with whom I have held discussions on the staff of: Aluminium Limited, Reynolds, Kaiser, Surinam Aluminium Company, OECD, L'Aluminium Française, Giulini, Metallgesell-schaft, Vereinigte Aluminium Werke, Bundes Ministerium für Wirtschaft (Bonn), Queensland Agent General's Office (London);

c. Mr Dudley Seers (whose concern with the role of export industries which dominate the domestic economy – like oil in Venezuela – helped stimulate his interest in the present study);

d. Mr R. A. Healing of the Overseas Geological Surveys (London), Mr H. P. Jacobs, President, Historical Society, Jamaica, and Mr K. B. Higbie of the U.S. Bureau of Mines, who have been of great help in aiding me with sources of information.

Finally I wish to thank the members of my family, my wife, my son and my daughter for the stimulation they gave throughout the long period which has elapsed between the start of this study and its appearance in print. My daughter, Anne, worked long and close with me in the summer of 1962 in Düsseldorf, Bonn and Frankfurt and the knowledge of the industry which she acquired was of great help.

Contents

Part Two: The Interaction of Developments in America, Europe and the Commonwealth Caribbean

List of Tables

19

Chapter V

Introduction

Weathering of aluminium-bearing rocks can lead to residual hydrated aluminium oxide. The resulting soil or rock if it consists of a high proportion of the oxide is called bauxite. An arbitrary limit observed in the industry is that a clay contains less than 32 per cent of recoverable alumina (the oxide); bauxite contains 32 per cent or more. Three types of hydrated aluminium oxide, gibbsite, boehmite and diaspore have a fairly well defined geographical distribution. The bauxites of the humid tropical and sub-tropical regions in the Caribbean, Africa, Asia, the Pacific (also the United States, which was warmer, geologically speaking, relatively recently) are made up mostly of gibbsite (Table I).

TABLE I *Properties and Distribution of Hydrated Aluminium Oxide*

	Gibbsite	Boehmite	Diaspore
Name	Trihydrate	Alpha Monohydrate	Beta Monohydrate
Parts of world in which there is a preponderance	Zone near the equator – including North and South America, Africa, South Asia, Australia, the Caribbean	Belt north of gibbsite zone including the Mediterranean region	Belt north of boehmite zone – including Russia, China, Hungary

Bauxites in which boehmite predominates are in the Mediterranean, with diaspore still further north. The colour of the ore varies from white and other light shades to brown or red depending on the proportion of iron compounds. While ores of varying composition are found in different parts of the world it is in the warmer regions that most of the really massive deposits have been discovered. Since in general the warmer countries of the world have thus far lagged behind in technological expertise it has meant

23

that the main producing countries of bauxite have not been the main manufacturers and consumers of aluminium.

In the early days of the industry most of the world's production of bauxite came from Europe and in Europe there was one producer of consequence – France. There were two other small producers, Ireland and Italy, but France's output was 90 per cent of Europe's total in 1900 and an even higher proportion by 1913. The First World War brought about a radical change. Not only did France's output decline relatively as well as absolutely but at one period it was below that of either Italy or Austria. Reacting to the war's demand for bauxite, the European output rose considerably higher than in 1911 but it was German together with Austrian and Hungarian supplies which markedly changed – from nothing at the outbreak of war to some 70 per cent of Europe's total in 1917. This change left the United Kingdom-French war effort with little bauxite. The United States miners made good use of the opportunity and by 1917 they had more than tripled their 1911 output, to a figure higher than the production of all Europe. One effect of this was to quicken the interest in bauxite deposits in the Western Hemisphere both in the United States and abroad. It was at this time, in British Guiana, that rich deposits which had been discovered and described some years before were first exploited. In 1917 British Guiana became the first producer in the Western Hemisphere, outside of the continental United States, and it remained the only such producer until after the end of the war. In 1922 Dutch Guiana also began exports to North America.

With the end of the war, demand for supplies of bauxite fell markedly and it was only in 1923 that world production again reached that of 1917. In the re-adjustment after the war Europe regained from North and South America her traditional place of main producer. Europe, producing one-quarter of the world's supplies of bauxite at the end of the war (with America producing three-quarters), essentially reversed the position and from the mid-twenties up to the beginning of the Second World War Europe yielded well over half of the world's consumption of bauxite. By the 1920s and 1930s, the structure of the European suppliers was restored in a reasonable image of the original, with France again dominant. It is true that France's output, over 60 per cent of Europe's total in 1931, fell to a little over 30 per cent by 1939 but Hungary's supplies being then the next in importance were only 60 per cent those of France. In America a different pattern had developed. Up to the end of the First World War the United States were almost the sole producers in the Americas. There was little change in the total output of the Americas between the years 1918 and 1928 but the Guianas (British and Dutch) while supplying a negligible quantity of bauxite in 1918 had in 1928 become a bigger producing region than the United States. The significance, in world supplies, of the territories bordering the Caribbean was not at first realized since European production continued to dominate the world position right up to the Second World War. In 1938 Europe's production was well over twice that of the Caribbean territories and the rest of the Americas combined.

In the Second World War as in the First there was a sharply rising demand for the ore and this, as in the First World War, Europe was unable to meet. In response a substantial increase in output took place in the United States. There was also a rise in production in the Guianas in the early years of the war but so destructive were the U-boat raids on shipping in the Caribbean that in 1944 the bauxite exports from the Guianas had fallen back almost to the 1939 level while United States production had increased sevenfold.

With the end of the war and with the sustained demand, increased production in Surinam and British Guiana returned sharply and Surinam attained and maintained leadership in world production. There was now the urge to find sources complementary to those in South America. Known and new deposits were examined and large scale geological studies undertaken to determine their quantity and quality. It was in this context that the Jamaica deposits, later found to be the biggest in the world, began to be worked.

Consumption of Bauxite

Bauxite is used primarily for the production of alumina, about 92 per cent of bauxite going into alumina. Of the 8 to 10 per cent of bauxite which is not used for alumina most is used in the chemical industry, for cement, refractory manufacture, oil refining (Table II).

TABLE II *Total (Domestic and Foreign) Bauxite Consumption in the U.S.*

Purpose for which used	Per cent total of bauxite consumed in the U.S.[1]					
	1956	1957	1958	1959	1960	1961
Alumina	92.1	91.3	92.6	93.1	91.6	93.2
Abrasive	3.6	4.2	2.6	2.5	3.2	2.2
Chemical	2.4	2.6	3.1	2.8	3.4	2.7
Refractory	1.1	1.1	0.9	1.0	1.1	1.3
Other	0.8	0.8	0.8	0.6	0.7	0.6
	100.0	100.0	100.0	100.0	100.0	100.0

1. Bureau of Mines, U.S.; *Minerals Yearbook: Minerals and Metals (except Fuels).*

Part I

Early and Orderly
Developments in the Industry

1 The Location of Alumina Plants — Some Causes and Effects

This discussion of the location of alumina production attempts to examine some of the relationships which have special reference to the British Commonwealth Caribbean territories and, more particularly, to Jamaica. This is not intended as a general study of the aluminium industry but the fact is that the Caribbean bauxite and alumina activities are an integrated part of the operations of North American aluminium firms. To see in perspective the Caribbean part of the industry and some of the causes and effects of the policy of the location of alumina production, one must keep in view events in North America and further afield. While the Canadian aluminium interests were always international in their outlook, both in the purchase of raw materials and in the export of the finished products, the United States companies have only slowly become international; and from the last quarter of the 1950s they became much more international in their activities than they ever were previously in peace-time.

In consequence it becomes necessary in looking at this question of alumina policy to examine the relationships between domestic (Caribbean), metropolitan (United States and Canada) and international happenings as if they were a composite whole. But in order to make the discussion manageable reference is made to the metropolitan and international factors mainly when they are relevant to the central argument – the effects on the Caribbean. Material which appeared to interfere with the flow of the central argument was extracted and put into self-contained appendices.

With the processes now in commercial use the production of alumina is one of the following four stages in the aluminium industry: (i) the mining of the ore, bauxite; (ii) the extraction by a chemical process of aluminium oxide or alumina from bauxite; (iii) the reduction, by an electrolytic process, of aluminium oxide (alumina) to the metal (aluminium), massive and cheap supplies of electric power being required for this process; (iv) conversion of aluminium, in the fabrication stage of the industry, into the industrial shapes and forms required on the market. There is no discussion in the present study of stage (iv).

Some alumina enters the chemical industry as hydrate of alumina (e.g. for conversion into aluminium sulphate for the paper industry, for water purification, for treatment of sewage and trade effluents, for waterproofing of textiles, or for the manufacture of catalysts used in the petro-chemical industries). Corundum, a form of alumina, has a hardness just a little less than that of the diamond and consequently abrasives are another source of demand. Use of alumina in refractories and special types of cement arises from the high melting point of alumina (2,040° C.) and its resistance to chemical attack. Alumina is also used in ceramics (e.g. gas radiants, imitation fire logs) and in high quality glassware. The requirements for high temperatures by jet and rocket units have sharply increased the demand for alumina through the ceramic insulation industry.

While these demands are not unimportant[1] about 95 per cent of the alumina produced in the United States goes into the production of aluminium. One of the major factors influencing location of alumina plants has thus far been proximity to aluminium smelters. Thus smelters in 1953–54 in the United States, Canada, U.S.S.R., France, West Germany and Norway constituted 86 per cent of the world's reduction plants and the capacity of the alumina plants in these six countries was 86 per cent of world alumina manufacturing capacity. Of these countries, only the United States, the U.S.S.R. and France produced bauxite in sizeable proportions – respectively 12 per cent, 6 per cent and 8 per cent of the world's total production in that period. On the other hand such major producers of bauxite as Surinam, British Guiana, Jamaica, with nearly 50 per cent of the world's bauxite had, until 1952, no alumina plants[2] in production. Historically, the availability of cheap and abundant electric power has controlled the location of smelters and also influenced the location of alumina plants. This has happened although the alumina process is essentially a chemical one and the electric energy (mainly thermal) required is relatively small.

1. Alumina is used in the United States in approximately the following proportions: for aluminium production (95%), chemicals (3%), abrasives (1%), refractories, ceramics (1%).
2. Alumina production began in Jamaica at the close of 1952, in British Guiana at the close of 1960.

Policy and the Location of Alumina Plants (up to the end of the Second World War)

The United States Producers
and some Determinants of Alumina Policy

Alumina production for the United States industry is closely bound up with the history of a small number of firms which are vertically integrated. For much of the industry's history and until 1941 the Aluminum Company of America, a vertically integrated firm, was the sole manufacturer of aluminium and alumina. The United States Government initiated anti-trust proceedings against this company, Alcoa, in 1937. It was only in 1945 that the case reached the appellate court and the judge handed down the now famous ruling that Alcoa, at the time that proceedings were begun, was an illegal monopoly[1] in the field of ingot production. In the interval the war had induced an expansion of smelter capacity in the United States of about one million tons (aluminium) about 60 per cent of which the Government owned. The court was conscious that the disposal of Government facilities in a manner such as to foster competition would influence the future structure of the industry, and so the court indicated that to this end there should be a judicious disposal of Government facilities. So effectively did the Government pursue its purpose that Alcoa, which had provided all the United States aluminium ingot in 1940, had a share amounting to only 50 per cent ten years later. With the increased demand of the war and the favourable climate for more competition in the industry, the Reynolds Metals Company, as an integrated producer, had entered the industry in 1941. Kaiser entered in 1946–1947. Both of these companies secured plants including alumina plants at something like 30 cents in the dollar.[2]

While the main measure of Alcoa's control of the market was ingot production, the anti-trust ruling had, understandably, far-reaching implications for alumina. The expansion programme left the Government at the end of the war, in 1945, with 54 per cent of the country's alumina capacity and 59 per cent of the smelting

1. The basis for this conclusion was that an appraisal of power in the market was the critical measure of monopoly, not a history of predatory conduct.
2. Thus Kaiser obtained for $36 million facilities which were estimated at 20 per cent of the then replacement costs. (Equity 85–73 Defendant's Exhibit No. 158, p. 24498, U.S. vs. Alcoa *et al.*, District Court of the U.S., Southern District, New York.)

capacity. The Government, acting on the court's ruling, proceeded to encourage firms which might have a chance of competing, both in the scale of operations and degree of integration. Each new entrant if it was to survive, the reasoning ran, must have recourse to alumina independent of Alcoa, and be vertically integrated so that each owned not only reduction but alumina facilities. Since the Government had only two alumina plants available for disposal, this effectively limited the number of firms attracted into the industry through the policy adopted towards surplus property. As Reynolds had been established in 1941, Kaiser was the only new entrant who may be said to have been influenced by the policy of disposal. Not only was the number of entrants limited but from the course of events both of the new entrants secured larger alumina capacity than their reduction facilities required. Kaiser obtained an alumina production plant of 700,000 tons a year to cater for its smelter capacity of 130,000 tons of ingot a year. Reynolds obtained a 750,000 ton alumina plant and, since they were already vertically integrated, they secured alumina capacity far in excess of requirements.[1] It was not simply that only one new firm, Kaiser, was added and that the market had moved from a monopoly to a Big Three but also that it still was not easy for the medium-sized firm or the firm which was not vertically integrated to enter the industry. Increases in the demand for aluminium were likely to be met by an additional number of pot-lines in the existing smelters of the existing firms. New firms were likely to survive only if the demand was brisk enough to absorb the supplies of the Big Three (including the increased output which these could effect with relatively modest expansion in capital and personnel) in addition to the output of the new vertically integrated entrant which must, of necessity, meet certain minimum requirements of scale. So substantial an increase in demand had, in the past, occurred only in the face of war or the threat of war. Conscious of this historical relationship the Government made great effort to induce new entrants by way of a guaranteed market over a five-year period and through accelerated amortization. Despite this, under the second round of expansion after the end of the war, the Big Three were allocated 92 per cent

1. It must have given small comfort to the advocates of a competitive industry that this major step to implement the Justice Department's behest should have been associated with the emergence of only one new producer, Kaiser. For a thoughtful discussion of this see Krutilla, John V. 'Aluminum, A Dilemma for Antitrust Aims?' *The Southern Economic Journal*, Vol. XXII, No. 2, 1955.

of the aluminium guaranteed market and the only other new entrant, Anaconda, obtained 8 per cent.

This inability to secure the entry of more new firms into the United States industry stems in great measure from the Government's pre-occupation with establishing vertically integrated firms. There is little doubt that the Government's success in facilitating the establishment of vertically integrated giants effectively limited the entry of new firms. Not only should the demand and promised demand be ample to attract the new firm but the new and independent firm could not expect to survive unless it were itself vertically integrated. Economies of scale affect mainly the alumina stage in production and an anti-trust policy which discouraged, rather than subsidized, vertical integration might have had quite different results. In 1956 it was still only the Big Three that were producing alumina in the United States; Ormet came into production later. Anaconda, a manufacturer of aluminium, secured its alumina, through a contract, from Reynolds and later from Kaiser (Table I.1).

Many chemical processes, including alumina extraction, effect substantial economies of scale. There must be large reduction and fabricating facilities if there is to be balanced production in an integrated firm.[1] But, the massive scale of total operations is determined essentially by the need to take advantage of economies of scale in alumina extraction. It is recognized that in the reduction process (from alumina to aluminium) the same considerations do not apply and that major economies do not result from scale.[2] It is typical that electrolytic and electric furnace processes usually have industrial application simply in the multiplication of small units. The reduction of alumina to aluminium is an electrolytic process in which essentially the output of the metal is proportional to the electric current used. It is feasible to use only a limited amount of current in an aluminium cell (an aluminium reduction pot is essentially a large electric cell) so that the optimum size of the individual cell is comparatively small. Hence if one aims for higher production one simply multiplies cells and there is approximately the same ratio of labour to output in the small as in the big plants. It is also true that in the smelters the proportion of energy to output is little affected by scale. Savings in labour and power have occurred but these derive from improvements in the design and

1. Krutilla, *op. cit.*
2. Wallace, Donald H. *Market Control in the Aluminum Industry*, p. 190.

TABLE I.1 *Alumina Capacity, Distribution by Industrial Groups in the United States*

	Alcoa		Reynolds		Kaiser		Ormet		The U.S.	
	Tons '000	% Total Capacity	Tons '000	% Total Capacity	Tons '000	% Total Capacity	Tons '000	% Total Capacity	Tons '000	%
1956	1,434	46	978	31	714	23	—	—	3,126	100
1958	1,255	36	1,140	33	759	22	322	9	3,476	100
1959	1,590	37	1,304	30	1,143	26	322	7	4,359	100
1960	1,590	37	1,304	30	1,143	26	322	7	4,359	100
1961	1,590	35	1,498	33	1,143	25	322	7	4,553	100

B

operation of the cells rather than from larger size of plants.[1] Hence in the reduction process capital tends to increase almost proportionately with output. It is even more true that at the fabrication stage there is wide variation in the scale of operation. Thus firms have rolling mills which range from 2,000 to 300,000 tons annual capacity. This holds in other forms of fabrication and is reflected in the existence of some 17,000 establishments which are able to survive, doing business in fabrication.[2]

As far as alumina extraction is concerned, Wallace[3] writing in the 1930s considered that after an alumina plant had become large enough (15,000 – 18,000 tons a year capacity), further enlargement simply meant duplication. He mistakenly concluded that cost would not vary appreciably between such a plant and larger plants. Wallace based his conclusion on a study published in 1930, a description of a plant in 1918, a personal visit to one plant, and 'one authoritative opinion'. In 1945, Engle, Gregory and Mosse estimated that on the basis of early 1940 prices there was a 20 per cent difference in cost between a 100,000 and a 500,000 ton a year alumina capacity.[4] Krutilla[5] considers that the difference was even greater and draws attention to an unpublished study estimating the cost of producing alumina at three different levels: 300, 500 and 1,000 tons a day. Admittedly the results could not be accepted as identical with costs derived from units which were designed to operate at these several levels, but the experimental results tried to omit all facilities not necessary at the lower levels of production. The conclusion from the experimental estimates was that the 300 and 500 tons output a day level had a unit cost 27 and 14 per cent respectively above the 1,000 tons output a day level. All in all the evidence is indicative that a smaller number of alumina plants than of metal smelters is required to supply, economically, a given requirement of the metal. Thus Alcoa, the one producer in the industry in the United States, had concentrated its alumina facilities

1. Wallace, *op. cit.*, observes that 'the reduction plant seems to present a clear instance of broad limits within which unit cost would vary hardly at all due to change in scale'.
2. A Study of Monopoly Power, Hearings before the Sub-Committee on Study of Monopoly Power, of the Committee of the Judiciary, House of Representatives, 82nd Congress, 1st Session, Serial No. 1, Part I, Aluminum (and quoted by Krutilla, p. 168).
3. Wallace, *op. cit.*
4. Engle, Gregory, Mosse. *Aluminum, An Industrial Marketing Appraisal.* Irwin, Chicago, 1945.
5. Krutilla, *op. cit.*

and, until 1938, operated only one alumina plant to meet the needs of its three reduction plants.

One may trace the history of the policy towards the location of alumina plants by considering another series of events. During the First World War the American producing company, beginning to supplement its requirements of bauxite by mining in British Guiana, could envisage neither economic, political nor traditional justification to erect an alumina plant in the Caribbean. The idea of establishing an alumina plant in British Guiana was not only raised with but pressed upon the Americans. When interest in the bauxite lands of Guiana was first aroused, the Americans, aware that the British Aluminium Company might be a possible competitor, proceeded with vigour ('persistent negotiation, litigation and compromise')[1] to secure control of most of the deposits which were either in public or private ownership in that territory. Aided by this threat of competition the British administration attempted to put pressure on the American interests to establish by 1923 an alumina plant on British territory. British Guiana thought and expected that the negotiations, while using the broad phrase 'British territory', meant in effect an alumina plant on British Guianese soil. The Americans agreed but, doubtless regarding their consent as given under duress, proceeded to implement their promise only in so far as it might be said that they kept the letter of the law. Their associate company established in 1928 an alumina plant on British soil – on the St Lawrence in Canada.

The American company's reservation about starting alumina manufacture in the Caribbean was understandable in the 1920s. It could with reason fear that, when the market readjusted itself after the war, France would rehabilitate her industry and there would then be the question of the extent, if any, to which the United States would need supplies of ore from overseas. For years after, the company had reason to think its fears well-grounded because up to 1923 the United States was almost entirely self-sufficient in ore and for the three-year period 1926–28 was a net exporter. With the depression of the 1930s the ore supplies coming into the United States from abroad were in 1935 little more than half those in 1925. While these imports, in absolute terms, were lower at the end of the 1925–35 decade, the position in relative terms had changed greatly. Up to the years just before 1925 the United States was largely self-sufficient but reliance on supplies from the Guianas thereafter was firmly estab-

1. Wallace, *op. cit.*, p. 70.

lished (Table I.2). By the early 1940s when the second United States company, Reynolds, had entered the industry the American producers were being shown how hazardous submarines could make the sea trip between the Guianas at the eastern end of the Caribbean and the Gulf Ports at the western. With the tradition (against the location of alumina plants overseas) established in peace now strengthened by the experiences of war, change to a new American outlook was, in 1940, improbable and Reynolds located its alumina facilities at Listerhill, Alabama (Table I.3). By this time the demand for aluminium had become pressing. The United States Government decided to take the lead in expansion and the military found no more justification than the private industrialists for locating alumina plants elsewhere than in the continental United States. As the war ended the policy of disposal of Government surplus property made it more unattractive than ever to locate extraction plants abroad. The new companies which were the producers that might conceivably take a new look at the policy of plant location were offered subsidized excess alumina plant capacity. This excess capacity was in operation in the United States and was added inducement to keep alumina processing in the United States.

TABLE I.2   *United States Self Sufficiency in Bauxite*[1]

Year	Self Sufficiency[2] %	Year	Self Sufficiency %
1925	47	1952	32
1926	58	1953	27
1930	45	1954	29
1935	55	1955	27
1938	41	1956	23
1940	41	1957	17
1943	80	1958	14
1946	56	1959	17
1949	30	1960	18
1950	35	1961	12
1951	40		

1. U.S. Bureau of Mines, *Materials Survey – Bauxite*, p. xi, 4 and *Mineral Industry Surveys*. (For the years 1938–60.)
2. Self sufficiency = (Domestic production × 100) divided by (Imports + domestic production).

TABLE I.3 *Capacity of Alumina Plants in North America*

(Capacity '000 tons)

Year	Alcoa			Reynolds Metals Co.				Kaiser	Ormet		Alcan
	Bauxite Ark. 1952*	East St Louis 1903*	Mobile Ala. 1938*	Point Comfort 1958*	Hurricane Creek 1943*	Corpus Christi 1953*	Lister Hill 1941*	Baton Rouge 1943*	Gramercy 1959*	Burnside 1958*	Arvida Canada 1928*
1939		N.A.	N.A.								N.A.
1940		N.A.	N.A.								N.A.
1941		N.A.	286				89				N.A.
1942		N.A.	N.A.				89				N.A.
1943		342	587		580		89	446			N.A.
1944		375	580		694		89	446			978
1945		375	580		695		89	446			N.A.
1946		375	580		695		89	446			N.A.
1947		N.A.	N.A.		N.A.		closed	N.A.			893
1948		N.A.	N.A.		N.A.			N.A.			N.A.
1949		N.A.	N.A.		N.A.			N.A.			N.A.
1950		163	538		465			393			N.A.
1951		163	538		554			393			N.A.
1952	357	163	587		652			393			1,027
1953	358	293	782		652	326		696			N.A.
1954	358	293	782		652	326		714			1,041
1955	358	293	782		652	326		714			1,071
1956	358	293	782		652	326		714			1,071
1957	375	closed	880		652	489		759			1,140
1958	375		880	335	652	489		759		322	1,140
1959	375		880	335	652	652		759	384	322	1,140
1960	375		880	335	652	652		759	384	322	1,140
1961	375		880	335	716	782		759	384	322	1,140

* Year of start of production.

The Canadian Producer
and some Determinants of Alumina Policy

The Pittsburgh Reduction Company (later Alcoa) began aluminium operations in Canada in 1900 and the Northern Aluminum Company became in 1925, the Aluminum Company of Canada. Alcan became a subsidiary of the holding company, Aluminium Limited which, registered in Canada, took over much of Alcoa's property outside of the United States. From the outset the Canadian company received an orientation towards international operations, including the necessity to look to external sources for their ore. This background made it probable (certainly more probable than in the case of the United States companies) that the Canadian company would have found it expedient to locate some alumina production overseas. Nevertheless, even up to the end of the Second World War these considerations had not affected the policy of Aluminium Limited. Aluminium Limited extracted its alumina at Arvida in Canada although it relied on its supplies of ore entirely from abroad, mainly from British Guiana. Even the decision of Canada to restrict to the mainland its conversion of bauxite to alumina was due perhaps in part to the policy of Aluminium Limited, traditionally in such close relationship with Alcoa. There may also have been lacking the disposition for bold adventure required for the initial step in locating a chemical plant such as an alumina unit in an under-developed territory such as the Caribbean rather than at home.

Policy and the Location of Alumina Plants (the late 1940s to the late 1950s)

The United States Producers
and some Determinants of Alumina Policy

When the war ended in 1945 the United States Government owned two alumina plants. The background of the acquisition of one plant by Reynolds and the other by Kaiser has already been discussed.

At the war's end there were grounds for pessimism as to the future of the industry.[1] By 1947 it looked as if these forebodings

1. Aluminium, as a commercial product, was conceived as a war baby and it took two world wars to provide the stimulus for vigorous growth. Bearing this history in mind, when the end of hostilities came in 1945, many feared that production in the industry would contract. The requirements for aluminium capacity in the United States in 1945 were more than three times those at the beginning of the war. Edward S. Mason, in his book, *Controlling World Trade*,

TABLE I.4   *Estimated Requirements of Alumina for Reduction to Aluminium in North America*

Year	Alumina Required[1]		Year	Alumina Required[1]	
	Canada '000 tons	U.S. '000 tons		Canada '000 tons	U.S. '000 tons
1938	121	245	1950	677	1,225
1939	140	279	1951	762	1,427
1940	186	352	1952	852	1,598
1941	365	527	1953	931	2,135
1942	581	889	1954	957	2,491
1943	845	1,569	1955	1,032	2,660
1944	788	1,324	1956	1,054	2,852
1945	368	844	1957	946	2,799
1946	330	699	1958	1,084	2,659
1947	510	975	1959	1,018	3,319
1948	626	1,063	1960	1,293	3,422
1949	630	1,029	1961	1,247	3,247

were justified because demand in the industry fell off sharply in 1945 and 1946. By 1949 the National Security Resources Board, on the basis of a survey, reported that an adequate alumina capacity was available and that the limit to further production (if wanted) was electric power for the smelters. In the immediate post-war period any company bargaining with the Government for the industry's war surplus plants could argue effectively for generous treatment. The general acceptance of the argument explains, in part, the liberal terms on which the Government disposed of its alumina producing equipment and related assets to private interests.

There were in 1945 few signs that new uses (peace-time, war and

p. 193 (McGraw Hill, 1943) wrote: 'No conceivable expansion in consumption can eliminate the vast excess production capacity that already exists for . . . aluminum . . . In fact despite continued high requirements, government-owned aluminum . . . plants were already closing down before the end of the war. The Tariff Commission foresees a maximum domestic consumption of . . . aluminum . . . might reach 700 million lb yearly as compared with the existing capacity of 2,300 million lb.' This consumption was about 5,000 million lb by 1960.

1. The conversion factor used is 1.91 tons alumina to 1 ton aluminium. See *Materials Survey – Aluminium*, p. V, 6.

the threat of war) would urge still more massive expansion upon the industry, but in 1949 the Government agreed to begin stock-piling aluminium and expansion was on. The outbreak of hostilities in Korea in 1950 helped. By the end of the year the Government agencies calling for so high an increase in output found it necessary to assure producers of a tax allowance providing for total amortiz-ation of capital invested in new facilities. There was, in addition, other financial support (such, for example, as substantial Govern-ment advances out of stock-pile funds) which was enough sometimes to meet total costs of construction. As a result the requirements for alumina capacity in the United States in 1955 were over three times those in 1945 (Table I.4).

In the 1940s and the early 1950s firms in the United States aluminium industry had gained both on the swings and on the roundabouts. At the end of the war they had received war surplus plants on terms partly conditioned by fear of contraction in the industry, and by 1949–50 were receiving even more generous finan-cial aid to encourage expansion. It is not easy to discover figures on alumina capacity for earlier years. The figures (Table I.3) show the capacity of the individual companies which make up the North American industry. It is seen that Alcoa, Reynolds, Kaiser and Ormet each built one or two new alumina extraction plants since the Korea expansion.[1] Not only is it not surprising that this ex-pansion occurred and that new alumina plants arose but it would have been surprising if they had not. What is notable is that all of the United States firms decided to locate their new alumina plants within the United States.

As previously shown, when the single United States producer, before and during the First World War, required expanded alumina facilities the United States was relatively self-sufficient in regard to supplies of bauxite. In the 1950s it was different (Table I.5). The geological surveys had shown that Jamaica[2] had extensive deposits

1. The two other American companies with smelters were Harvey which imported alumina from Japan and Anaconda which had an arrangement for supplies with Reynolds, later with Kaiser.
2. The relatively recent recognition of these deposits took a strange course. Nearly twenty years before Hall in the United States and Héroult in France independently discovered the means of commercially producing the aluminium metal and so ushered in a new industry, geologists in the 1860s drew attention to the alumina content of the red soils in Jamaica. In 1938, the Jamaica Depart-ment of Agriculture troubled by low crop and livestock yields on these red soils recognized that these agricultural lands were in reality low-grade bauxite. Later, the Jamaica Government, not having a geologist of its own, invited

of bauxite – then the known biggest in the world. The two United States firms which were mining bauxite in Jamaica expanded their alumina capacity by building new alumina plants in the 1950s – Reynolds in 1953 and Kaiser in 1958 – but neither elected to locate an alumina plant in the Caribbean. Some of the considerations which, one surmises, must have contributed to such a decision are:

Security Reasons: In the 1940s the sinking of ships carrying bauxite from the Guianas to North America was one of the major problems of the war. It was a worrying enough experience for the United States aluminium reduction units to be dependent on ore from overseas and, one argument runs, it would have been even more so if, in addition, caustic soda and other material would have had to be transported to the Caribbean for alumina production. On the other hand if the problem was shipping – and it was[1] – there would be some argument for conversion to alumina near the source of the ore since only one ton of alumina would have to be transported for two to three tons of bauxite.

A second argument on grounds of security was that alumina capacity located in the United States should be adequate to meet the current or immediately future needs for aluminium and to process domestic ores which the country might wish to fall back on in time of crisis. In 1950, the year of Korea-induced expansion, United States production of aluminium was somewhat under

Aluminium Limited as their agent to carry out a systematic geological recon- naissance and this survey showed that bauxite was widespread. Aluminium Limited organized a subsidiary (Jamaica Bauxites Limited) and Reynolds came later, followed by Kaiser, still later by Alcoa.

Aluminium Limited and its subsidiaries would seem to have led in this exploration and in opening up the new mining industry in Jamaica, but Reynolds (in its publication: *Reynolds Jamaica Mines Ltd., its Origin and Development*, 1943–53) claims credit for much of the pioneering work in Jamaica and for the drive in bringing bauxite into commercial production. Thus, Reynolds reported to the Governor of Jamaica that its 'preliminary investigation indi- cates bauxite reserves of more than 100 million tons in contrast to the prevailing view at the time that there were between 5 and 10 million tons' (p. 4). 'If the Aluminum Company of Canada expects to mine only 3,000,000 tons of bauxite . . . If there is even a possibility that 100,000,000 tons may be found on the entire island . . .' and 'Reynolds Metals Co. was apparently virtually alone (1943) at the time in its willingness to develop and try to use Jamaica bauxite' (p. 14).

1. Reynolds Metals Co., *op. cit.*: 'The problem during World War II was not of bauxite reserves, but of shipping and processing facilities . . . The prime concern was not for more reserves but for ways and means of getting the bauxite to the United States ports.'

TABLE I.5   *Bauxite Production in North America, The Caribbean
and South America, 1917–1961*

Percentages of combined output of North America, Caribbean, South America
produced in:

	North America	Haiti	Dominican Republic	Jamaica	British Guiana	Surinam	Brazil
1917	99.64				0.36		
1918	99.31				0.69		
1919	99.48				0.52		
1920	94.32				5.68		
1921	91.85				8.15		
1922	94.36					5.64	
1923	81.85				15.71	2.44	
1924	61.63				27.36	11.01	
1925	54.91				30.36	14.73	
1926	63.07				29.93	7.00	
1927	48.40				24.26	27.34	
1928	49.97				22.02	28.01	
1929	48.28				24.44	27.28	
1930	46.53				16.83	36.64	
1931	39.86				25.46	34.68	
1932	34.00				22.06	43.94	
1933	52.69				12.33	34.98	
1934	52.65				15.74	31.61	
1935	52.46				23.83	23.71	
1936	48.23				21.58	29.32	0.87
1937	37.93				26.83	34.47	0.77
1938	29.02				35.13	34.66	1.19
1939	27.34				34.67	36.68	1.31
1940	26.31				37.41	36.28	0.00
1941	29.51				32.88	37.16	0.45
1942	51.67				23.76	23.99	0.58
1943	63.31			0.02	19.19	16.55	0.93
1944	64.65				20.92	14.10	0.53
1945	41.89	0.02			28.52	28.75	0.82
1946	35.93	0.01			36.45	27.47	0.14
1947	28.11				30.34	41.40	0.15
1948	26.68				34.30	38.75	0.27
1949	22.91				35.04	41.73	0.32

TABLE I.5   *Bauxite Production in North America, The Caribbean and South America, 1917–1961—cont.*

	North America	Haiti	Dominican Republic	Jamaica	British Guiana	Surinam	Brazil
1950	26.78				31.77	41.09	0.36
1951	28.44				30.81	40.45	0.29
1952	21.99			4.49	31.49	41.85	0.18
1953	19.19			14.02	27.43	39.17	0.19
1954	20.50			20.90	23.68	34.65	0.27
1955	18.01	0.00		26.65	24.53	30.36	0.45
1956	16.13	0.00		28.55	22.96	31.72	0.64
1957	11.94	2.22		38.74	18.56	28.02	0.52
1958	11.01	2.35		48.05	13.32	24.70	0.57
1959	13.09	1.96	5.85	39.47	12.89	26.00	0.74
1960	13.61	1.82	4.62	39.12	16.87	23.15	0.81
1961	8.33	1.78	4.90	45.20	16.11	22.73	0.95

750,000 tons. Its alumina capacity in 1951 was over 2 million tons, i.e. nearly a million tons excess alumina capacity.[1]

A third argument was that the military could be expected to be conservative in experimenting overseas with the processing of a strategic raw material like alumina and it was improbable that, in the late 1940s when these decisions were being taken, Caribbean representatives had the degree of experience required to argue the case with United States logistics experts. The circumstances in the late 1940s and early 1950s surrounding the United States Government's encouragement for an expansion programme (including stock-piling, financing, allocation of certificates) gave organizations like the Office of Defence Mobilization ways and means of ensuring that their wishes in the aluminium industry were respected. While aware of the wishes (and the power to use its influence) of the United States Government, one must not conclude that the individual producers did not have room for manoeuvre. Even if security considerations carried much weight earlier, by the time that the expansion of the 1950s was taking place peace-time considerations were already imposing an appropriate influence.

1. At that level of production the ore from domestic sources was already only one-third 'self sufficiency' (Table I.2).

The argument – that the Caribbean territories possessing the bauxite deposits should, for United States security reasons, be denied the development of alumina extraction facilities – is difficult to support if the Reynolds method of financing its Jamaica expansion is to be defended. Reynolds sought at first to finance this expansion with aid from the Colonial Development Corporation and later with Marshall Plan funds. The Colonial Development Corporation did not accept the invitation to participate but the Marshall Plan authorities loaned some £4 million and this (p. 28 of the Reynolds statement) was enough to cover in full the costs of the Reynolds Jamaica project. The Marshall Plan was established to encourage, and did encourage, the building of production facilities in countries even more likely to be vulnerable if there were an outbreak of hostilities in the Western World. Oil, presumably, is no less strategic than aluminium and United States firms have not hesitated to invest in oil refining in the Caribbean.

Security reasons were not alone responsible for the decision of United States firms not to locate alumina plants in the Caribbean.

Costs: It may well be that in considering their long run profits the United States firms found it necessary to give more consideration to the wishes of the Government than a straightforward analysis of cost-pricing would justify. Having examined the influence of the Government, one needs next to consider whether the United States firms, although erecting new plants in the 1950s (some explicitly for Jamaica bauxite), refrained from the location of alumina production in the Caribbean because, or in spite, of cost factors.

For the United States firms the problems of costing of alumina plants in the rapid peace-time expansion were considerably simplified because of the undervalued fixed costs which resulted from the method of acquisition of alumina plants and from other hidden subsidies. The extra capacity in alumina would appear at first to explain sufficiently why the United States firms would not contemplate location of alumina plants in the Caribbean, but on this question Reynolds has some relevant comments: '. . . because of its peculiar chemical and physical properties, Jamaica bauxite cannot now be processed economically in existing alumina plants.'[1] Then in 1950[2]: 'While Reynolds was then preparing to use Jamaica bauxite in a section of its (existing) alumina plant it had not yet

1. Reynolds Metals Co. Economic Research Department, *op. cit.*, p. 15.
2. *Ibid.*, p. 36.

had any regular processing experience with Jamaica bauxite. If it decided to build a conventional alumina plant to use already proven bauxite, it would have meant a correspondingly smaller use of Jamaica bauxite.'

Reynolds solved the problem by building a new alumina plant 'which has been using Jamaica bauxite ever since'.[1] The older plant was in Arkansas, the new plant in Texas. The new plant with a capacity of 330,000 tons in 1953 was planned to expand to 730,000 tons. Kaiser, the other United States firm operating in Jamaica, had acquired an alumina plant at Baton Rouge which they adapted to the combination system to use Jamaica bauxite. In addition, Kaiser established in 1958 a new alumina plant, in Gramercy (also in Louisiana) whose entire bauxite requirements, it was expected, would be supplied from Jamaica.[2] Alcoa's main source of supplies of bauxite continued to be Surinam so that the technological difficulties of processing the Jamaican type of bauxite was not a problem as far as they were concerned.

Up to the outset of the 1950 expansion the existence of excess alumina capacity could well have been a determining factor, but in the 1950s separate new and independent alumina plants with a new technique were being erected. Hence, as far as overhead costs were concerned, the problems for consideration would not be greatly different whether the new plants were established in the United States or in Jamaica.

In special reference to variable costs, there is a carefully documented study carried out in 1956 by Dr Peter M. Stern.[3] He compiled structures of comparative cost for hypothetical plants in Jamaica and at a port in the United States on the Gulf of Mexico. He found the aluminium industry 'close-mouthed about the structure of its operations' but believed that he had found enough checks to make the cost data plausible and comparable. The estimates in Table I.6 show the variable costs. The estimates of variable costs apply to the delivery of a short ton of alumina manufactured from Jamaica bauxite and delivered at a United States Gulf Coast aluminium plant. The estimates are that such a ton of alumina costs $45.49 if manufactured at a Gulf Coast port and $39.91 if manfactured in Jamaica, a difference in favour of Jamaica production of

1. *Ibid.*, *p.* 36.
2. Kaiser Aluminum and Chemical Corporation. *Prospectus*, June 26, 1957, p. 10.
3. Stern, P. M. *The Bauxite Industry in Jamaica*, May 1956 (unpublished).

$5.58 per ton. Table I.7 shows the differential in costs when the alumina is delivered to smelters in different geographical areas.

TABLE I.6   *Estimated* (1956) *Comparative Variable Costs of Producing One Short Ton Alumina, U.S. Dollars*[1]

		Location of Plants	
		U.S. Gulf Coast $	Jamaica $
(1)	Cost of Jamaica bauxite[a]	14.21	14.21
(2)	Transport of bauxite to alumina plant[b]	10.88	
(3)	U.S. port charges[c]	2.90	
(4)	U.S. duty on bauxite (suspended)[d]		
(5)	Labour[e]	5.40	2.70
(6)	Fuel[f]	3.10	4.62
(7)	Administration and miscellaneous costs (including costs of soda ash, lime, starch, filter cloth)[g]	9.00	9.00
(8)	Transport to Gulf Coast reduction plant[h]		3.38
(9)	U.S. port charges		1.00
(10)	U.S. duty on alumina		5.00
(11)	Variable costs of one ton of alumina delivered at Gulf Coast plant	45.49	39.91

1. Based on Stern, P. M., *op. cit.*, Table VIII.

a Cost of mining, drying and delivering 2.9 tons bauxite (12.13 per cent moisture) to port, Jamaica.

b 2,500 miles round trip at costs given by Johnson, A. F. 'Cost Factors in the utilization of Foreign Bauxite to make Aluminum', *Mining Engineering*, June 1954, p. 600.

c Johnson, A. F., p. 599.

d Kurtz, H. F., Blue, D. D. *Bulletin* 556, 1955, p. 14. Bureau of Mines, Washington.

e Blue, D. D. 'Raw Materials for Aluminum Production', 1954, Bureau of Mines Information Circular 7675, Washington.

f Blue, D. D., p. 4. The Reference is to natural gas in the United States, oil in Jamaica.

g Johnson, A. F., p. 602. A part of administration should be allocated to fixed costs but it is not easy to disentangle these.

h Johnson, A. F., p. 600.

TABLE I.7   *Differential[1] in Variable Costs of Jamaica Alumina Delivered to Smelters at Different Locations*

	Differentials (in favour of Jamaica made alumina) between variable costs of 1 short ton of alumina manufactured from Jamaica bauxite in a United States plant and in Jamaica
Site of Smelter	$ $
A. Gulf Coast Port	5.58 + 5 (tariff suspension)
B. U.S. Pacific Northwest	7.64 + 5 (tariff suspension)
C. Ohio Valley	4.44 + 5 (tariff suspension)

The differentials, higher for smelters in the Northwest and in the Gulf Coast, are slightly lower for the Ohio Valley, but substantial for all three locations. These locations are representative of operations of the United States aluminium industry. The relatively low differential for the Ohio Valley is due to high internal United States rail charges on Jamaica alumina.

Tariff: When Stern in 1956 carried out his calculations on the relative costs of manufacture of alumina in the United States and in Jamaica, there was in force a tariff amounting to $5 per short ton of alumina imported into the United States. He thought this tariff one of two important reasons why the United States companies did not embark on alumina production in the Caribbean. This tariff has since been suspended so that the differentials shown would, on the basis of the 1956 figures, be increased by $5 in each case.[2] The estimates indicate that, with the removal of the tariff,

1. Stern, P. M., *op. cit.*, Tables VIII, IX, X.
2. In 1956 Public Law 725 suspended for the first time the duty on alumina entering the U.S. (see *Mineral Markets Reports* MMS No. 2683, 1957, Bureau of Mines, Washington). This suspension therefore came into force after the U.S. firms had taken their decisions about the location of their alumina plants in the post-1950 expansion period and could not presumably influence those decisions. On the other hand, while one used to hear a good deal from the industry in the early 1950s about the restrictive force of the alumina tariff there seems to have been no major problem in securing its suspension as soon as producers so desired. The suspension preceded the agreement, signed in 1957, by Harvey Aluminum Co. to import 105,000 short tons of alumina a year for 5 years from the Sumitomo Chemical Co. of Japan. Harvey has its smelting facilities in the U.S. Northwest and was the first American company to operate entirely on alumina produced in a foreign country.
One might add, as a postscript, that Harvey with no alumina capacity of their own decided to build an extracting plant in 1960–63 and undertook major explorations to determine if Jamaican supplies of ore would meet their requirements. They abandoned these explorations and negotiations in 1958. One

the variable costs of production of alumina, on 1956 calculations, would have been some 20 per cent lower on alumina manufactured in Jamaica than on alumina (derived from Jamaica bauxite) manufactured in the United States.

The conclusion is that in the decision of United States firms not to locate alumina plants in the Caribbean differentials in variable costs did not receive the weight which one would normally expect.

Taxation: Under the United States tax law[1] miners of bauxite are allowed an annual deduction of 23 per cent of the gross income derived from mining (not from manufacture) if the mineral is drawn from deposits in the United States. If the deposits are not in the United States the depletion allowance on gross income is 15 per cent. In both cases the deduction is subject to a maximum limitation equal to 50 per cent of the net income from mining operations.[2]

A United States company mining bauxite is entitled to a depletion allowance whether the bauxite is mined in, or outside of, the United States. The fact that the bauxite may be transported from a foreign

possible reason for this abandonment was that competing companies had earlier set about securing ownership of bauxite lands in Jamaica. A new company like Harvey is said to have found difficulty in securing in the island large enough blocks of contiguous land rich in bauxite. Whatever the reasons for Harvey's change of plans, anyone interested in the policy of location of alumina plants will feel that an interesting case for study was lost because Harvey would have had stronger economic inducements to locate an alumina plant in Jamaica than either of the other U.S. firms (see Table I.7). Harvey would also have had fewer disincentives because reasons of security (discussed above) were almost certain to have been pressed home with more vigour in the late 1940s than in the late 1950s.

1. Internal Revenue Code of 1954, Sections 613 (b) (2), 613 (b) (6), 613 (a).
2. These liberal allowances have done much to encourage United States interests to undertake risk for profit in mining particularly in oil and an illustration of its effectiveness is the concentration of millionaires in Texas. Those who defend these depletion allowances point out that the reward for risk is not demonstrably more favourable than the corresponding system in Canada. By the tax law in Canada, a taxpayer who operates base metal mines or industrial mineral mines may deduct 33.3 per cent of net profits derived from such mines. A new mine of this type is allowed a tax-holiday for the first three years of operation. In addition a deduction is allowed against the dividends received from a corporation doing business in Canada equal to 10 per cent of the dividend if the mineral profits of the corporation represent 25 to 50 per cent of its income, 15 per cent of the dividend if the mineral profits represent 50 to 75 per cent of its income, and 20 per cent of the dividend if mineral profits exceed 75 per cent of the total. Dividends received from a non-resident subsidiary are not included in the taxable income of a Canadian company if it owns more than 25 per cent of the shares having full voting rights of the non-resident company paying the dividends.

source to the United States for conversion into alumina would not affect the depletion allowance. If, however, the mineral is mined abroad by a foreign company which does not pay any United States tax there is no depletion under the tax law whether the mineral is processed abroad or transported to the United States for processing by another company. It would seem from this that the depletion allowances, restricted as they are to mining operations, are unlikely to have a positive effect on the location of the alumina plants. In the case of the United States firms, operating in Jamaica, the subsidiary in each case is registered in the United States.

Politics: Nationalist movements are active in many parts of the world, in the West Indies as elsewhere. United States investors have many experiences to illustrate the risks abroad which their investments run. Thus even in mining enterprises there was, at about the time that decisions were being taken on alumina plants, the topical example of oil installations in the Near East and the concern caused by wrangles over the Suez Canal. Doubtless the United States oil interests found the controversy discouraging and the developments certainly such as they would not have chosen, but this did not prevent them from transferring large investments in oil refining to Trinidad.

An example even more analogous than the oil refinery in Trinidad is Alcoa's policy in Surinam. The discussion thus far pointing to the resistance of United States firms to process the ore in the Caribbean refers primarily to the policy of Reynolds and Kaiser. The third United States firm with extensive interests in the Caribbean area is Alcoa, with its chief source of supply in Surinam. Alcoa has gone further than either Reynolds or Kaiser with plans for processing in the Caribbean. Alcoa in 1957 signed a letter of intent to build a smelter in Surinam. The condition for this was that the Dutch and Surinam governments would first put up the funds to harness the Surinam River to provide hydro-power. These proposals agreed to in 1957 ran into the 1957–58 recession and discussions have taken place on modification of this Brokopondo project. The plans included eventual construction of an alumina plant.[1]

It is almost certain that nationalist movements abroad caused United States investors to pause but investments by United States private enterprise both in the Caribbean and elsewhere continued.

1. Alcoa. *Annual Report*, 1957.

Politics could therefore not be regarded as the limiting factor preventing the location of alumina extraction in Jamaica.

External Economies: The question of external economies affects costs and often has an important bearing on policies of location. Alumina extraction, while not employing a large labour force, does require a limited number of highly trained technicians and these skills are not readily found in sufficient quality and quantity in places such as Jamaica or the Guianas. The absence of such skills is often more of a deterrent than it should be because there are now many examples of skilled operations proceeding satisfactorily in communities less advanced than the Caribbean bauxite-producing territories. Entrepreneurs in and out of the Caribbean have found by experience that training programmes associated with imported technical assistance, can give rapid and effective results. There is, however, another aspect of this question of external economies in that an alumina plant located in the United States would be part of a complex of other industries in a way that such a plant in the Caribbean would not and this would influence the thinking of the United States firms who were making the decisions. Alumina extraction is essentially a chemical process and one of the main chemicals used is caustic soda. In the post-1940s when the aluminium firms were giving thought to new alumina plants the chemical firms were finding themselves with excess caustic soda and would presumably be interested in increasing domestic demand, the kind of demand which new alumina plants in the United States would provide. There is close affiliation between some of the aluminium and the chemical firms. In the case of Kaiser, the company has placed a good deal of emphasis on the expansion of its chemical activities and, in establishing its new alumina plant in Gramercy in Louisiana in 1958, built a caustic soda plant as a part of the unit. There were two advantages to this. The caustic soda output would in part go to the alumina process. Secondly, the electrolytic process by which caustic soda is produced secures certain economies in the production of power from association with the alumina operation.

One suspects that the considerations relating to external economies and the participation of alumina extraction in a larger United States industrial complex, played a major part in the decision ultimately taken by United States firms to locate their alumina plants at home even if costs were higher than in Jamaica.

The Canadian Producer
and some Determinants of Alumina Policy

As noted earlier the Canadian producer in the industry had come into being, from the outset, with more of an international orientation than the American. In 1950 three families (Mellon, Davis and Hunt) owned 45 per cent of the shares in Alcoa and 35 per cent in Aluminium Limited. Arising out of the United States anti-trust litigation a court order in 1951 ruled that these families should divest themselves of their shares in one company or the other. Given this choice, one Davis brother elected to choose Aluminium Limited and set the course of the company. With all supplies of the raw product coming from abroad and a limited demand for the finished product at home, the Canadian company adopted a policy that was more conscious of its international relations than the United States counterpart.[1]

During the period of expansion of the 1940s and 1950s Aluminium of Canada embarked on a policy that was different in two respects from the tradition in the United States. One was the emphasis on hydro-electric development which was company financed and which the company (rather than the government or a public utility) controlled. Both in North America and in Europe the aluminium industry had in the past pioneered in plans for hydro-electric development and later competitive demands had raised the price of power and it was the cost of power which dominated the cost of operation of the aluminium smelters. In order to avoid rising costs of production in future, Aluminium of Canada put investment into localities which had potential for hydro-power (Arvida, Kitimat) and outright ownership meant that future operating and plant costs were controllable in a way that would not be possible under public ownership.

A second and important difference in Aluminium Limited's policy was the company's election not to increase its alumina capacity at home but to establish extraction facilities near to its chief supply of ore. The erection of an alumina plant in Jamaica

1. The production and distribution relationships were very different in the United States and the Canadian industry when the post-war expansion was being planned. In both countries expansion was rapid, but more so in the United States than in Canada. The rate of increase was about twice as fast in the United States as in Canada for the years 1950–53. The United States exports were not only negligible (1 ton exported for every 680 tons produced) but were a small fraction of her imports. Canada on the other hand exported over 80 per cent of her production.

was indeed a notable event because it was the first time in the history of the industry that the decision had been taken to establish an alumina plant at so great a distance overseas from the reduction facilities.

The company's subsidiary in Jamaica first drew up its plans on the basis of mining and shipping part of its ore in the crude state to the Arvida plant. Only a part of the ore was to be converted into alumina in Jamaica. The company, however, later changed its plans and decided that all extraction from Jamaica ore would be done locally[1] and at the end of 1952 its alumina plant in Jamaica came into operation. The company increased the capacity of the plant by successive stages to 480,000 tons of alumina a year and in 1955 decided to erect an additional plant of approximately half the size at another site in Jamaica, thus bringing the Jamaica capacity to something under 800,000 tons. Shipments from this plant have gone to Canada (East and West Coast), Norway, Sweden and elsewhere. The company followed this with an alumina plant in British Guiana of 220,000 tons capacity.[2]

Some Differences in Alumina Policy
between United States and Canadian Producers

It is striking that the Canadian company pursued a policy in regard to the siting of alumina plants, so different from that of the American companies, Reynolds and Kaiser, which in the 1950s also secured their major supplies of bauxite from Jamaica. It is even more striking that the difference should have evolved since it meant that the Aluminium Limited policy in the years succeeding the Second World War became a complete reversal of that in the inter-war years. During the years following the First World War, the Canadian and United States policies were in close association and although there was some official pressure to locate an alumina plant in British Guiana, the pressure was resisted and the plant located in Canada. In the inter-war years the policy of the Canadian producer was not different from that of the United States producers.[3]

1. Zans, V. A. 'Bauxite Resources of Jamaica and their Development', *Colonial Geology and Mineral Resources*, 1952, Vol. 3, No. 4, pp. 307–333.
   2. Aluminium Limited. *Annual Report*, 1956.
   3. It can be argued that the decision of the Canadian producer to have established an alumina plant in Jamaica before British Guiana, was influenced by the relative difference in position of deposits in Jamaica and in British Guiana. The deposits in British Guiana are at Mackenzie, which is 65 miles from the mouth of the Demerara River – that is farther from Georgetown than Kirkvine (the Jamaica alumina plant) is from Kingston, and much farther than Kirkvine is from its deep-water harbour, Port Esquivel. The Demerara although

The Canadians were because of the nature of their market more sensitive to the implications of international change. The situation which evolved from the Russian incursion (to which we shall refer again) into the foreign aluminium market from 1956 justified this awareness. Another circumstance which indicated that not only the Canadian but also the United States integrated firms were becoming increasingly involved in the international trade was the British Aluminium-Alcoa-Reynolds contest in 1958. Each of these episodes in its way had significant implications for the industry as a whole – including implications for alumina and the location of alumina plants in the Western Hemisphere – and deserves further attention.

It is probable that no single factor was responsible for the difference in policy that grew up between the Canadian and United States producers but rather a combination of several. In the early years their policy was the same (alumina plants on the mainland) but when the expansion in the 1940s and 1950s came about, the Canadians had at Arvida a plant that was already large, with a capacity of a million tons of alumina a year. They needed a new plant and must have been for some time giving thought to new capacity. The two United States companies that we are chiefly considering, Reynolds and Kaiser, had on the contrary been faced for a long time with excess and heavily subsidized alumina capacity. It can be of little consolation to the Caribbean that this policy of the United States Government which was intended to promote free enterprise and competition, succeeded merely in converting a duopoly into an oligopoly at home, while helping abroad effectively to discourage the type of alumina policy that keener competition would have brought and the possessors of bauxite deposits would have deserved.

a great river has across its mouth a bar which large ocean-going vessels cannot cross. Kirkvine had railway facilities including a spur line specially constructed for it, but the spur line was practicable, like all spur lines, because the main line was already there. Mackenzie, only ten feet above sea-level, had some of the natural discomforts and health dangers of a tropical littoral and it was here that an artificial urban community had to be created. Kirkvine, in a healthy plateau area, pleasanter for Canadians than most of Canada, had good secondary schools, and was a tolerable shopping centre. As far as availability of skilled labour was concerned, there was no comparison. Kirkvine was in the midst of long-settled country, Mackenzie was in the wild. British Guiana's outstanding potential always was hydro-electric power but this, it was said, had its sources too far from Mackenzie. It may therefore well be that the proposal for an alumina plant in British Guiana after the First World War had a good deal to be said against it on general grounds.

As far as the security considerations go, the same arguments doubtless had to be examined by the Canadians as by the United States firms.

The cost structure is a complicated one in the vertically integrated firms. It is particularly difficult to determine costs of bauxite which is not a homogeneous product. The evidence is that the influence of cost, if operating freely, should have encouraged the location of alumina production in the Caribbean. There are two items connected with cost to which the literature often attributes a major influence in bringing about the difference between the Canadian and the United States policy: distance and tariff.

In regard to distance the round trip from Jamaica to Kitimat is 10,000 miles; to New Orleans 2,500. The distance to and from Kitimat may be 10,000 miles but to and from Canada's East Coast reduction works at Arvida is only 5,000 miles. The discrepancies in distance are further complicated in that the American producers were already aware in the early 1950s that increased prices of power were driving their smelter facilities further and further from the Gulf Coast in the direction of the coalfields of the Ohio Valley and even towards the North West Coast. Thus on the Pacific Coast Kaiser had a reduction plant near Spokane in Washington and Reynolds one at Troutdale in Oregon. One company, Harvey, with smelters in the North West, apparently could secure its alumina cheaper from Japan than from United States producers who manufactured their alumina on the Gulf Coast (from bauxite brought from Jamaica). In any event the cost of sea transport is not dominated by distance travelled as much as by the loading and unloading charges. If distance were such a dominating factor Reynolds' involvement, in 1958, in reduction facilities at Baie Comeau in Canada might have induced that company to consider alumina manufacture in Jamaica but one has seen no evidence of this.

In regard to tariff, unlike the United States industry the Canadians did not try to raise the odds against alumina manufacture abroad by securing a tariff on alumina imports at home. Against a $5 a ton tariff in the United States the Canadians imposed none.

The question of external economies was a major factor working against the location in the Caribbean, but although the influences should have been at work both in the United States and in Canada there was a difference. The alumina plants located in the Gulf Coast area filled a complementary role in the heavy chemical industry complex based on the salt deposits in the area. Electrolysis of the salt yielded caustic soda which was in excess supply and alumina was a heavy consumer of caustic soda. Thus, in this particular, external economies might have been a more powerful influence in determining the policy of the United States industrial groups than in the case of the Canadians.

Taxation policies in the United States and Canada are sufficiently alike not to have had a markedly different influence on alumina policy. Political movements and the trend towards independence in the emerging countries had been observed in Canada as in the United States and may have caused uncertainties in both, but should not have caused more in the one than in the other. It is possible, however, that while the Americans were just as interested as the Canadians in the idea of independence for a British colony like Jamaica, the Canadians would have fewer secret emotional reservations. The Americans would think of some of the neighbouring republics as a guide to the future of a Caribbean Dominion, the Canadians of their own past and that of the other older Dominions.

A most important factor influencing the location of secondary industries in a territory is the policy of the government. This may well be one of those cases in which a deciding factor could be the action taken (or omitted) by the government. At a level above the aluminium companies was the action of the United States Government which through its wish to implement the ruling of the Court subsidized Reynolds and Kaiser in a manner that did little to help the country's anti-trust policy but much to discourage the processing of bauxite to alumina in the Caribbean. The subsidy was especially effective in the 1940s and early 1950s, the crucial years for planning expansion in the aluminium industry's capacity.

Admittedly, the governments of the economically advanced countries (e.g. that of the United States) were much less sensitive in the 1940s than they have later become to the wisdom of encouraging rather than of impeding the diversification of the economies of the less advanced countries. But even then, and certainly later, it would have seemed desirable for the point to be made – at the highest level, with resourcefulness and importunity – of the harm that had been done the Jamaica economy by the action of the United States Government. This action had made it highly improbable that the United States companies Reynolds and Kaiser would at an early stage establish alumina extraction in the Caribbean. The harm has proved a lasting one because the more set the pattern became the more the resistance to change grew. One must necessarily be uncertain how much in this general sphere may have been left undone by Jamaican policy-makers since negotiations would in large measure be confidential. It is difficult to determine whether or not Jamaica allocated enough resources and effort to bringing to Jamaica alumina manufacture by the United States companies. Nevertheless, in the absence of a thorough study of market potential and interdependence, Jamaica might easily not have recognised the powerful hand it held. In the absence of this recognition Jamaica seemed to have been hesitant in demanding with enough importunity that more alumina plants should be sited in Jamaica.

2 Two International Trade Episodes and some Implications for Western Hemisphere Aluminium and Alumina

In the 1940s and early 1950s when the main post-war expansion of aluminium capacity was being planned, the Canadian producer was complementary to rather than competitive with the American. The American industrial groups concentrated on the home market and left the international trade in aluminium to the Canadian producer and others. The Canadian producer, regarded benignly by the United States producers, helped to meet the deficiencies in domestic supplies for the United States market and looked elsewhere for the disposal of the remainder of his output. If this general pattern changed and if the United States producers began to supplant Canadian exports not only on the United States market but abroad as well, the United States decisions that had been taken not to locate alumina plants in the Caribbean could have major implications for the pattern of trade. Two episodes, while perhaps not causing, were certainly heralding in precisely such a change in the pattern of trade in aluminium and alumina on international markets.

The Soviet Aluminium Episode

From the point of view of the aluminium producers, 1956 was a good year. In the United States the consumption of aluminium, increasing spectacularly, had doubled between 1950 and 1956 and the major problem which the aluminium firms faced was the struggle to keep up with their domestic demand. The United States firms were conscious that it was possible for them not to send their fabricators empty away only because Canada, their good neighbour, was sending them some 0.2 million of the 1.8 million tons which their consumers required. For the North American producers the price was right, the demand was right and they were all one happy family. In Europe the outlook also was good, in some ways better. Consumption of aluminium in 1956 had not only doubled that in

57

1950 as in the United States but had grown proportionately more (2.3 times that in 1950). The United Kingdom was the second largest consumer of aluminium in the Free World, second only to the United States and the biggest importer of the metal. While of the other big consumers the increase in demand was greatest in West Germany (a consumption of 55 thousand tons in 1950 and 229 thousand in 1956) the United Kingdom was still the biggest in Europe.

The United States and the United Kingdom had in common a dependence on imports which were dominated by Alcan. To Alcan these two markets were important, taking together in 1956 about 89 per cent of her exports. Of the two the United Kingdom market was even more important to Canada.[1] During 1956 the Canadians raised the price of aluminium on the United Kingdom market from £171 to £179 to £189 a ton. This happened in a period when prices of the other non-ferrous metals were falling, which somewhat irritated the United Kingdom purchasers who began to wonder, in print, whether the rise was not as much attributable to opportunism as to increased costs.[2] The higher prices in 1956 did not seem to affect demand. Alcan was able to maintain the one price system and continued with assurance as the stabilizer of the world price-structure. Nevertheless there was this concern about supplies by the United Kingdom fabricators and an indication of this was that a British company had already decided to erect a smelter in Canada to tap the hydro-power of the St Lawrence and to have its own independent supplies of ingot.

During the year the Soviet Union had shipped aluminium abroad. This at first received little notice since the amounts were small and had gone only to the United Kingdom. But the event in itself was surprising since the Soviet Union's aluminium industry with that of its satellite countries was even more self-contained than that of the United States. The domestic consumption of the metal per head was relatively low (Table II.1) and so aluminium was not a commodity with regard to which it was anticipated the U.S.S.R. would become a factor in international trading. This did not mean that the world was not aware of the increasing U.S.S.R. production. While the United States production had risen by approximately 3 to 4 times between 1945 and 1956, the U.S.S.R.'s had risen by

1. Thus in 1955 the United States imports from Canada were some 71 per cent of the corresponding imports into the United Kingdom.
2. *Light Metals* (London), January 1957, p. 18.

6 times and the United States and Canada were the only producers which, individually, had an output higher than the U.S.S.R.

TABLE II.1   *Consumption (per head) of Aluminium in* 1956

Country	lb per head
United States	21
United Kingdom	13
Canada	11
West Germany	8
France	6
Italy	5
U.S.S.R.	6

By 1957 the United States recession had begun. This was associated with supplies of aluminium running so far ahead of demand that the industry reduced output to well below capacity and there then occurred a breach in the one-price system: Aluminium Limited dropped its price in all countries other than the United States, the United Kingdom and Canada.[1] In this situation Alcoa also dropped its price making it clear that it was doing so as a result of Alcan's action. By 1957 some people were asking whether the entry of Soviet aluminium into Western markets was necessarily a temporary phenomenon and whether it might affect the whole structure of aluminium prices on the world markets. The reaction to the Soviet entry was different in Europe from that in North America. West European purchasers rationalized that there had been little cause to impute improper motives to the Soviet conditions of trade; that the price the Russians quoted was no lower than what everyone had for some time been saying Alcan could and should have fixed, intervention or no intervention; that the falling off in demand for aluminium had been partly due to the too high price of the metal; that this pressure was in fact a good thing if it induced Alcan to be more sensitive to world consumer opinion. On the other hand many in North America interpreted the Soviet incursion as just another political ploy for which the Soviet Government was prepared to pay. The view received support from the wording of an

1. *Light Metals* (London), December 1957, p. 395.

escalator clause in the Russian contract which could be taken to mean that for one year the Russians were prepared to offer aluminium to the West at £10 per ton below any price Canada quoted.

Convinced of the rightness of its cause Alcan applied early in 1958 to the United Kingdom Board of Trade for an anti-dumping duty on aluminium imported from the Soviet Union. There were several arguments which Alcan could put forward in support of its application: that the long-run interests of the United Kingdom market were best served by assured and adequate supplies of the metal at stable prices; that the price to United Kingdom users of Canadian aluminium had risen over the years not only because of higher costs of production but also because of the devaluation of sterling in 1949; that the company's net income during the nine months ending September 30, 1957 – representing less than 2.5 per cent of the net value of assets – was not easily reconciled with the accusation that Alcan had taken advantage of shortages of aluminium to charge higher prices simply because the market would bear it; that in 1955 and 1956 when the metal was scarce the Russians delivered only small quantities in the United Kingdom, 2,468 tons in 1955 (at £219 c.i.f.) and 197 tons (at £248 c.i.f.) in 1956, compared with deliveries in the United Kingdom by Alcan at £171 in 1955 and at £179 in 1956; that the United Kingdom had the first call on about 275,000 tons a year of Canadian metal and this right extended to 1970; that in 1957, when the Russians had increased their exports, the United Kingdom demand for Canadian metal was only about half the figure which the Canadian industry had to reserve in case the United Kingdom required it; that there was provision under GATT which required members to impose anti-dumping measures if failure to do so imperilled free competition in a third country.

On the other hand there were several problems which Alcan's application posed. A first requirement was for the Board of Trade to determine whether or not dumping as defined in the Act[1] was in fact taking place, i.e. whether the 'fair market price' of aluminium in the Soviet Union was greater than the price being quoted to importers. Alcan, if it was to prove this, had set itself a difficult task. In its simplest terms the problem facing the Board of Trade was to determine whether or not it was in the best interests of the United Kingdom economy to force the Soviet prices up to those which Alcan was charging and which the consumers had been protesting were too high. The industry's leaders in the United

1. The Customs Duties (Dumping and Subsidies) Act, 1957.

Kingdom had more than once appealed for the discounts for quantities, cash payments and forward deliveries which were common in other metal markets. It also became clear that, even if the Board of Trade granted Alcan's application and an anti-dumping measure came into force, this would be specifically against Russian imports and would not interfere with imports, say, from Belgium or West Germany fabricated from Russian metal. As developments showed, before the Board of Trade handed down its ruling, some countries of the Soviet allied Bloc (notably Hungary) were quoting prices even below Russia's and even China was offering aluminium at competitive prices on the United Kingdom market. To complete the inconsistencies of the situation, by late 1958 the French Customs Board reported brisk sales of French aluminium to China. An anti-dumping duty, if allowed by the Board of Trade, would probably have led to a position where Aluminium Limited would be selling her metal on the United Kingdom market at a figure higher than she would have to offer in Western Europe. There were also the political aspects of a discriminatory duty of this kind at a time when the United Kingdom's political thinking was in favour of increased opportunities for trade and other intercourse with Russia.

In October 1958 the Board of Trade announced its ruling – that it would not impose an anti-dumping duty against Russian aluminium and that it had received assurances from the Russian authorities that they would limit their exports to the United Kingdom to 15,000 tons a year. Although the exports from Russia for the twelve month period ending September 1958 exceeded 15,000 tons the rate of imports had declined after that and the opinion became increasingly accepted that the Russians, having regard to their domestic demands, were in any case not planning to export more than this amount to the United Kingdom. Admittedly, the appearance of Russian metal occurred at a time when there was considerable deterioration of the aluminium market and it may well be that many of the events might have taken place Russian metal or no Russian metal. The history of the aluminium industry is one of lumpy capital investment providing, in periods of optimism, capacity ahead of requirements which later catch up only to have production take another leap forward. Excess capacity had occurred before and the North American producers had in such circumstances managed to close ranks and to make an orderly retreat. There was now, however, a breaking of ranks and much disarray, and one is inclined to associate a certain amount of this – while not venturing to say how much – with the unexpected appearance of Russian metal in the West.

The appearance of Russian exports while having much effect on events in the United Kingdom market was associated with – through the notable changes in attitudes and policy of the United States producers – even more profound implications for the location of the alumina plants of the North American producers. It is necessary to consider next some of the changes in attitudes and policy which took place at this time among the North American producers.

The quantities of Russian exports to the United Kingdom although not great (Table II.2) affected both the Canadian and, through the Canadian, the United States aluminium producers markedly and there seemed to be a continuing apprehension that these marginal sales might for some time exert an effect on prices not only in the United Kingdom market but also in the American market.[1] The North American producers regarded this threat[2] seriously and Alcan announced a cut in price of two cents a pound

TABLE II.2   *Imports into the United Kingdom of Primary Aluminium*

Exporter	1957 Tons '000	1957 % Total	1958 Tons '000	1958 % Total	1959 Tons '000	1959 % Total	1960 Tons '000	1960 % Total
Canada	152	79.6	147	70.0	145	57.6	163	52.2
U.S.	1	0.5	21	10.0	45	17.9	97	31.1
Norway	17	8.9	20	9.5	34	13.5	37	11.9
U.S.S.R.	17	8.9	11	5.2	17	6.7	7	2.2
Other countries	4	2.1	11	5.2	11	4.3	8	2.6
Total	191		210		252		312	

1. Thus the Canadians had made no attempt to alter prices when, not long before, Formosa had been making sales on the South African market below the Canadian fixed price. (*Metal Bulletin* (London), November 12, 1957, p. 27.) There were discounts which took various forms. There was, e.g. a 'loyalty rebate' of 2 per cent allowed to a consumer who did not make purchases from any other supplier during a twelve month period.

2. There was increasingly in the literature an expression of the point of view that there was no indication of any deliberate intention of the U.S.S.R. to disorganize the metal market. The official American view was that Russia was exporting metals primarily to pay for their increasing imports from the West since Russian trade with Western Europe had been rising sharply.

or nearly 9 per cent, effective in the United States and in the United Kingdom.[1] The United States producers made a corresponding price reduction, but with sharp and unfavourable reaction to what Alcan had done, and began agitating at home for high duties[2] and even quotas on aluminium imports. For the reasons mentioned before the United States producer was much more concerned with the domestic market than was the case in Canada and there was good reason why developments on the United States market made it expedient for him in 1958 to urge the claims for a higher tariff: protection was needed not so much against the Canadian product as against semi-fabricated material which was said to be finding its way into the United States from Western Europe but which, they claimed, was based on Russian metal; a labour agreement called for automatic wage increases later that year; under the terms of the GATT agreement aluminium duty was due not for an increase but for a decrease from 1.3 cents to 1.25 cents by mid-year. The industry's claims for higher duty did not get very far with Congress.[3]

1. Several considerations seem to have induced this decision:
a. There was, in 1957, a reduction of 3 per cent of the Free World's consumption of aluminium and a sharper fall in demand as inventories were run down. There was therefore something to be said, on general grounds, for the need to increase consumption by reducing prices.
b. Canada exported most of her output and had to be sensitive to conditions on the United Kingdom market which in 1957 absorbed about 43 per cent of her exports. A policy of tight money in Britain had encouraged low stocks so that while United Kingdom totals fell by 26 per cent between 1955 and 1957 aluminium imports from Canada fell by 35 per cent. In addition the trade in Britain continued to complain about the Canadian price.
c. The movement of related prices had probably influenced the decision. The London price of copper then approximately that of the reduced price of aluminium was, two years previously, twice that of aluminium. A contemporary cut in general steel prices had taken place in the United Kingdom and, though small (one and a half per cent), was the first since 1939.
d. The U.S.S.R. exports to the United Kingdom, negligible in 1956, had risen during the 8 months period, July 1957 to February 1958, to an equivalent of an annual rate of 25,000 tons.
e. The position of the Canadian exporters in their appeal for anti-dumping measures in the United Kingdom would be strengthened by this evidence of the determination to meet competition.
2. Lobbyists talked in terms of a really substantial increase, from the existing 1.3 cents a lb to 4 cents (a figure which had been in existence in 1930).
3. One proposal was put forward in United States legislative circles that 150,000 tons of aluminium should be stock-piled at a figure up to 27.5 cents a pound for pig, the ruling price being 24 cents a pound and that this stock-pile might be used as an economic counter-measure by the United States and sold (either abroad or even in the United States) at competitive prices with metal coming from the U.S.S.R. See *Metal Bulletin* (London), June 27, 1958, p. 22 and July 25, 1958, p. 24.

The United States producers in this period made it clear that they were far less disposed than the Canadians to accept the possibility of the retention of the lower price for which international trade had been mainly responsible. In an editorial, the United Kingdom magazine, *Metal Bulletin*, referring to the efforts being made by the United States producers in mid-1958 to increase aluminium prices on the domestic market, wrote:

> 'The Americans, of course, are worried about what attitude the Canadians would take to any such move (i.e. a rise in price). They know that the Canadians, with their much more international outlook on world aluminium markets, are fully alive to the problems like those created by the availability of Russian aluminium as a competitive raw material for European fabricators. It is presumably for this reason and no other that the American aluminium industry is suddenly exhibiting great concern over the presence of cheap Russian aluminium in Europe. We refuse to believe that the direct impact of these Russian sales on the United States markets . . . is sufficient to cause any real concern.'

Alcoa announced a price increase in August (1958) applicable to the United States. Alcan followed suit on the United States market but did not pass on these increases to the United Kingdom market, an unusual step for Alcan who so quickly was once again called on to break its tradition of not altering prices on a piecemeal basis.

For North America this was not the end of the affair. Russia had come into international trade in aluminium and new influences would have to be reckoned with. Previously, only three events in the history of the industry had caused United States producers seriously to give thought to the rest of the world. Two were World Wars. In both cases the result had been the same: the United States producers were expected to come to the aid of Europe by increasing their production and their market. Each such association had had a benign influence on the course of the United States industry. The third event was in the distant past when in 1912 the French company had tried to get a footing in the United States and possibly to bring with them inconvenient foreign complications and competition. By good management and effective strategy the French interests had been prevailed upon to withdraw from the United States scene. The Canadian industry had been sired by the United States producers and there was on the whole a happy relationship in which some of the hydro-electric resources of Canada helped supply aluminium that was complementary to production in a United States where competitive demand was pricing hydro-power out of aluminium reduction. Up to this time Canada, fitting in so neatly into the scheme of things, could hardly be thought of as anything other than a part of the domestic industry. Canada had helped confirm the image of the beneficent influence of international trade and the conviction of the United States producers that theirs was a self-contained industry.

For the United States industry, as the conditions governing the supply of and demand for the finished metal had been orderly from the point of view of international trade, so were the conditions governing the raw product. When home supplies of the ore had run low, deposits in the Caribbean had provided further evidence that international trade was a convenient thing. The events of the late 1950s brought a different set of relationships which showed that the United States producers would experience, in a way that they had not previously, some of the pressures as well as the advantages of international trade. There were even signs that the United Kingdom market which had, by a gentleman's agreement, been regarded as Alcan's preserve would be invaded by United States producers. This was a development which did not seem probable in the late 1940s and early 1950s when the Caribbean territories were negotiating their relationships with the aluminium companies. Such a development would necessarily have implications for the location of alumina plants and it is this development – the invasion by United States producers of the United Kingdom aluminium metal market – and its implications for the location of alumina plants, which one must next examine.

The Reynolds – Alcoa – British Aluminium Episode

British Aluminium although relatively small was none the less the sole producer of ingot (30,000 tons a year) in the United Kingdom, a relatively large fabricator of its own and other producers' metal, having a fabrication output second only to Northern Aluminum's (a subsidiary of Aluminium Limited). In the 1930s, before the outbreak of war, British Aluminium was a completely integrated company in the sense that it produced enough aluminium to meet

C

its requirements for fabrication. In 1956, however, it was producing less than half of its ingot needs and the company wished to be assured of supplies to meet the current as well as anticipated demand. In consequence Canadian British Aluminium Co. Ltd. came into being and established in Canada a smelter, in Quebec, which with an ultimate capacity of 160,000 tons a year was to make British Aluminium independent in regard to ingot supplies and to have some left over for sales. In this new company British Aluminium owned 60 per cent of the shares (the other 40 per cent being owned not by other aluminium interests but by a Chicago Tribune paper-making subsidiary). In connection with these activities British Aluminium decided in mid-1957 to float a large issue of new shares but the international situation made the market for aluminium uncertain and the prospect for such massive financing difficult. Canadian British Aluminium decided not to establish, in the first stage, an alumina plant at Baie Comeau, but made an agreement to deliver 20,000 tons of aluminium a year to Alcan in return for alumina.

Simultaneously a quite independent but comparable set of developments was taking place. One of the larger fabricating companies in the United Kingdom, Tube Investments Limited, was (by the end of 1957) complaining that its aluminium division was being hampered by not having close association with a prime producer of aluminium. This lack, in the company's view, confronted them with the worst of both worlds: unreliable supplies when business was buoyant and a competitive disadvantage when there was a buyer's market. In the latter half of 1957 Tube Investments and other buyers were encouraged by the Russian episode to complain loudly that the traditional suppliers (i.e. Alcan) could justifiably quote lower prices. In order to remedy these 'frustrating'[1] circumstances Tube Investments decided to enter into an agreement and association with the Reynolds Metals Co. of the United States. To do this they formed a new company (Reynolds Tube Investments Limited) with a nominal capital to be held by Reynolds of the United States and Tube Investments in equal proportions. The new arrangement, the companies stated, was that with Tube Investments Reynolds would assume equal responsibility and would with its full resources back the development of the new company's aluminium activities in the United Kingdom. It is true that by the end of 1958, there was less talk in terms of an excessive Russian threat to the

1. Tube Investments Limited. *Annual General Meeting*, 1957.

aluminium export markets of Western Europe and even a disposition to assume the possibility of net Russian aluminium imports
in the years immediately ahead. The threat to the old order posed
by the Reynolds and Tube Investments association was, however,
another matter and more was to follow.

The position now was that Alcan and Reynolds had outlets in
the United Kingdom but Alcoa and Kaiser had not. British
Aluminium had erected its new installations in Canada and, bent
on expansion, needed to raise capital. It decided to look for its
capital not from its shareholders (possibly remembering its difficulties with the Baie Comeau financing) but as a direct investment
from Alcoa who would presumably assume a degree of control of
British Aluminium. These negotiations were rather hush-hush and
it may well be that Alcoa had pangs of conscience about such
activities in the United Kingdom market which up to then had
always been recognized as Alcan's special sphere of activity.
News leaked out. A buyer (later identified as the Reynolds-Tube
Investments combine) began to collect British Aluminium shares
quietly but industriously and later the battle for control of British
Aluminium came into the open. On the one side the British
Aluminium Board of Directors had come to an unpublicized
arrangement to issue to Alcoa its unissued shares which would
have given Alcoa a one-third interest in British Aluminium.
Reynolds and Tube Investments countered by making an offer
also for these unissued shares, and made its offer public in terms
which indicated that its proposals would be more advantageous
from the point of view of the shareholders than Alcoa's.[1] The issue

1. The offer from Alcoa was that Alcoa would provide capital required by
British Aluminium for expansion by acquiring the unissued shares over a 3–4-year
period at a price of 60s a share. The Reynolds associates offered direct to British
Aluminium stockholders for each £2 of British Aluminium ordinary stock: one
Tube Investment ordinary £1 share (market value £3 18s 3d) plus £3 18s 0d
in cash, the shares being put up by Tube Investments and the capital by Reynolds.
The shares of British Aluminium so acquired would be vested in a holding
company of which Tube Investments would own 51 per cent and Reynolds
49 per cent, thus maintaining the form of British control and ownership. The
arguments and counter-arguments surrounding these negotiations made it clear
that control of the policy of British Aluminium would pass to an American
company, Alcoa or Reynolds. A further complication arose when on December
31, 1958 a group of United Kingdom bankers decided to throw their support
behind the Alcoa proposals and offered 82s a share for one-half of any holding
of British Aluminium stock if the shareholder agreed not to sell the other half.
Reynolds increased their cash offer to 88s and by mid-January, 1959, the
Reynolds-Tube Investments combination had won the battle and control. Alcoa

of the shares to Alcoa might have gone through except that it was necessary for British Aluminium to secure permission of the British Treasury for the transaction and it was during the period when this consent was being sought that Reynolds and Tube Investments submitted their offer for shares of British Aluminium.

Reynolds-Tube Investments won the struggle. The fabrication facilities of British Aluminium and of Tube Investments, the smelter capacity of British Aluminium in Britain and of Canadian British Aluminium in Canada, added to the resources of Reynolds of America (who, it was clear, were going aggressively after the United Kingdom aluminium market) now constituted a unit of potential dominance in the United Kingdom industry.

This discussion has had special reference to fabrication and smelting capacity and might seem to have little relation to alumina since neither Tube Investments nor Canadian British Aluminium were involved in alumina production and British Aluminium only to a modest extent, but few events in the history of the industry were likely to have more repercussions on the policy in the British Caribbean relating to the location of alumina processing.

Aluminium imported into the United Kingdom had thus far been made chiefly from alumina manufactured either in Canada (from Caribbean and West African bauxite) or in Jamaica from Jamaican bauxite. Even Canadian British Aluminium had a long-term contract relying on these same two sources of supply of alumina.[1] One effect of the new alignment was almost certainly that the Reynolds interests would wish to increase their competition in the United Kingdom market via aluminium manufactured at the Canadian British Aluminium's plant in Canada[2] which would, understandably, look to Reynolds for supplies of alumina in excess of what Canadian British Aluminium was committed to take from

withdrew and the British Treasury gave official approval to the new alignment. The fight had not ended as the directorate of British Aluminium had hoped because they had been with Alcoa 'on the closest terms of mutual trust and friendship for many years'. The decision had been, in many ways, a difficult one for the stock-holders. The Reynolds offer presented them with a higher immediate gain. The British Aluminium directorate believed that the Alcoa offer would have brought participation in an expanded British Aluminium and higher long-term gains for the shareholders.

1. A long-term contract by the British Canadian plant at Baie Comeau to supply to Alcan until 1977, 20,000 tons of ingot a year in return for alumina. Baie Comeau plans were for a 160,000 ton capacity. The alumina commitment was therefore relatively small.

2. British Aluminium owns 60 per cent of the shares in Canadian British Aluminium.

Alcan. Reynolds chief source of bauxite was Jamaica. The expansion of Reynolds' participation in the United Kingdom market would be in the form of providing supplies which would otherwise have come from Alcan. The outcome would necessarily be that alumina extracted in the United States by Reynolds (chiefly from Jamaican bauxite) would replace alumina extracted in Jamaica by Alcan (from Jamaican bauxite). Put in another way, the new merger (Tube Investments, British Aluminium, Canadian British Aluminium, Reynolds) implied an increase in exports of Jamaican bauxite to be converted into alumina in the United States to supply metal for an expanding market which, before the new constellation appeared, Jamaica had reason to hope would depend not only on Jamaica produced bauxite but also on Jamaica produced alumina. Jamaica was now faced with the less desirable alternative of having the United Kingdom market supply of aluminium depend on Jamaica bauxite converted into alumina in the United States replacing Jamaica bauxite converted into alumina in Jamaica.

In the future, international competition was likely to increase and come to exert still further pressure on world trade in bauxite, alumina and aluminium. Jamaica, used by the American companies as a source of bauxite but enjoying none of the secondary processing and additional income involved in alumina extraction, would be placed at a disadvantage with territories (like those in Africa, South America, Australia) whose ore deposits were being processed locally with value added to the benefit of the domestic economies.

The outcome of the Reynolds-Alcoa-British Aluminium episode was affecting adversely the long-term position of the Jamaican industry *vis-à-vis* alumina production.

Part II
The Interaction of Developments in America, Europe and the Commonwealth Caribbean

3 Expansion, in the late 1950's and early 1960's, of U.S. Firms into the Export Market in Aluminium

The earlier part of this discussion has dealt with events in the aluminium industry which particularly affected the Caribbean. The points made have centred largely on Jamaica, one reason being that her recorded bauxite deposits are not only greater than those in all the rest of the Caribbean combined but are also some of the most extensive in the world. The discussion has brought us to one of the turning points in the history of the North American industry, to the point where one United States firm, Reynolds, had entered international trade in aluminium and had given a clear indication of competing in the United Kingdom market and elsewhere with the Canadian producer, Alcan. The conclusion drawn was that this had major implications – and of a disadvantageous kind – for the Caribbean part of the industry.

In the late 1950s and the 1960s, the North American industry was engaged in development in two distinct directions. One related to the building of new capacity abroad as part of a programme of expansion through participation in the integrated domestic industries that were burgeoning in Brazil, Surinam, Greece, India, Japan, Australia and elsewhere. The other line of development and the one which is the subject of discussion in this chapter was urged on in part by North America's excess capacity at home: the new policy of the United States producers to compete aggressively in the United Kingdom and other markets abroad. The earliest indication of the new trend was the Reynolds incursion into the United Kingdom market and this has been discussed. The two other United States companies operating in the Caribbean, Alcoa and Kaiser, soon followed suit. In the United Kingdom operations Alcoa entered into an association with I.C.I. and Kaiser with Booth.

In 1960 the North American smelters worked at only 75 per cent of capacity but, in spite of this, production was in excess of demand. The United States producers affected by the recession cut back production so that the 1958 output instead of continuing on its upward trend was some 5 per cent lower than that of 1957 (Table

III.1). In 1959 the United States production again advanced (by some 25 per cent) more than in 1958. The relationship that made its appearance, for the first time, was that the United States production in 1960 exceeded its consumption. The United States no longer accepted the Canadian producer as complementary, but as a competitor at home who would increasingly have to be challenged abroad.

TABLE III.1   *Aluminium Production and Consumption in North America*

	Quantity ('000 tons)				Percentage change annually		
	1957	1958	1959	1960	1958–1957 %	1959–1958 %	1960–1959 %
United States							
Production	1,471	1,398	1,745	1,799	− 5	+ 25	+ 3
Consumption	1,586	1,617	1,917	1,563	+ 2	+ 18	− 19
Canada							
Production	497	566	530	680	+ 14	− 6	+ 27
Consumption	70	91	79	102	+ 30	− 13	+ 30
United States and Canada							
Production	1,968	1,964	2,275	2,479	− 0.2	+ 16	+ 9
Consumption	1,656	1,708	1,996	1,665	+ 3	+ 17	− 17

It is therefore not surprising that the United States producers began to seek an export outlet and if United States exports in 1957 were taken as 100, exports in 1960 were nearly 1,000 (Table III.2). In 1958 the United States producers were freely offering surplus production at substantial price discounts[1] but despite the new export outlet continued to work at less than full capacity. The United Kingdom was the largest market for aluminium in Western Europe and, in addition, traditionally looked abroad for its main supplies of the raw metal. The United Kingdom therefore was the logical outlet to be explored in the first instance and this is what

1. McCurda, D. B. *The Changing Logistics of the North America Aluminum Industry.*

happened in the late 1950s and early 1960s. In 1957 the proportion of the United Kingdom's supplies from the United States was negligible, while 80 per cent came from Canada. In 1960 the United Kingdom imports had increased considerably (well over 60 per cent) but Canada's proportion of the market had fallen – from 80 per cent in 1957 to 52 per cent in 1960. Meanwhile the United States had increased its share of the market to nearly a third. Although the industrial recovery in the United Kingdom led in 1959 to an increase of 15 per cent in the consumption of aluminium (Table

TABLE III.2   *Total Exports of Aluminium from the United States*

	1957	1958	1959	1960
Exports ('000 tons)	26.0	47.1	108.3	254.5
Index (1957 = 100)	100	181	417	979

II.2), Alcan did not share proportionately in that increase. In his report to shareholders for the first six months of 1961, the President of Aluminium Limited reported that while sales improved in Canada and the United States[1] they declined in the United Kingdom. The result of all this was to modify the traditional pattern of trade and prices in the industry.

From the point of view of the Commonwealth Caribbean the new situation was even worse than it looked because a part of the Canadian exports was now emanating not only from Alcan but also from Canadian British Aluminium, an associate of Reynolds. In 1961 British Aluminium announced that its subsidiary Canadian British Aluminium would expand its capacity at Baie Comeau by 45,000 tons at a cost of $36 million. An increasing portion of Canadian exports to the United Kingdom would therefore be based on Jamaica bauxite converted into alumina in North America. In

1. Canada, faced with the challenge, was conducting aggressive competition on her own account also. Thus in 1961, Aluminium Limited announced that they would be selling ingot at the United States-Canadian border at 23.80 cents per lb. The United States producers, led by Alcoa, soon after reduced their price from 26 cents to 24 cents a lb (i.e. £208 to £192 per ton). It was clear that this action, open to interpretation as provocative by United States producers, probably reflected Aluminium Limited's intention to get outlets for the increased outputs of which her long-term planned capacity was capable and to secure these before the new capacity of competitors was in production.

1962 it was reported that if the latest take-over bids were successful, Reynolds would own nearly one-third of the Canadian extrusion capacity and that for the first time in more than 25 years Alcoa was establishing a sales subsidiary in Canada.[1] The United States producers were indeed carrying the fight to the other fellow's camp and in the first quarter of 1962 the President of Aluminium Limited drew attention to the 'severe competitive conditions'. The sources of imports for the United States market were also undergoing a change. In 1957, Canada was providing 92 per cent of total United States primary aluminium imports, 84 per cent in 1958, 70 per cent in 1959, 68 per cent in 1960.

TABLE III.3   *Proportion of Primary Aluminium – By Producers in North America*

	Percentage United States Production				Percentage North American Production			
	1948 %	1958 %	1960 %	1961 %	1948 %	1958 %	1960 %	1961 %
Alcoa	52	33	36	35	33	24	26	26
Reynolds	27	32	25	23	17	22	18	17
Kaiser	21	28	24	24	13	20	18	18
Anaconda		3	3	4		2	2	2
Ormet		3	9	10		2	7	8
Harvey		1	3	4		1	2	3
Alcan					37	27	24	22
Canadian British						2	3	4

There was a situation then in the North American industry of temporary pauses and even declines but with a trend to push production upwards since there was excess capacity available. Changes had taken place in the structure of the industry (Table III.3). In the early post-war years Alcoa was still the dominant producer, her output in 1948 being some 52 per cent of the total United States figure, but by 1958 both Reynolds and Kaiser had

1. *Light Metals* (London), April 1962, p. 88, December 1962, p. 5.

expanded output so that their proportion of the market had risen from 48 per cent to 60 per cent and Alcoa's had fallen to 33 per cent. This change had little significance for the Caribbean end of the industry since apart from Alcoa's development in Surinam, the United States companies pursued the same policy in the Caribbean. Therefore even had there been a redistribution of production within the United States this would have made little difference to the Caribbean. But Alcan's proportion of the North American total fell by 10 per cent between 1948 and 1958 and this trend did have unfavourable implications for the Caribbean.

The North American domestic market in many ways was a most attractive one. Perhaps it was because of aggressive sales policies of the producers (and in this sphere Reynolds was outstanding). Perhaps it was because, in the United States, the metal entered the 1950s with a reputation for glamour and success which arose from the pride that the American people had come to feel in their mass production of a metal whose versatility had proved so effective in the winning of the war. Perhaps it was because of the higher incomes. Whatever the reasons were the demand for the metal in America was high. The consumption was about 24 lb a head a year, some 2–3 times that of Western Europe, some 30 times that in Latin America and some 40 times that in Asia. While this high consumption held advantage for the present it probably meant that future demand, on a per capita basis, could be expected to rise less rapidly than abroad. It was, of course, possible that some innovation might bring about increased mass consumption in the United States, but failing this the demand for aluminium in the United States was likely to be more closely tied to proportionate increases in population than in most other economies.

A characteristic of this period was that the United States industry decided to meet its problem of excess capacity by aggressive competition abroad. On some of these markets the influence of the change in policy of the United States producers was, as we have shown, considerable. But even at home the United States industry was facing problems and developments which were affecting policy. In 1961 it was reported[1] that a United States aluminium spokesman had called on the United States to combine with other aluminium producing nations to secure international quotas in order to enable the United States industry to develop its market potential. The claim was that this was necessary because the United

1. *Light Metals* (London), September 1961, p. 232.

States industry was at a disadvantage because of inequalities in taxes, depreciation allowances and labour costs. To complicate further the conditions on the domestic market of the United States it was reported that the Swiss company, AIAG, was contemplating plans for a subsidiary to establish reduction works in the United States (at Johnsonville, Tennessee).

With much excess capacity at home lying idle, with domestic prices being cut in a way that the industry had not experienced before, the United States firms decided that it was a good hedge to invest in expansion abroad despite conditions at home. There were the attractions of the Common Market in Europe, the vast potential increase in consumption in the Far East, the juxtaposition of raw material and power in Africa and Australia and the planned economic development in Latin America. But by the 1960s both nationalism and sophistication had grown and there was little promise of participation in these opportunities unless the United States[1] producers were prepared to exploit the resources and the market in joint collaboration with the natives, whether the natives were of India, Australia, Guinea or the Argentine. Thus if Alcoa wished to participate in the Common Market it would have to do so by undertaking the processing in plants within the Community and this they were doing in Surinam. Reynolds, if wishing to get into the Indian Market, had to follow a corresponding course. Kaiser was doing the same in Australia, and there were other illustrations of this. The feature of the 1960s for the North American industry was, therefore, massive idle capacity at home and expansion in plants abroad. The following is not a complete list but gives an indication of the order of expansion with which in 1962–63 the North American companies were being associated abroad (see Appendix B, Table IV):

a. *Alumina plants:* Alcoa: plants of about 116 and 220 thousand tons in Surinam and Australia respectively; Reynolds: plants of 100 thousand tons in Greece, 60 thousand tons in India; Kaiser: plants of 40 thousand tons in India, and 360 thousand tons in Australia; Harvey: plant of 100 thousand tons in U.S. Virgin Islands; Aluminium Limited: expansion of plants in Norway and India, totalling about 60 thousand tons capacity.

1. Reference is made to United States producers because the Canadian company, Aluminium Limited, had long ago adopted a policy of international dispersal of its production activities.

b. Smelters: Alcoa: expansion of plants in Brazil, Mexico, Surinam, India, Australia, totalling some 130 thousand tons; Reynolds: expansion in Canada (Baie Comeau), Argentina, Venezuea, Mexico, Norway, Greece, Ghana, India, Japan, totalling about 350 thousand tons; Kaiser: expansion of plants in Argentina, Spain, Ghana, India, Japan, Australia, New Zealand, totalling some 430 thousand tons; Aluminium Limited: expansion in Brazil, in Norway, Sweden, India, Japan, totalling about 150 thousand tons.

4 Supply and Demand in Western Europe and the Interplay of the Policy of the Aluminium Industrial Groups of America

The discussion in the previous chapter on the developments in the industry in North America concerned itself primarily with the inter-related problems of excess domestic capacity, the United State's invasion of markets abroad (some captured from the Canadian exporter) and a possible flattening off of domestic demand for aluminium in the United States. These developments meant that although some relationships of supply and demand caused concern, the United States aluminium industrial groups (with their Caribbean enterprises) were now much more actively involved in international operations than even a short while previously. Even if North American producers were in a mood of restraint in production at home they had become engaged in strategically placed expansion of capacity on an unprecedented scale abroad. The other major producers of the world industry were also involved in massive expansions. The order of increase is shown in Table IV.1. It is estimated that the smelter capacity in the Western world which would be about 5 million tons in 1965 would be 7.5 million in 1970, a further increase of 50 per cent.[1] This expansion is based on the conviction that consumption per head is likely to increase substantially in most parts of the world. Although substantial developments are world wide, of direct concern to this exercise are those in Western Europe and their ramifications in so far as the North America and Commonwealth Caribbean enterprises are concerned.

Production and Consumption in Western Europe

Until the Second World War Western Europe was the world's largest producer of aluminium, producing 55 per cent of the world

1. Hamer, R. D. (President of Alcan, S.A. Zurich). *The Future Development of the use of aluminium in the European Market.* Fourth International Light Metals Congress, Leoben, Austria, 1961.

TABLE IV.1 *Aluminium Production and Estimated Planned Expansion*

('000 Tons)

	1950	1957	1958	1959	1960	1965	Index 1960 = 100 1965
America							
United States	641.6	1,471.3	1,397.8	1,744.8	1,798.7	2,332.7	129.7
Canada	354.4	497.1	566.2	530.0	680.4	935.0	137.4
Brazil		8.8	11.7	17.8	17.9	59.1	330.2
Western Europe							
a. **EFTA Countries**							
United Kingdom	29.5	29.4	26.4	24.5	28.9	32.5	112.5
Austria	17.7	55.5	56.0	64.5	66.9	66.9	100.0
Norway	46.3	94.1	119.5	143.7	162.2	295.3	182.1
Sweden	4.0	13.4	13.5	15.3	16.4	17.1	104.3
Switzerland	18.9	30.6	31.0	33.8	39.1	39.1	100.0
b. **EEC Countries**							
France	59.7	157.4	166.2	170.3	231.5	290.4	125.4
West Germany	27.4	151.4	134.6	148.8	166.3	242.1	145.6
Italy	36.5	65.2	63.0	73.8	82.3	137.8	167.4
c. Spain	2.1	15.6	15.9	22.3	23.6	43.3	183.5
Yugoslavia	1.9	17.9	21.3	19.0	24.7	37.4	151.4
Africa		7.5	31.4	41.7	43.3	196.9	454.7
Asia							
Formosa (Taiwan)	1.7	8.1	8.5	7.4	8.1	19.7	243.2
India	3.6	7.8	8.2	17.1	18.0	80.7	448.3
Japan	24.4	66.9	83.3	98.6	131.1	393.7	300.3
Australia		10.6	10.9	11.4	11.7	39.4	336.8
Western World	1,269.7	2,708.6	2,765.4	3,184.8	3,551.1	5,259.1	148.0
Soviet allied Bloc	201.0	616.0	697.3	826.8	911.4	2,214.6	243.0
World	1,470.7	3,324.6	3,462.7	4,011.6	4,462.5	7,473.7	167.5

total. From 1938 to 1943 Europe's production rose by only 40 per cent, the North American production more than five times. This major leap forward in capacity, achieved during the war and immediate post-war years, created a difference which Europe has thus far not been able to modify substantially and in 1960 Western Europe was third in the three great blocs.[1]

	Percentage World Production %
American Continent	56
Soviet allied Bloc	20
Western Europe	19
Rest of the World	5

Although this substantial difference between the output of America and Europe remains, the rate of expansion in Europe has been greater than that in America (Table IV.1). The production in America more than doubled between 1950 and 1955, but between 1955 and 1960 rose only by about 28 per cent. Between 1955 and 1960 the output in Western Europe rose by nearly 55 per cent.

Production of aluminium occurs in 10 countries in Western Europe and only two of these – Spain and Yugoslavia with a combined production in 1960 of 48,000 tons – are not involved in either the European Economic Community or in the Free Trade Association. The Big Three are France, Norway and West Germany which are the only countries in Western Europe with a capacity of more than 200,000 tons.

As far as consumption in Western Europe is concerned, projections indicate steady increases in the demand for aluminium during the next decade. In 1959 the chief use was in transport followed by construction. It is projected that a higher proportion in 1970 will be used in construction than in transport. Following in importance would be the electrical industry (Table IV.2).

The capacity in both aluminium and alumina of the countries of the EEC is shown in Table IV.3.

The EEC countries had a capacity of alumina plants in excess of the requirements of their aluminium reduction plants in 1960. This excess was considerably reduced by 1961. On the basis of their past policy this meant almost certainly expansion of alumina facilities

1. For a fuller discussion see de Vitry, Raoul (President of Pechiney). *Present and Future of the Aluminium Industry in Europe.* Paper presented at Fourth International Light Metals Congress, Leoben, Austria, 1961.

TABLE IV.2   *Trend in Consumption of Aluminium[1] in Western Europe*

	Consumption 1959		Estimated consumption 1970	
	'000 Tons	%	'000 Tons	%
Building and Construction	113	10.1	650	24.5
Transport	312	27.8	575	21.7
Household and Commercial Appliances	104	9.3	300	11.3
Electrical Industry	151	13.4	375	14.2
Packaging	123	10.9	325	12.3
Other End-User Categories	320	28.5	425	16.0
Total	1,123	100.0	2,650	100.0

in some (or all) of the Community's member and associate countries: France, West Germany, Guinea, Greece.

The EFTA countries were in 1960 and 1961 in deficit as far as their alumina capacity (required to meet the demands of their aluminium reduction plants) was concerned. This deficit was substantial and is one of the major relationships to which the present study is directing attention.

The Producers in the European Economic Community

France: Due to her expertise in aluminium metallurgy France is the oldest producer of the metal; she has deposits of the ore – bauxite being named after the French town of Les Baux; there are hydro-electric resources and supplies of gas available within her boundaries. This combination has given France a tradition of leadership in the aluminium industry not only in the Common Market but in Western Europe. It is a position which she recognizes and which by shrewd and aggressive planning she gives every indication of maintaining. She is with Norway and West Germany one of the Big Three producers in Europe, her capacity (in Europe)

1. Hamer, R. D., *op. cit.*

being about 300,000 tons. Her production of 275,000 tons in 1961 was over four and a half times that in 1950 and makes her the fourth largest producer in the world (after the United States, the U.S.S.R. and Canada).

TABLE IV.3   *Capacity and Requirements in Aluminium and Alumina in EEC and EFTA Countries, 1960 and 1961*

	Aluminium Capacity in Operation		Alumina[1] required for Aluminium Capacity		Alumina Capacity in Operation		Excess Alumina Capacity over Requirements	
	1960	1961	1960	1961	1960	1961	1960	1961
	'000 tons		'000 tons		'000 tons		'000 tons	
EEC Countries								
France	240	296	458	565	567	572	109	7
West Germany	167	210[2]	319	401	510	512	191	111
Italy	85	93	162	178	189	236	27	58
Total (EEC)	492	599	939	1,144	1,266	1,320	327	176
EFTA Countries								
U.K.	35	35	67	67	105	105	38	38
Norway	189	221	361	422	18	18	−343	−404
Switzerland	40	40	76	76			− 76	− 76
Sweden	16	16	31	31	8	8	− 23	− 23
Austria	74	74	141	141			−141	−141
Total (EFTA)	354	386	676	737	131	131	−545	−606
EEC and EFTA	846	985	1,615	1,881	1,397	1,451	−218	−430

France has a large alumina capacity, some 20 per cent higher than her domestic needs for reduction to aluminium. In addition she is a large importer, primarily from Guinea and so she continues

1. Conversion: 1 ton Aluminium requires 1.91 tons of Alumina.
2. Includes 40,000 ton capacity which came into operation in 1962.

to be a major exporter of alumina, her chief customers being Spain, Switzerland and Norway.

The giant of the French industry is Pechiney. The company has nine smelters (with a total capacity of some 243,000 tons) and in 1961 produced 227,000 tons or 80 per cent of France's total. Of the smelters, that at Noguères is the most recently built and has attracted world-wide attention because of advances made through technological improvement and innovation. The company has three alumina plants in metropolitan France. Another factor adding to Pechiney's dominance in the industry is the control by the company of a large proportion of the fabrication capacity. This is unlike West Germany where much of the fabrication is in the hands of small operators. Ugine has two smelters in operation (with a total capacity of 53,000 tons a year) and in 1961 produced 52,000 tons or 20 per cent of the country's total. The company operates one alumina plant.

France's consumption is only two-thirds of her capacity. She is therefore an exporter on a substantial scale but so buoyant was the demand for her aluminium that in 1960 Pechiney had to import 10,000 tons of metal.

West Germany: The other major producer in the Common Market is West Germany. Unlike France, West Germany has practically no bauxite and secures her supplies mainly from Yugoslavia, Greece, France and Surinam. The main source of energy is not hydro-power but lignite. Production in 1960 was 166,000 tons compared with France's 232,000 tons. Expansion has since about 1950 been steady and even more impressive than in France. This is hardly a meaningful comparison since France's output at the end of the war was higher than in 1938 while West Germany's production had become so disorganised after the war that even as late as 1950 it was only about one-sixth of what it was in 1938. From such a low level the West German production could be expected to increase at a faster rate than that of France, and this it has done. France's output in 1961 was over four and a half times that of 1950, while in West Germany the figure was more than six times as high. West Germany's production in 1960 for the first time was as high as her peak production before the war.

West Germany is a producer of alumina and has a capacity in excess of her requirements even greater than that of France. Her main supplies of bauxite come from Yugoslavia (42 per cent in

1961), Greece, France and Surinam – in that order in 1961. Her exports of alumina go essentially to Austria and from 1961 she imported nearly half of her total alumina exports from Guinea.

West Germany has three industrial groups in alumina or aluminium. These are: VAW, mainly Government-owned with a smelter capacity of about 125,000 tons and with two alumina plants; AIAG, a Swiss company with a smelter capacity of 45,000 tons and one alumina plant; Giulini, a family-owned corporation with the quite exceptional characteristic of not being vertically integrated, operates an alumina plant but has no reduction plant (at any rate none in West Germany). West Germany's consumption of aluminium is well above her production which in 1961 was only 60 per cent of requirements, the rest coming from imports.

Italy: Like France Italy has bauxite deposits and power resources. She has a capacity of about 90,000 tons a year and in 1961 produced 82,000 tons of aluminium. In Italy there are three industrial groups in aluminium, Montecatini, Sava and Alcan. Montecatini announced in 1961 plans for a 100,000-ton smelter to be located in one of Italy's under-developed areas (Sardinia), some 10,000 tons more than Italy's total existing capacity. Her consumption in 1961 was in excess of her capacity so that, like West Germany, she was a net importer.

Her alumina capacity is in excess of her smelter requirements and this surplus is shipped primarily to Austria and Switzerland.

The Benelux Countries: None of the three Benelux countries in 1962 was a producer of aluminium in continental Europe. The discoveries of gas in the Netherlands had, however, led to a decision by the Billiton group to establish a smelter in North Holland. The long-range capacity was said to be 60,000 tons a year. Holland does not have bauxite deposits and the preliminary plans were that her smelter would secure its alumina either from Surinam or the United States. In 1961 she imported about 14,000 tons of the metal but should become a net exporter when her planned capacity comes into production.

Belgium is not a metropolitan producer of aluminium. She is, however, a major fabricator and was therefore one of the main importers of the metal. In 1961 she imported 69,000 tons, approximately half as much as West Germany.

The Producers in the European Free Trade Association Countries[1]

The capacities in both aluminium and alumina of the countries of the EFTA are shown in Table IV.3.

Norway: From the point of view of production, present and potential, Norway is the most important producer in the Association and ranks with France and West Germany as one of the Big Three. The Norwegian industry has much in common with the Canadian – no domestic supplies of the ore, generous supplies of hydro-power obtainable at competitive cost, a domestic consumption which compared with production is small, and exports which had grown up in a special relation with the United Kingdom market. In 1961 the capacity was estimated at over 200,000 tons a year. Production at 170,000 tons (i.e. nearly four times that in 1950) makes Norway approximately tied with West Germany for second place in production in Western Europe. Of all the countries in Western Europe, Norway gives promise of the most spectacular increases in capacity and production. The plans in existence call for an increase in capacity to about 300,000 tons in 1965 and to 700–800,000 tons in 1970. Norway has a small alumina capacity in relation to her requirements for reduction. In 1961 the imports of alumina came mainly from Jamaica.

The Norwegian aluminium production is in the hands of four industrial groups. Ardal og Sunndal is the largest, owning some 66 per cent of the country's capacity. It produces no alumina but imports all its requirements on the basis of long-term contracts with Aluminium Limited (Canada) and Alcoa (United States). The agreement calls for the repayment by Ardal og Sunndal with aluminium for the alumina received. Mosjöen Aluminium, while the newest, now has the second largest capacity. The Swiss group, AIAG, has minority interests but the controlling investment is by Norwegian capital. It has under discussion plans to double its capacity. Det Norske Nitridaktieselskap (DNN) is third in size. The company is owned in equal shares by Aluminium Limited and British Aluminium (which is now a part of the Reynolds constella-

1. G. A. Baudart's writings on the structure of the European industry well deserve study and the discussion here has secured much of its basic material from that source. See particularly 'L'Aluminium dans le Marché Commun', *Revue de l'Aluminium*, p. 288, 1961 and 'Les Developments de l'Industrie norvegienne de l'Aluminium', *Revue de l'Aluminium*, p. 455, 1962. M. Baudart is, of course, in no way responsible for my interpretation of the basic information.

tion). French interests were at one time involved but have now been withdrawn. The company has no alumina plant. Norsk Aluminium Company (NACO) is notable in that it is the only company producing alumina in Norway (using not the Bayer but the Pedersen process). It announced plans in 1961 to double its smelter capacity to 26,000 tons. Aluminium Limited owns 50 per cent of the shares.

Austria: The industry gives little indication of expansion in the immediate future. Production in 1960 was 67,000 tons, of which about a third was exported. There are two firms with production plants, one of which is a subsidiary of AIAG (Swiss).

Switzerland: The country is a relatively small producer but is important in the aluminium world since its financial group has major interests in several of the main producing countries, e.g. West Germany, Norway, Austria, and more recently the United States. There are plans for some expansion of its present domestic capacity. With a production in 1960 of 40,000 tons, exports were 8,000 tons. She imports her alumina requirements mainly from France. There are two companies with smelters. The larger of these is AIAG which is responsible for 80–90 per cent of the country's output.

Sweden: This, the smallest of the European producers, has a capacity of 16,000 tons with plans for modest expansion.

The United Kingdom: The industry in the United Kingdom has some similarities to that in Belgium: minimal interests in metropolitan reduction; high consumption; dependence essentially on imports. This analogy cannot be pushed too far since on the consumption side the United Kingdom's demands, present and potential, are on a much grander scale and on the supply side the United Kingdom unlike Belgium, is engaged in smelting. The United Kingdom has an aluminium capacity of about 25,000 tons. Her internal consumption in 1960 was 353,000 tons. This demand was met mainly from Canada and Norway up to 1957 (when imports from the United States were negligible) and, after 1957, from Canada, the United States and (in much smaller quantities) from Norway.

The structure of the industry has been discussed elsewhere. It was shown that the production side of the United Kingdom industry was now in the closest association with North American corporations and that the trend was towards a progressive sphere of influence of United States producers at the expense of the Canadian. This applied increasingly not only to primary aluminium but also to the fabrication side of the industry.

Aluminium and Trade Groupings of Western Europe

Britain applied in October 1961 to be admitted to the European Economic Community and early in 1963 her admission was refused, or indefinitely postponed. One cannot, in advance, know how permanent this refusal may be and it has therefore been decided to examine the question: What are some of the implications of the Common Market, including the possibility of its enlargement by the EFTA countries, for suppliers of the metal and of the raw materials?

In 1957 six countries signed the Treaty of Rome setting up the European Economic Community: France, West Germany, Italy and the three Benelux countries (Belgium, Netherlands and Luxemburg). Article 3 of the Treaty stated:

> 'The activities of the Community shall include . . . (a) the elimination between Member States of custom duties and quantitative restrictions in regard to the importation and exportation of goods, as well as of all other measures with equivalent effect; (b) the establishment of a common customs tariff and a common commercial policy towards third countries . . .'

It was clear that the influence on international trade would be profound and the OEEC Council, even before EEC formally came into being, set up a Committee to consider possible association between the projected Community and other countries. The Committee reported that it was feasible to work towards the freeing of trade between countries and at the same time to make it possible for the countries involved to deal individually with the outside world as far as trade and their internal economic and tariff policies were concerned. The idea was to secure a reduction of restrictions on trade in manufactured goods of the Free Trade Area. Each member would, however, have been able to determine its trade policy with non-members. Agricultural products were not included and this would have meant that the United Kingdom's relationships with Commonwealth trade in agricultural and non-manufactured products would not suffer violent dislocation. Negotiations, however, broke down and in 1959 seven countries brought into existence the European Free Trade Association (EFTA). The seven were: the three traditional neutrals (Sweden, Switzerland, Austria), the remaining Scandinavian countries (Norway and Denmark) with Portugal and the United Kingdom.

Since the EEC was a Customs Union and since progressively closer political union was envisaged the traditional neutrals in EFTA might not find it expedient to wish for full membership of the EEC. It was probable that Denmark would seek full membership and what was much more significant, from the point of view of the aluminium industry, both the United Kingdom and Norway had applied for admission and might one day be members. There has been a good deal of discussion on the envisaged effects – some great, some small – of the enlargement of the Community by the admission of the United Kingdom. There were few industries which would be as profoundly affected by this enlargement as aluminium and especially Commonwealth Caribbean alumina.

When Britain applied for admission to the EEC in 1961 the position was roughly as follows:

	Primary Aluminium '000 tons
Community's capacity for aluminium production (including 48,000 tons for Cameroun)	620
Demand in the Community	680
Deficit in the Community's supply of aluminium	60

The admission of the United Kingdom to the Community would have changed the outlook materially. In 1959 the United Kingdom had imported about 25 per cent more aluminium than all of the EEC countries put together and in 1960 her total imports were only slightly (about 10 per cent) below the Community's total. Britian's consumption due to subdued economic activity was lower in 1961 than in 1960 but even then, if she had been a member, the Community would have had a deficit not of 60 thousand tons but of some 300 thousand tons. If one accepts the trend in consumption of an increase of 7.2 per cent a year, and if one makes projections for 1966, consumption in the Community should be about 960 thousand tons and Britain's consumption should have increased to about 500 thousand tons. The position as projected then would be:

	Primary Aluminium '000 tons
Capacity for production of the Community + U.K. in 1966	1,070
Demand in the Community + U.K. in 1966	1,500
Deficit in supply in the Community + U.K. in 1966	430

The United Kingdom would therefore be an attractive addition to the Community from the point of view of aluminium because this large market was not one in which the main EEC producers had in the past participated to a substantial extent. The prospect of the opportunity to help supply this demand behind a protective tariff was indeed a pleasing one.

The aluminium producers of the Six, and especially those in France, argued that the picture was even more complicated. It was probable that Britain's entry into the Common Market, if allowed, would have been accompanied by Norway's admission. Although Norway's production in 1961 was 170,000 tons and her exports 144,000 tons, her anticipated capacity in 1966 was about 350,000 tons. This would have meant that by 1966 the output of the Community, enlarged by Norway, would have been about 130,000 tons short of the demand of the Common Market enlarged by Britian. In such a situation the North American industry, urged the Community's spokesmen, could, with its strong influence in Britain and Norway, become a threat to domestic EEC production. They pointed out that North America's capacity trebled itself in a decade rising from 1 million tons in 1950 to 3 million tons in 1961 and that in the same period consumption had risen from 900,000 tons to only 1,900,000 tons with the consequence that about three-quarters of a million tons capacity (out of the total of 3 million) was not used in 1961; that the Common Market would therefore be in constant threat of dumping and that one positive step for discouraging this was to establish an adequate safeguard through a high enough external tariff; that the absence of such a tariff would inevitably lead to unfair competition with a consequent deterioration of the structure of aluminium prices within the Common Market; that it would be a policy inimical to orderly development in the Community to establish the Common Market as a depository for excess North American production; that the dumping of North American aluminium would mean the abandonment of increased production in projects which had already been embarked upon not only in the Six but in the enlarged Community; that a vigorous North American industry nurturing and nurtured by its domestic consumption would be a demonstrable contrast to the Community's industry which, subject to harassment and unfair practice, would be denied such opportunity; that a foreseeable consequence would be the EEC's industrial groups finding themselves in economic difficulties and losing their independence; that, while Canada's relationship with the United Kingdom had been a long, traditional and understandable one, the assumption of extended control by the United States producers of the supplies, as well as of the fabrication in Britain, was evidence of what could and would happen in the Common Market; that the evidence did not indicate that North America could contribute to the well-being of the Community through its large and economic production of aluminium, since during recent years the price of aluminium in France had been below the international price and this had happened although France's tariff was higher than the common external tariff.

The tariff on aluminium in each of the member countries at the time of the Treaty of Rome was: France, 20 per cent; West Germany, 10 per cent; Italy, 28 per cent; Benelux, nil. The common external tariff based on the arithmetic mean of these would be 14.5 per cent but a figure of 10 per cent was negotiated in 1960 and further negotiations through GATT in 1962 led to a reduction to 9 per cent. The members of the Common Market, especially those members who were or expected to be exporters, were making it clear that they were opposed to a further reduction of the tariff.

Even spokesmen of the Six who were ardent supporters of an adequate common external tariff were conscious that the relationship between Aluminium Limited and Britain was a special case. After all, not only was Aluminium Limited traditionally accepted as a part of the United Kingdom complex but United Kingdom Government funds had been deliberately allocated to the expansion of capacity in Canada in much the same spirit as they might have been allocated to Wales if Wales had possessed the conditions appropriate for the location of aluminium reduction. Britain had made it a condition that she should have first claim on a quarter million tons of Canadian produced metal a year. This, in the early 1950s, was about half of Canada's production and 60–70 per cent of her exports. The Six might have found the problem easier to countenance if only Canadian supplies to the United Kingdom were involved but the situation was now complicated. From 1958 the United States exporters had begun taking over an increasing portion of the United Kingdom market and, to confuse the situation still more, a Reynolds-British Aluminium complex now operated a smelter in Canada. Therefore, argued the French and other leaders of the Community's industry, while there were special circumstances as far as Canada *vis-à-vis* the United Kingdom was concerned, the Six had previously rejected the principle of a Free Trade Area as an alternative to a customs union and the supply and demand conditions made it clear that a common external tariff, and an adequately high one, was required by the Community's producers and consumers of aluminium.

On the issue of a high external tariff the view of the United Kingdom Government was markedly different from that of the Six. The United Kingdom had admitted aluminium free of duty regardless of whether it originated in the Commonwealth, in EFTA (i.e. mainly Norway) or in other countries. Britain supported a continuation of this arrangement. The matter was thought important enough for Mr Heath, the British Minister in charge of negotiations, to refer to the concern the problem was causing and he made mention of it in his opening address in which he was submitting an application for Britian's entry into the Community. He then listed aluminium as one of the raw materials which should not, in his view, be subjected to an external tariff. The British argued[1] that it was inconsistent to have a tariff on aluminium since there was an accepted policy of having lower tariffs on basic materials which had of necessity to be imported; that the claim for the need of protection against lower cost aluminium from North America did not ring true since French prices were about 3 per cent below Canadian and 5 per cent below United States; that transportation costs from Canada were equivalent to about a 5 per cent tariff; that even if France could compete, Norway's costs were even lower and if the Community could hold its own against Norwegian aluminium it could do so against anybody's; that, even if Norway joined, the Community would still need to import aluminium for some time to come and that a tariff would discriminate against those countries which were net importers of the metal; that this discrimination would hit Britain hardest; that the United Kingdom's consumption was about half the EEC figure; that the United

1. *The Times*, London, June 12, 1962, p. 17.

Kingdom's imports were in some years as high as and higher than the total of all the EEC countries combined and this tariff would amount to a surcharge of 9 per cent on a raw material already costing more than 50 per cent of the price of its end product; that Italy supported France in claims for a high duty primarily because Italy's costs of production were high; that from the French point of view a high tariff would be of material aid in enabling her to expand her smelting capacity and to undersell the British fabricating industry not only on the Continent and on third markets but in Britain itself.

Apart from the considerations above, which apply in the case of primary aluminium and fabrication in the United Kingdom, there were also the implications for alumina. The Caribbean area and Canada were the chief Commonwealth communities supplying the United Kingdom with the basic requirements of the industry – bauxite, alumina and aluminium. The Canadian aluminium supplied to the United Kingdom market was largely based on bauxite and alumina from the Caribbean (primarily Jamaica and British Guiana). The imposition of a 9 per cent tariff (and there have even been rumblings of quotas) would probably mean that Canada would expand, within the confines of the Enlarged Community, the smelter capacity in which she already had interests. Because the Aluminium Limited side of the Canadian industry had adopted a policy of making alumina in the Caribbean and because there was already the traditional trade in this alumina with Norway, the Caribbean had reason to hope that Canada would continue to depend on alumina from the Caribbean rather than from elsewhere in the coming expansion (in Western Europe) of the production of aluminium and the consequent demand for alumina.

There were, however, hazards which these developments in the negotiations held, via Canadian aluminium, for alumina from the Caribbean. They are the types of problems to which Meade[1] drew

1. Meade, J. E. *U.K., Commonwealth and Common Market*, p. 24. '. . . Some raw materials in their processed forms (aluminium, leather, newsprint, for example) are admitted free into the United Kingdom but would be taxed under the present EEC tariff on import into the EEC. If these arrangements were continued, the United Kingdom would have to import aluminium from France free of duty while Canadian aluminium would be taxed. Such duties are proposed in order to protect the relevant processing industries in the EEC countries . . . The products of tropical agriculture present a rather different set of problems . . . There is real danger that the EEC arrangements would be such as to use the EEC market including the very important United Kingdom market as a means of protecting the French ex-colonies against other, including Commonwealth, producers of similar products.'

attention. Britain offered no preference to aluminium imported from the Commonwealth and if the only consequence of the new relationships was that there would be an end to these conditions then the Commonwealth (i.e. that part of it involved) could have no grounds for complaint. But there was more to it than that. The new relationships would have meant that not only did Canada and the West Indies lose their neutral position of no preferential treatment but continental European countries and some of the associated territories would have enjoyed a protected position in the aluminium Common Market. To rub salt into the wound the imports would be mainly for Britain. At present the United Kingdom could import Italian aluminium free of duty but could do the same for Aluminium Limited's aluminium (made mostly with Jamaican bauxite). Had Britain become a member this Canadian company, unless manufacturing in one of the countries of the EEC, would have to pay on its product a surcharge of 9 per cent (the common external tariff). This disadvantage would not have been suffered in the case of several Commonwealth products which were to be used in later stages of manufacture. Many raw materials (e.g. Australian wool), now admitted free on to the United Kingdom market, would on the basis of the negotiations have been similarly admitted to the Common Market. There was also the case of tropical agricultural products. The Six agreed that these were a special case and that the arguments in favour of non-discriminatory action against them were as acceptable as the corresponding argument in the case of aluminium was not. It would seem, however, that the analogy between alumina (i.e. the Commonwealth alumina involved in supplying the United Kingdom market with aluminium and coming primarily from the Caribbean) and tropical raw products was a close one. The main suppliers of alumina for Western Europe were – apart from domestic suppliers – the Caribbean and, increasingly, the Pechiney and associates' capacity in West Africa. The French alumina plants were already vertically integrated with aluminium production facilities in the Common Market. The Caribbean's plants were not so integrated and would be able to participate in the protected aluminium EEC imports (which are mainly United Kingdom imports) only to the extent that Aluminium Limited might decide to invest in expanded reduction facilities in the area of the Community and/or to increase her sales of alumina to EEC industrial groups.

To complicate the problem further the bauxite of the Commonwealth Caribbean was mined by the United States companies Reynolds and Kaiser, neither of which had elected to process bauxite into alumina in the territories providing the ore. That part of the Caribbean's output handled by the United States companies was, from the point of view of the Common Market, even more vulnerable. The Commonwealth Caribbean had reason for disappointment when United States aluminium (made largely from Jamaican bauxite converted into alumina in the continental United States) supplanted Canadian aluminium (made largely from Caribbean bauxite converted into alumina in the Caribbean) on the United Kingdom market. In the Common Market the threat would be that United Kingdom supplies of aluminium would not be based on Commonwealth Caribbean alumina (Canadian aluminium) and not even on Commonwealth Caribbean bauxite (United States aluminium) but on bauxite and alumina from France, Italy, Greece, Guinea. The relationship with the United States producers and the effect of their policy on the economy is a separate question and is discussed elsewhere in special relation to Jamaica.

Implications for Aluminium and Alumina of inter-relationships in EFTA

It is easy to be wise after the event, and as one looks back at the formation of these two European economic groups there can be little doubt now that the Commonwealth Caribbean involved in alumina production would have been well advised to explore with vigour possibilities for expansion of trade ties when EFTA was being formed.

For the five EFTA countries producing aluminium (Austria, Switzerland, Sweden, Norway, United Kingdom) the tariffs on alumina are shown (Table IV.4). The principle of protection for alumina was accepted in two (the United Kingdom and Switzerland) of the five. The United Kingdom protection was on the *ad valorem* basis. The Swiss was specific and the duty on alumina from non-EFTA countries was 50 per cent higher than on that from the EFTA countries. In regard to tariffs, these could be of only academic interest as far as the Caribbean was concerned since the conditions of the Association did not apply to non-European territories. While, therefore, protection on the Swiss market might apply to alumina processed in the United Kingdom it would not apply to alumina processed in the Commonwealth Caribbean.

TABLE IV.4   *EFTA Tariffs on Alumina*

| EFTA countries producing aluminium | Duty on alumina imported from | | |
	Other EFTA countries	Countries not in EFTA	The British Commonwealth
United Kingdom	7%	10%	Nil
Sweden	Nil	Nil	Nil
Switzerland	0.20 sfr[1]	0.30 sfr[2]	0.30 sfr[2]
Norway	Nil	Nil	Nil
Austria	Nil	Nil	Nil

In addition, while the purpose of the Association was to promote economic activity and to work towards the elimination of duties between Member States it was explicitly understood that there would be no common external tariff. The opportunity for admission of Caribbean alumina into EFTA was not to be gained on the grounds of protective tariffs. Rather was it to be gained by negotiating new trade arrangements for meeting potential demands which were demonstrably in the offing. In the same way that the French industrial groups and their associates had planned to look to Guinea for complementary supplies of alumina even before the days of the common external tariff of a Common Market, so might the Commonwealth Caribbean have tried to get itself accepted as the logical supplier of the needs of the EFTA countries. To accomplish this the Caribbean would have required two conditions: enough alumina capacity for the Caribbean to meet the demand; secondly sustained advocacy on behalf of the Caribbean product among the industrial groups with aluminium plants in the EFTA countries.

It is probable that with their traditional French ties the Swiss would not have too strongly encouraged proposals for changing the old and creating new ones for Caribbean alumina.[3] One would

1. 34.5 pence or 50.8 cents (U.S.) per long ton.
2. 51.8 pence or 76.2 cents (U.S.) per long ton.
3. In August of 1962 a shipment of some 5,138 tons of Jamaican alumina was made to Switzerland; future events will show to what extent this may have been part of a trend.

guess that Austria, with its alumina trade connections already well established, would also have been lukewarm. Sweden might have been more amenable than either Austria or Switzerland in the light of Aluminium Limited's participation in the Swedish facilities but in any event Sweden's demand would not be high. The prize to have gone for, however, was Norway. This was the country with the greatest potential in Western Europe for expansion in aluminium production. It possessed no bauxite of its own. The Commonwealth Caribbean's interest in this market was that the Caribbean was uniquely eligible for meeting the excess requirements of Norwegian smelters. In 1959–60 when the EFTA convention was drawn up the Commonwealth Caribbean was a territory for whose international relations the United Kingdom was responsible, and it was the only such territory which produced alumina. This, therefore, gave the Caribbean a specially high claim for alumina trade with Norway and for Britain's advocacy of this claim. The Caribbean had already established trading relationships in alumina and, from the outset of its production activities, had been shipping alumina to Norway. It would have been good if Norway's industrial groups had been persuaded to offer a more secure place for expanding supplies of Caribbean alumina in the expanding output of aluminium. This would have encouraged a greater production of alumina in the Commonwealth Caribbean, over and above Aluminium Limited's requirements, and for consumption by smelters in Norway whether they were associated with Aluminium Limited or not. One needs to evaluate some of the arguments and considerations for or against the proposals for arrangements for securing a generous proportion of the Norwegian market. It is almost certain that the chief question mark would be about the attitude of the United States firms which have interests in Norway. Alcoa is associated with Ardal og Sunndal and Reynolds with DNN. Even though Kaiser, as far as the writer knows, did not have financial interests in any of the Norwegian reduction plants, their position in fabrication in the United Kingdom would make their United Kingdom associates sensitive to developments relating to Norwegian metal. Their support one way or the other could have some influence. It was not conceivable that the United States industrial groups could be expected to support with enthusiasm a scheme whose net effect would be an increased demand for their competitor's product, the Caribbean producer Aluminium Limited being the sole processor of alumina in the Commonwealth Caribbean. It would appear that, in the EFTA and EEC alumina

D

plans for the future, the interests of Aluminium Limited were identified with, or at any rate did not greatly differ from, those of the Commonwealth Caribbean. By the same token the combination of circumstances which occurred in EFTA could result in the policy of the United States corporations (who mined but did not process bauxite in the Caribbean) conflicting with the economic advantage of the Commonwealth Caribbean.

Point is given to the argument that the Commonwealth Caribbean enterprise is at a disadvantage if one looks at what the relationships have been between the French metropolitan industrial groups and the suppliers of their raw material in Africa. France is the only large producer of bauxite within the Community and, with her African enterprises, expects to be still larger. She is therefore within the Community the main architect for alumina policy. There is no ambivalence in the attitude of the French aluminium producers, Pechiney and Ugine, to the conversion of EEC bauxite into alumina and to this process being protected within the Common Market. Under the French leadership the arrangement arrived at in the Common Market is that the ultimate common external tariff[1] on alumina will be 11 per cent and that there should be no duties within the Community. At July 1, 1962, the French tariff on alumina was 11.5 per cent from non-member countries and 7.5 per cent from member countries. The external tariff in the EEC was higher even than the protection which the United Kingdom Government, whose consumption of alumina was in any case low, gave to Commonwealth alumina. This meant that the United Kingdom would, if given entry into the EEC, adopt progressive stages of protection for alumina. When the final stage was achieved Britain would afford alumina produced in any of the member countries (e.g. France and her African associate producers, Belgian and Dutch overseas associate producers) higher protection than she had provided to her Commonwealth alumina. Only to a modest extent was the Commonwealth Caribbean bauxite-alumina enterprise vertically integrated into aluminium production within EFTA. Only that portion of the Commonwealth Caribbean enterprises which was so integrated would not be discriminated against if the EFTA countries joined the EEC. Britain, being the largest importer of aluminium, would in such an event be imposing severe discrimination indeed against Commonwealth Caribbean alumina in favour of corresponding alumina from enterprises integrated into the EEC

1. No. 28.20, under the Brussels Tariff nomenclature.

aluminium industries. Nor was that all. Just as Britain was the chief importer of aluminium, Norway was second in consumption of alumina only to France and expected in the not distant future to be greater. Since France had substantial supplies of raw materials itself the Norwegian market for alumina was therefore potentially the most attractive even if one looked at both the EFTA and the EEC countries. The Commonwealth Caribbean alumina would have been in a better bargaining position for the Norwegian alumina market, if at the time of entry into the EEC better supply terms for the future had been negotiated with Norway. The outlook for the future was that if the United Kingdom and Norway were admitted to the EEC, a Commonwealth Caribbean which did not convert more of its output of bauxite into alumina for integration into aluminium production in the EEC would suffer two forms of discrimination:

a. indirect discrimination on the United Kingdom market in relation to those supplies of aluminium which were produced in the EEC in large part from vertically integrated EEC producers;
b. direct discrimination on the Norwegian alumina market which would be supplied increasingly from EEC and other European alumina.

As one followed the negotiations for the admission of Britain and of Norway into the EEC one recognized that if Britain was admitted into the EEC there was probably no sector of the Commonwealth's economy for which the forebodings were more sombre than that sector of the Commonwealth Caribbean depending heavily on the bauxite industry. There was also probably no problem connected with European trade for which the solution was more clear.

Implications for Aluminium and Alumina of inter-relationships in the EEC and Britain

Early in 1963 the French announced their veto of Britain's application for admission into the EEC. It is neither easy nor wise to attempt crystal gazing but as hazardous as this may be there is little alternative in the present context to putting forward some guesses about the possible implications of this situation for the future course of bauxite–alumina–aluminium trade and production *vis-à-vis* North America, the Caribbean and Western Europe.

One alternative set of possibilities is that the admission of Britain and other EFTA countries into the EEC (either as full or associate members) is not refused but only delayed briefly. Were this the course of events there would be little modification of the considerations which have been discussed before. After all there were few who, even when Britain's negotiations on her application for admission seemed to be making progress, did not conceive it as probable that the application would continue to encounter delays. One probable consequence of the new level of resistance to Britain's admission was that if or when the question of admission was re-opened the aluminium industrial groups of the Six would be more resolved than ever to oppose any further reduction in the external tariff on the metal.

The second alternative is that the admission of Britain and other EFTA countries into the EEC will continue to be refused or indefinitely postponed. At the time of this writing the consensus was that this second alternative was the more likely. An obvious consequence would be that the combined consumption of the Six would be met, and planned to be met, by the expanding output of aluminium and alumina in France, West Germany, Italy, Greece (and perhaps Holland), in West Africa (French Guinea and Cameroun) and in Surinam. The French are reputed to be resolved to make it difficult for North American capital to buy its way into the Community's production complex and are vocal in their opposition to the idea of the kind of participation which has taken place in Britain. Already, however, Reynolds is involved in Greece, Alcoa in Surinam, Reynolds and Ormet in Guinea. It may well be that faced by giants like Pechiney in France and VAW in West Germany the North American producers may elect to divert their attention elsewhere and concentrate on some of the other expanding aluminium markets of the world, but it is unlikely that the North American producers will accept, without a struggle, the view that they should keep out of one of the most attractively expanding markets of the world. They will probably continue to invest in fabrication plants,[1] to send in the metal over the 9 per cent tariff wall and to secure[2] interests, controlling or otherwise, in reduction

1. Kaiser has recently invested in a fabricating mill at Koblenz in Germany and this should provide an outlet for some Kaiser primary metal. In addition Kaiser Aluminium Werke planned to build an aluminium reduction plant in Germany. *Light Metals* (London), December 1962, p. 7.

2. Since this was written there were reports that Alcoa had taken steps to buy its way into Pechiney.

as well as extraction plants, within the Community. If there is greater participation of United States companies in supplies to the Six, there will be a greater outlet for Commonwealth Caribbean bauxite in so far as United States manufactured aluminium is exported to the Common Market. For aluminium supplied to the Community, and manufactured there by United States companies and their subsidiaries, the bauxite of the Commonwealth Caribbean is unlikely to compete successfully with alumina produced in plants in which United States companies have interests in Surinam, Greece, Guinea. One could envisage even the possibility that, as the United States industrial groups' financial involvement in alumina plants overseas became greater, their relatively lower investment in the bauxite operations in, say, Jamaica might become increasingly expendable. As far as the Canadian industrial group is concerned, their involvement in alumina processing in the Caribbean is likely to mean that greater participation by that group in supplies to the EEC will have favourable implications, in the long and the short term, for the outlook of the Commonwealth Caribbean economies. Thus far, Aluminium Limited has based its policy, to a major extent, on production of its alumina in the Caribbean. Aluminium Limited already has interests in fabrication capacity in West Germany and this is likely to afford an outlet in the Community for more Canadian produced metal.

While many interests will be dismayed by the non-entry of Britain into the Common Market the North American aluminium industrial groups are not. North American aluminium entered Britain free of duty, but, had Britain been admitted to the Community, this aluminium would not only have ceased to enjoy a nil tariff but would have had to compete with a French, West German, Italian, Greek product which did. Since in 1960 exports to Britain made up 33 per cent of Canada's aluminium exports and 40 per cent of the United States aluminium exports, the disorganisation of the United Kingdom market would have added to the discomfiture of the North American producers. As far as the Commonwealth Caribbean enterprises were concerned the continued admission of duty free North American aluminium to the United Kingdom market was an item on the credit side because the smelting operations of the large industrial groups, apart from Alcoa, are based predominantly on Commonwealth Caribbean raw materials. As has been pointed out above there are, however, important differences which result from the proportion in which the United Kingdom market is shared between United States and the Canadian producer. It is only relatively recently that the United States producers have entered the United Kingdom aluminium market and their proportion of the total imports has increased sharply.

Since the United States companies do not convert their bauxite into alumina in the Commonwealth Caribbean while the Canadian company does and since the local disbursements per ton unprocessed bauxite are approximately £1.4 compared with £4 per ton converted into alumina, the Commonwealth Caribbean stands to lose substantially by the displacement on the United Kingdom market of Canadian by United States aluminium.

As far as Western European trade in aluminium is concerned the net effect of the refusal (or indefinite postponement) of the United Kingdom's entry into the European Economic Community is the situation which has been discussed above when the implications of the EFTA supply and demand relationships were considered.

The Latin America Free Trade Association came into being with the signing of the Montevideo Treaty in 1960. Seven countries comprising the bulk of Latin America are members – Argentina, Brazil, Chile, Paraguay, Peru, Uruguay and Mexico. Some regard this as the first step in bringing about a Common Market for the twenty countries of Latin America. In Argentina some three smelters with a capacity of about 60,000 tons are reportedly being planned for construction. While some Argentine capital is involved, Kaiser, Reynolds and Pechiney are participating. In Brazil Aluminium Limited has one reduction plant in operation and so has a local company, both of which companies have plans for expansion. Alcoa and Kaiser have plans for reduction plants of their own. In Mexico both Alcoa and Reynolds have reduction plants under construction. There are two alumina plants in Brazil and one alumina plant has reached the active planning stage in Argentina (the capital being Argentinian). From the known reports the deposits of bauxite in Latin America are not high, although all that this may mean is that geological surveys have been inadequate thus far. In this context it can be expected that the United States companies will supply, to their Latin American subsidiaries, alumina made in the most part from Caribbean bauxite which is converted into alumina either in the United States, or perhaps in Latin America. In LAFTA as in EFTA the outlook for Caribbean processed alumina is not bright except in the case of those smelters in which the United States companies do not have financial interest and influence.

5 The Bauxite-Alumina Enterprises and the Jamaica Economy

The Historical and Institutional Background

The commercial possibilities of Jamaica's bauxite deposits were recognized in about 1942 but this was not the date of the discovery of the deposits. The first official geological survey of Jamaica was reported on in 1869[1] and noted the widespread occurrence of aluminium ore, but the announcement attracted little attention since the processes for extracting the metal aluminium from the ore were still uncertain and only came into commercial operation some 20 years later, in the 1880s. The rediscovery of bauxite in Jamaica came when the new demands for the metal encouraged a search for new sources of the ore. In 1938 the Agricultural Chemistry Division of the Department of Agriculture found that certain infertile red soils had a high aluminium content, and in 1942 some of these were identified as low grade bauxite.[2] This attracted the attention of aluminium interests abroad because the demand for aluminium during the 1939–45 war had stimulated interest in possible new sources of the raw material. During the Second World War there had been heavy losses of ships hauling bauxite from Surinam and British Guiana to alumina plants in North America. Jamaica was less than half the distance from the Gulf Coast ports and therefore had a considerable strategic advantage.

Various delays which prevented the war-time exploitation of Jamaican reserves were only temporary, and four companies became interested from an early stage.[3] The Dutch Company, Billiton, first in the field, subsequently abandoned its concessions, but the other companies prospected and acquired concessions on bauxite-bearing lands. Most sections of the community viewed with

1. Brown, Charles B., Sawkins, James G., *et al*. *Report on the Geology of Jamaica*. Longmans Green & Co., London, 1869, p. 167. 'Parish of Manchester – *Red Ferruginous Earth*. This very peculiar deposit is seen persistently covering the white limestone formation everywhere in the parish . . . In composition it is principally a mixture of iron and alumina.' Alumina was also identified in various mineral samples (Appendix III).
2. Zans, V. A., *op. cit*.
3. Stern, Peter, *op. cit*., Table II, p. 16.

little enthusiasm the prospect of bauxite being mined in the island, such discussion as there was being concerned mainly with the probable ill effects of mining. Apart from the pressure brought to bear by the companies themselves, there was little agitation for quick action. An emergency regulation which had been proclaimed during 1942 to control mining in Jamaica[1] was rescinded early in 1944 and not immediately replaced by any permanent legislation. The delay may in part have been the result of difficulty in obtaining expert advice, and the Government's desire to avoid the evil consequences of inadequately controlled mining, but in a community which had no continuous mining tradition and whose previous major experience with extractive industries was limited to stone-quarrying, it was not surprising that the potential value of the bauxite industry to the economy was not generally realized.[2]

The Mining Laws of 1947[3] followed fairly closely the pamphlet on Colonial mining policy[4] which had been published by the Colonial Office in 1946. They vested the ownership of minerals in the Crown, so that mining could take place only under Government lease, fixed the royalty which was to be paid on bauxite mined and regulated the conditions under which it could be mined.

The bauxite companies had been buying land and acquiring options since 1944 and by 1946 the price of bauxite land had risen to between two and three times its former value.[5] After 1947 the companies intensified their activities further. The Aluminum Company of Canada had in 1943 formed a subsidiary, Jamaica Bauxite (1943). This was reorganized in 1952 under the name Alumina Jamaica Ltd, and in 1961 renamed ALCAN (Jamaica) Ltd. It had begun acquiring land, and by 1950 was preparing not only to mine bauxite, but to convert it into alumina in the island. Reynolds Metals Co. had been interested in the Jamaican bauxite reserves

1. Regulation No. 21 of November 1942.
2. Benham, F., *et al. Report of the Economic Policy Committee*, January 1945 – 'Mining operation may begin in, say, two years' time; output may be around a million tons of bauxite per year for a very long period of years. The numbers employed in actual mining are unlikely to be much more than a thousand.'
The general gloom of the Benham report reflected, in part, the opinions of many in high places. Jamaican planters with limited bank credit feared competitive activity which might put up the rate of wages and place a strain on their working capital. However the idea that bauxite was not likely to involve extensive operations was less distasteful than might be expected.
3. Minerals Vesting Law, Cap. 38 of 1947. Mining Law, Cap. 41 of 1947.
4. *Memorandum on Colonial Mining Policy*, HMSO, Col. No. 206, 1946.
5. Benham, F., *et al., op. cit.*, p. 4, para. 23.

since 1943, and in 1950 a subsidiary, Reynolds Jamaica Mines Ltd, was formed to conduct operations in Jamaica. Kaiser Aluminum and Chemical Corporation began buying land through its subsidiary Permanente Metals in 1947, and in 1950 it formed a subsidiary, Kaiser Bauxite, to undertake development in Jamaica.

Thus in 1950 three companies awaited the completion of the legal framework in which they were to operate and hard bargaining preceded the drawing up of the 1950 Bauxite and Alumina Industries Encouragement Law, and its accompanying regulations.[1] The Hicks Report considered that 'it looks as if a better bargain could have been made by the Jamaican Government'[2] and it seems fairly certain that the bauxite companies would have mined in Jamaica under terms more favourable to Jamaica than were imposed in 1950. The companies based much of their claim for low income tax rates on the low alumina content of Jamaican bauxite. Whatever may have been the justification for these claims, an important compensatory factor was the low cost of mining Jamaican bauxite which has little overlay and is surface mined. Under the 1950 law the companies were given duty concessions and the regulations fixed the income tax liability of the bauxite companies on the basis of a notional profit per ton of bauxite. No special arrangement was required to assess the alumina company's income tax liability as alumina had a market price and the company's profits were assessed in the normal way.

The initial investment of the companies had created employment and provided a fillip in the economy, but the industry was capital intensive and the amount of permanent employment it offered limited. Nor was it a consumer of local products to any great extent. The main long-term advantage which would accrue to Jamaica from the bauxite industry was in tax and royalty revenue. These were, as the Hicks Report pointed out, not only inadequate but unfavourable if comparison were made even elsewhere in the Caribbean. The Report discussed the rôle of the industry in the economy, and served to encourage the Government to negotiate on Jamaica's behalf better possible revenue from the industry. In 1956 the Government undertook a detailed study of the industry, and obtained information which enabled it to conclude that not only should the royalty be revised, but that the companies could be persuaded to agree to a revision of the income tax arrangements.

1. Bauxite and Alumina Industries Encouragement Law, Cap. 53, 1950.
2. Hicks, J. R. and U.K. *Report on Finance and Taxation in Jamaica*, p. 101.

The Bauxite and Alumina Industries Encouragement Law, which provided that income tax arrangements could be revised only with the agreement of the company concerned, could of course have been amended, but the Government was presumably reluctant to take a step which might undermine the confidence of foreign investors in undertakings given by the Jamaican Government. It therefore opened negotiations with Reynolds Jamaica Mines Ltd and Kaiser Bauxite in January, 1957. The Government and its advisers had grown in sophistication and were in a stronger position than had been the negotiators in 1950.

The 1957 agreement revised the royalty rate on bauxite, which had formerly been 1s per ton on bauxite exported, 10d per ton on bauxite processed locally. The rates were now placed on a sliding scale, and the differential in favour of locally processed bauxite was slightly increased:

a. Royalty on Bauxite charged on Tonnage mined during calendar year

A. On bauxite processed into alumina in Jamaica per long dry ton

On first million tons   2s   6d
On second million tons   2s
On any amount in excess of two
million tons   1s   6d

B. On bauxite exported unprocessed per long dry ton

(i) *Fixed royalty*
On first million tons   2s
Where production more than one
million tons, entire tonnage up
to 2 million tons   1s   6d
Where production more than two
million tons, on tonnage in
excess of 2 million tons   1s

(ii) *Variable royalty*
As in (i) above, plus or minus an amount varying directly with the price of aluminium pig as quoted in the *American Metal Market*, the base price being 25 cents per lb.

Thus if the price rose to 26 cents per lb the royalty on less than one million tons would be per long dry ton:

Variable royalty $= \dfrac{26}{25} \times 2s = 2.08s$ per long dry ton.

Fixed royalty $\qquad\qquad = 2.00s$ per long dry ton.

Total royalty $\qquad\qquad = 4.08s$ per long dry ton.

The royalty is computed in sterling.

b. Income Tax for Bauxite Companies

Pre 1957 – 40 per cent of notional profit of 60 cents per ton
= 24 cents or 1s 8d per ton.

Post 1957 – 40 per cent of notional profit of \$3.85 per ton
= \$1.54 or 11s per ton. Half of the notional profit,
\$1.925, is assumed to vary with the price of
aluminium pig. Thus if the price of aluminium pig
rose from the base price of 25 cents per lb to
26 cents per lb the income tax per ton of bauxite
would be:

40 per cent of \$1.925 $\qquad = \$0.770$ per ton.

40 per cent of $\dfrac{\$1.925 \times 26}{25} = \$0.801$ per ton.

Total Income tax $\qquad = \$1.571$ per ton.

Income tax is computed and payable in U.S. dollars.

No change was made in the arrangements under which the
alumina company paid income tax at normal company rate on its
profits, but the assumed rate of profit of the bauxite companies was
increased to \$3.85 (27s 6d) per ton of bauxite, and the tax liability
was to be computed in dollars which provided against further
devaluation of the pound sterling. (This must have caused some
misgiving in 1961 when the dollar showed signs of weakening.) Half
the income tax and royalty payments were on a sliding scale which
was to vary with the price of aluminium pig in the New York
market. For each 1 cent per lb increase in the price of aluminium
pig on the New York market there would be an increase of 3.36
pence per ton of bauxite accruing to the Jamaican treasury.

The course of aluminium pig prices from 1950 led the Jamaican
negotiators to hope that this arrangement would result in substantial gains in revenue. It carried with it the disadvantage that
revenue would be adversely affected during a recession, not only by
a falling off in the quantity of bauxite exported but also by a falling
off in the revenue per unit of exports. The immediate result of the

new agreement was to increase revenue per ton of bauxite mined by more than 500 per cent.

Simultaneously with the increase in output of bauxite and alumina there had been an increase in investment activity as the two bauxite companies expanded their plant and transport facilities and increased their land reserves, and after a lull in 1954 bauxite investment reached a new high level in 1956. Alumina Jamaica Ltd commenced building a new 240,000-ton extraction plant. Reynolds Jamaica Mines Ltd installed a second tramway, two new drying kilns and increased storage capacity. Kaiser Bauxite extended its storage and wharf facilities at Port Kaiser and expanded its mining operations. Soon after this the American Metal Climax Inc. (through its subsidiary Caribex Ltd) and Harvey Aluminum of America began prospecting for bauxite. ALCOA formed a local subsidiary, ALCOA Minerals of Jamaica Ltd, which acquired options and in 1959 announced its intention of commencing mining in 1963. In 1960 the company took over the lease formerly held by Caribex Ltd.

Agricultural and Related Activities

It was one of the stipulations of the original agreements signed by the mining companies with the Jamaican Government that all land not immediately subjected to mining operations should be kept in a condition consistent with good agricultural practice. This require-ment had several implications for husbandry and tenancy arrange-ments. All three companies have developed beef herds although Kaiser was less involved in this aspect of development than the others. This has resulted in the improvement of several thousand acres of pasture land in the case of Reynolds and Alcan. The Reynolds herd amounted to over 20,000 head on improved pastures of over 25,000 acres. The Alcan herd totalled over 6,000 head (nearly three times as many as were purchased with the properties) on 8,000 acres. Both companies have sub-divided large pastures, planted grass, applied fertilizer, improved water supply, and intro-duced rotational grazing. The total acreage of improved pasture land in Jamaica was 90,000 acres in 1958, while the estimated total beef cattle herd was 101,500 head. From this it can be seen that the mining companies contributed materially to the economy. Alcan established irrigated pastures near the port that it built and Reynolds established a meat processing plant in St Ann. Reynolds has also been an important producer of poultry.

In addition to these livestock operations both Reynolds and Alcan planted extensive acreages of economic trees. Reynolds has concentrated in the past on afforestation schemes. Alcan planted over 200,000 hard wood seedlings and has under cultivation 500 acres of citrus groves in Manchester. Alcan is the largest grower of ortaniques, the special Jamaican orange-tangerine hybrid, and its nurseries have supplied Government and local nurserymen with budwood for 100,000 ortanique buddings. Sales of citrus increased from 8,600 boxes in 1946 to 45,573 in 1961.

Another agricultural scheme which brings the mining companies into close contact with the social and economic life of the people of Jamaica is their resettlement scheme: the practice of keeping tenants on lands (purchased or leased for mining purposes) until required. Where land has previously been mined out and the top soil replaced under the agreement tenants may also be resettled. Thus Reynolds made small tracts of farmland available to between 1,600 and 2,000 small farmers at a nominal rental on two to three years tenancy agreements with the stipulation that the land must in fact be cultivated. No tenant was allowed to stay indefinitely on his allotment, but he was assigned other land to plant while he took off the last crop. He was thus enabled to farm continuously. Alcan also had lease arrangements embracing about 2,500 tenants and involving over 3,500 acres.

There was an important difference between the position of Kaiser and that of the other two companies. While Alcan and Reynolds consolidated a number of large properties and bought very few small farms, Kaiser began to contract to buy several thousand small parcels of land. The company was aware that, if it carried on agriculture itself, it must disturb the whole socio-economic pattern by consolidating large numbers of small properties under modern systems of farm management, with displacement of population. Accordingly, it concentrated on leasing land, usually to the former owners. By the beginning of 1963, Kaiser had leased two-thirds of its holdings, as follows:

	No.	Acres
Leases covering over 100 acres	36	23,980
Leases covering under 100 acres	2,502	18,520
	2,538	42,500

In addition, Kaiser followed a resettlement policy: the company bought properties of some size which were not 'bauxite properties' at all, and on these resettled families displaced from land. By the beginning of 1963, nearly 7,000 acres had been transferred to resettle small farmers and over 7,000 acres more were being prepared for resettlement. The area occupied by the Company's mining activities (including land in process of rehabilitation after mining) was only about 5,000 acres, and some of this area had never been agricultural land. In addition, the Company has agreed to transfer 3,000 acres to Government for forestry and watershed protection purposes.

Every small farmer selling to Kaiser is given the option to buy an equivalent holding in a resettlement area at standard prices of £10 and £12 an acre.

About 300 acres are mined annually. All land mined must be rehabilitated. This takes five years. The top soil is replaced, fertilizer is applied, grass is sown, and cattle are grazed. The only other farming operation carried out by Kaiser is the growing of experimental crops (sweet potatoes, yams, corn, cassava) on land *before* it is mined. The rehabilitated land is ideal for settlement, as roads and other facilities, created during the mining operations, are already in existence.

In these various ways the companies have engaged in agricultural pursuits and reduced to a minimum the area of disruption in the lives of the people inhabiting the regions involved in mining operations. In their agricultural activities the mining companies engage altogether about 2,000 persons in full or part-time employment.

The interests of the companies in community activities have extended into the sphere of industrial training. Perhaps the most important aspect of industrial training to which the mining enterprises have contributed has been in the sphere of providing a foundation of industrial discipline to a small work force which had received little experience in this direction. Improved factory management methods have been made available to other Jamaican enterprises through work study courses. The insistence of the companies on formal education as the basis of success in training an industrial work force has also been of significance.

The Economic Background

The impact of bauxite and alumina operations on the Jamaican economy has been from their inception a subject of speculation varying from the pessimistic pronouncements of those who feared that mining would ruin the agricultural potential and the beauty of large tracts of Jamaica without adequate economic gain, to the rosy pictures relating particularly to the balance of trade painted by others. Since 1958 the companies have been obliged in theory to supply the Government with details of their costs and local outlays. To what extent this has happened in practice those not in government do not know since most of whatever information is supplied is confidential, and therefore not available to the public. The research worker in consequence finds it an extremely difficult task to disentangle the activities (and so the contributions) of the bauxite companies from those of the alumina enterprise. There are, however, now available to the public sufficient data which, when co-ordinated with cost structures for corresponding activities abroad, enable some assessment to be made of the rôle the companies have played in the Jamaican economy over the past ten years, and more particularly in recent years (Table V.1).

TABLE V. 1. *Gross Domestic Product, by Industrial Origin, at Factor Cost in Jamaica*[1]

Sector	Percentage Total Domestic Product				
	1953	1955	1957	1959	1960
	%	%	%	%	%
Agriculture, Fishing, etc.	21.2	19.2	13.9	13.5	12.9
Central and Local Government	6.4	6.6	6.5	7.0	6.8
Construction and Installation	9.6	9.5	13.6	11.3	11.3
Distribution	17.1	16.8	16.6	17.0	17.2
Manufacturing	13.8	13.4	12.7	13.1	12.8
Bauxite Mining and Alumina Manufacture	2.3	4.6	8.4	7.4	8.5
Miscellaneous Services	14.1	13.9	12.6	12.9	12.9
All Other	15.4	16.1	15.7	17.5	17.8

The bauxite and alumina enterprises were increasing their production throughout the period 1952–1960 and it was a period of

1. Department of Statistics, Kingston, Jamaica. *National Accounts*, Income and Expenditure 1950–57, and *Economic Survey*, 1960.

expansion and diversification of the whole economy. The GDP rose from £95 million in 1952 to £231 million in 1960 (Table V.1A). Part of this rise was due to the fall in the value of money, but calculations of GDP at constant prices showed that there was a substantial increase in real income. The part played by bauxite and alumina in this expansion is shown in Table V.1, which gives the proportionate share of the main items of the GDP. The total value of each sector rose over the period, but the increase was much greater in the sectors Mining, Construction and Government than in the other sectors.

The contribution of the bauxite industry to over-all economic activity in Jamaica is shown (Table V.1A) in terms of current and constant values. Together with agriculture, manufacture and construction, mining ranks as one of the four main providers of income in the island's economy. As far as the contribution to the country's trading position is concerned the valuation of the ore for export purposes and for the assessment of taxes on profit is notional. Both these valuations were revised by the agreement in 1957 which has been discussed above. The effects of these changes have been

TABLE V.IA   *Bauxite and Alumina, at Factor Cost, in Jamaica*[1]

	GDP at Current Prices			At Constant Prices		
	(1)	(2)	(3)	(4)	(5)	(6)
		Bauxite Mining and	Column (2) as per-centage of		Bauxite Mining and	Column (5) as per-centage of
Year	Jamaica £'000	Refining £'000	Column (1) %	Jamaica £'000	Refining £'000	Column (4) %
1952	94,962	N.A.	N.A.	99,743	N.A.	N.A.
1953	106,692	2,467	2.3	114,411	2,737	2.4
1954	119,682	4,586	3.8	127,411	5,475	4.3
1955	136,411	6,276	4.6	140,911	7,165	5.1
1956	158,496	8,051	5.1	158,496	8,051	5.1
1957	191,862	16,135	8.4	182,045	11,642	6.4
1958	198,710	16,472	8.3	184,000	14,516	7.9
1959	211,521	15,577	7.4	195,000	13,336	6.8
1960	231.251	19,650	8.5	207,222	16,770	8.1

1. Department of Statistics, Jamaica. *National Accounts.*

demonstrated not only on the Government's revenue but even more notably on the valuation for export purposes. Table V.2 sets out the movement in absolute and percentage terms of bauxite exports in relation to total exports. There was a sharp increase in value both of bauxite and of alumina in 1957 but in the case of bauxite while the volume of exports increased by nearly one half, the value more than doubled, which meant that a good deal of the difference was to be attributed to the revaluation of the product. In the case of alumina, both the volume and the value showed a rise in 1957, approximately double the corresponding figures for 1956, so that little change in product value took place in 1957.

The new level of values arising from the agreement of 1957 changed markedly the place which the product of the bauxite enterprises held in total export values. The value of exports moved sharply from a share of 2.4 per cent of total exports in 1952 to a share of 49.6 per cent in 1961. A jump of over 16 per cent in the share of total exports took place between 1956 and 1957 for reasons which have been explained.

Table V.3 presents a picture of the growth of investment in the bauxite operations from 1950 to 1960. Of particular interest was the effect of net annual investment on total net investment. There has been a decline in this last magnitude from a high point of nearly £49 million at the end of 1958 to £45 million in 1960. Even at this lower level bauxite remained the most highly capitalized enterprise in the Jamaican economy. It must be emphasized, however, that only a small share of the value of capital purchases has accrued in the form of income shares to Jamaica. In the case of the item Land and Buildings, only in the construction of buildings is income created. This income arises in the form of wages to building labour and profits to contractors, as well as the derived income which accrued to producing factors in the case of materials (e.g. cement) used. Small amounts of income are created from the element of Exploration, Research and Land Development in this item.

In the case of the item Machinery and Equipment all income created arises from transportation and installation of plant. This income constitutes a minor share, usually under 30 per cent of the final value of the item.

A matter of further interest is the share of the bauxite enterprises in the total Gross Domestic Fixed Capital Formation. This proportion is shown on an annual basis (Table V.3A). The high capital bias compared with the rest of the economy is marked, particularly

TABLE V.2 *Bauxite and Alumina Exports from Jamaica*[1]

Year	Exports Bauxite '000 tons	Bauxite £'000	Alumina '000 tons	Alumina £'000	Total £'000	Total Exports Jamaica £'000	Bauxite percentage of Total %	Alumina percentage of Total %	Both as percentage of Total %
1952	240	420			420	17,258	2.4		2.4
1953	1,253	2,756			2,756	24,535	11.3		11.3
1954	1,728	3,086	124	2,899	5,985	29,942	10.3	9.7	20.0
1955	2,172	3,888	184	4,784	8,672	32,427	12.6	14.8	27.4
1956	2,575	4,600	207	5,803	10,403	38,234	12.0	15.2	27.2
1957	3,641	9,563	436	11,911	21,474	49,535	19.3	24.0	43.3
1958	4,799	12,597	373	9,132	21,729	46,756	26.9	19.6	46.5
1959	4,197	11,016	399	9,406	20,422	45,268	24.3	20.8	45.1
1960	4,148	10,887	665	16,634	27,521	55,713	19.5	29.9	49.4
1961	4,975	13,059	703	16,885	29,944	60,387	21.6	28.0	49.6

1. Department of Statistics, Jamaica. *Trade Reports.*

TABLE V.3   *Fixed Capital Invested in Bauxite and Alumina in Jamaica* (£'000)

Year	Annual Investment					Net Accumulated Investment		
	Land and Buildings	Machinery and Equipment	Total Invested (gross)	Depreciation	Investment[1] Increment Rate %	Land and Buildings	Machinery and Equipment	Total Net Investment
1950	N.A.	N.A.	1,000	N.A.		N.A.	N.A.	N.A.
1951	N.A.	N.A.	3,700	N.A.		N.A.	N.A.	N.A.
1952	N.A.	N.A.	7,500	N.A.		N.A.	N.A.	N.A.
1953	N.A.	N.A.	6,250	N.A.		N.A.	N.A.	28,241
1954	N.A.	N.A.	1,300	1,699	4.6	N.A.	N.A.	28,640
1955	N.A.	N.A.	4,174	1,717	14.6	N.A.	N.A.	26,183
1956	4,584	9,309	13,893	2,061	53.1	N.A.	N.A.	38,015
1957	3,980	7,909	11,889	2,640	31.2	N.A.	N.A.	47,264
1958	1,906	2,713	4,619	2,995	9.8	N.A.	N.A.	48,888
1959	885	654	1,539	2,913	3.1	N.A.	N.A.	47,514
1960	525	645	1,170	3,637	2.5	16,928	28,119	45,047

1. Total gross investment in year 2 expressed as percentage of total net accumulated investment in year 1.

in the early years of the decade when capital increments in other sectors were relatively low.

TABLE V.3A   *Gross Domestic Fixed Capital Formation in Jamaica*

Year	(1) All Economy £'000	(2) Bauxite and Alumina £'000	(3) (2) as percentage of (1) %
1950	6,930	1,000	14.4
1951	12,160	3,700	30.4
1952	13,695	7,500	54.8
1953	14,150	6,250	44.2
1954	17,300	1,300	7.5
1955	21,470	4,174	19.4
1956	38,783	13,893	35.8
1957	52,104	11,889	22.8
1958	47,397	4,619	9.7
1959	46,072	1,539	3.3
1960	51,705	1,170	2.3

In the accumulation of capital over the ten-year period the pattern of costs of mining underwent a change. This was the result of developments in which economies of scale began to have a major effect. The other significant cause of changing cost patterns was the revision of the original mining agreement mentioned above. There have in addition been several revisions of wage structures as trade unions came to place increasing emphasis in wage negotiations on ability to pay. This too is brought out when one looks at the changes in cost structure over time.

A study of the cost and value pattern for mining by the bauxite companies shows that in Table V.4 items 1 and 2 (Mining, Transport, Drying and Loading) moved from 17.14 per cent of total value in 1954 to 18.43 per cent in 1955. By 1957 these two items stood at 14.11 per cent but after the revaluation of total costs in 1957 it rose to 22.2 per cent in 1958 and by 1960 stood at 27.7 per cent of total costs. Interest has in the same period fallen from a ratio of 11.02 per cent of total value in 1954 to 8.36 per cent in 1955 and after standing at 5.95 per cent in 1957 was less than 1 per cent in 1958. Government revenue excluding income tax fell from 3.47 per cent total costs in 1954 to 2.92 per cent in 1955, reaching 2.04 per cent in 1957. After the revision of costs in 1957 this item rose to a share in costs of 5.88 per cent in 1958 and by 1960 amounted

TABLE V.4   *Proportions of Value of Bauxite in Bauxite Mining Enterprise in Jamaica*[1]

Cost Items Making up Value	1954 % Value	1955 % Value	1957 % Value	1958 % Value	1960 % Value
1. Mining Transport Drying }[2] 2. Loading	17.14	18.43	14.11	22.20	27.7
3. Net Cost of Agriculture		3.01	2.15		N.A.
4. Insurance		0.68	0.35		N.A.
5. Interest	11.02	8.36	5.95	0.92	
6. Government Revenue excluding Income Tax	3.47	2.92	2.04	5.876	6.85
7. Exploration and Development		2.21	1.33		0.64
8. General Administration and Research	17.14	13.81	10.86	7.50	N.A.
9. Depreciation Normal	18.37	16.56	9.18	7.59	11.55
Depreciation Accelerated		19.80	8.36		N.A.
10. Net Cost	77.34	85.79	54.32	46.77	N.A.
11. Jamaican Income Tax	4.29	5.16	N.A.	20.44	20.82
12. Net Profit	18.37	9.06	N.A.	32.78	N.A.
13. **Total Profit**	22.66	14.21	45.68	53.22	N.A.
14. **Total Nominal Cost**	100.00	100.00	100.00	100.00	100.00

1. Estimates for 1954, 1958 and 1960 from *Surveys of Business Establishments*. Estimates for 1955 and 1957 from National Income Work Sheets, Department of Statistics.

2. Restatement of Items 1 and 2 for

		1960 % Value
A	Wages and Salaries	12.3
B	Maintenance	8.2
C	Transport	7.2
	Total Items 1 and 2	27.7

to 6.85 per cent. General Administration and Research, which stood at 17.14 per cent in 1954 fell to 13.81 per cent in 1955. By 1957, the year of revaluation, this item took a share of 10.86 per cent of cost and by 1958 had fallen to 7.5 per cent. Depreciation should be studied in relation to the movements in capital formation set out in Table V.3, but with some qualification. This item (Table V.4) stood at 18.37 per cent of value in 1954 but fell to 16.56 per cent in 1955, to 9.18 per cent in 1957 and to 7.59 per cent in 1958. As a result, however, of the large capital investment in 1956 and 1957 (Table V.3) it rose sharply in absolute and relative terms after 1956. Much of the increased investment took place in alumina refining installations, but a fair proportion was in the form of bauxite equipment. The effect on Depreciation was to increase its share in total costs to 11.55 per cent by 1960.

Jamaican Income Tax payments stood at 4.29 per cent of total value in 1954 and averaged 5.16 per cent in 1955. By 1958 they had risen to 20.44 per cent of total costs and remained at the same level in 1960 when they were 20.82 per cent.

The movement of the total nominal cost is an important point of interest since it affords a basis for the foregoing analysis apart from demonstrating the changing level of costs over the years. The cost of mining bauxite moved from an estimated £1.71 per ton in 1954 to an estimated £1.78 in 1955. In the year of cost revision, 1957, the total estimated cost rose to a value of £2.63. By 1958 it had risen further to about £2.68, but by 1960 it had fallen to £2.62 per ton. The revaluation of bauxite for export purposes brought about a basic change in cost structure so that by 1958 Net Cost, before Gross Profit was added, amounted to less than 50 per cent of Total Cost where before it had comprised 77.34 per cent of Total Cost (in 1954). The changes in Table V.4, where the ratios of costs and values relate to an averaging of estimated mining opera-tion costs in Jamaica, do not refer to the refining process.

When alumina refining was first established in Jamaica it was assumed that the conversion ratios of bauxite into alumina would be more or less stable but the ratios have over the years altered significantly. They have moved from 2.9 tons of bauxite to 1 ton of alumina in 1954 to 2.4 to 1 in 1960. This presumably must have made for economies in the refining process and affected costs. Table V.5 presents selected items as percentages of total costs in alumina refining for some recent years, the average for 1956–58 and then for comparison cost ratios for 1954. The items do not reveal the complete picture relating to alumina production. There are some points of similarity between the two patterns although in the absence of exact ratios for Interest and General Administration in 1956–58 and for Maintenance in 1954 reconciliation was impossible until the exercise described below was undertaken.

TABLE V.5   *Proportions of Value of Alumina in Alumina Enterprise in Jamaica*

Cost Items making up Value	Average cost per ton	
	1956–58	1954
	%	%
1. Wages	4.27	5.57
2. Interest		8.47
3. Maintenance	1.13	*
4. Bauxite	42.45	29.34
5. Fuel	9.42	9.54
6. Depreciation	8.60	14.25
7. General Administration ⎫		18.58
8. Other Costs ⎭	34.13	14.25
9. **Total Costs**	100.00	100.00

* Not available separately and included in item 7.

Table V.6 shows for bauxite and alumina production, the broad position of the development in factor use as revealed by the crude allocation, between two major factors labour and capital, of

TABLE V.6   *Bauxite Output (Exported and Converted) and Factor Payments*[1] *in Jamaica*

Year	Total Output		Factor Payments	
	’000 tons	Annual Change %	Labour Wages £’000	Capital[2] £’000
1954	2,075.2		1,110	1,777
1955	2,687.2	29.5	1,519	2,927
1956	3,086.3	14.9	1,681	4,309
1957	4,717.9	52.9	2,143	11,352
1958	5,700.3	20.8	2,571	10,906
1959	5,182.5	9.1	2,638	10,021
1960	5,790.5	11.7	2,966	12,749
1961	6,711.4	15.9	3,225	12,963

1. Department of Statistics, Jamaica. Factor Payments, *National Accounts*.
2. Including interest, rent, dividends, profit; rent is negligible.

monetary payments. It also shows the movement in physical terms of bauxite production since 1954 and also the rates of change in production.

The figures on factor payments show capital payments moving from a position of less than double that of labour in 1954 to one of more than four times the payments for labour in 1960. Continued exploitation of bauxite and its processing will have a tendency to call for even greater quantities of capital in relation to labour.

The nature of the open pit mining operation made it unlikely that the bauxite mining would ever employ large numbers of labourers and the production of alumina, a continuous chemical process, also has a low labour : capital ratio. Nevertheless the employment opportunities offered by bauxite and alumina have been greater than was at first expected (Table V.7). The companies have been almost continuously expanding since they began opera-

TABLE V.7   *Persons Employed in the Bauxite and Alumina Enterprises in Jamaica*[1]

Categories	1958	1959	1960
Mining and Related Activities	2,565	3,105	2,990
Construction	2,098	669	69
Agriculture and other	2,178	2,119	1,577
Prospecting			47
Total	6,841	5,893	4,683
Population of Jamaica	1,564,747	1,599,781	1,624,280

tions. While there has been a sharp drop in the number of persons employed in certain items the companies have engaged in non-mining activities which are labour-intensive. Their agricultural undertakings employ almost as many people as their mining and related operations. While therefore the number of employees in construction (in bauxite and alumina) in 1960 was only a small proportion (3 per cent) of the comparable figure in 1958, the total number of all employees in bauxite and alumina in 1960 was nearly 70 per cent that in 1958.

1. Central Planning Unit, Jamaica. *Economic Survey*, 1962.

The number of workers employed in mining and related activities does not rise above 3,000 but, although the companies have not had any great effect numerically on the labour force, their influence has been greater than the numbers would suggest. The highly mechanized nature of the mining and alumina operations has made it necessary for the companies to train labour and a nucleus of trained workers has been created. It was feared that bauxite might draw off skilled workers from the sugar industry,[1] but there has been collaboration between the industries in their training programmes and it appears that there has been a small amount of movement from bauxite into other avenues of employment. Jamaica had little tradition of industrial skills, apart from those acquired in the sugar industry, and employers have in general paid too little attention to training their workers.[2] The alumina and bauxite enterprises showed that with adequate preparation for the job, and good prospects of continued high earning-power, the performance of Jamaican labour was encouraging.[3]

The rates of wages paid in bauxite and alumina are in general higher than the rates paid to similar categories of workers in other sectors. The workers, through their unions, pressed for rates of pay on a par with those paid to bauxite and alumina employees in Canada and the United States. The companies resisted this claim, but the compromise reached has given the bauxite workers a lead over other industrial workers in the island. It is probable that this has in turn led to pressure for higher wages in other industries, and has been in part responsible for maintaining the share of wages in the GDP.[4]

The stimulating effect of the spending of bauxite and alumina workers on retail trade and services in the mining areas is notice-

1. Aaronson, Robert L. 'Labour Commitment among Jamaican Bauxite Workers.' *Social and Economic Studies*, Vol. 10, No. 2, June 1961.
2. Campbell, Ella. 'Industrial Training . . . Methods and Techniques.' *Social and Economic Studies*, Vol. 2, No. 1, 1953.
3. Aaronson, Robert L., *op. cit.*
4. Any disruption caused by sudden local rises in wages and prices was less than one would have expected – for several reasons. One was that the companies preferred to give employment to local people. If large numbers of people had immigrated they would probably have congregated in particular areas and limited their spending to those areas. Many of those who found employment were content to live at a distance, improve their houses and buy bicycles and cars. This stabilizing effect did much to counter-balance the disruption which might have arisen and credit should be given to the companies for their employment policy. So far as Reynolds is concerned, that policy appears to have been conscious and deliberate.

able. Unfortunately, no information is available on their consumption patterns. Aaronson made some enquiries about the consumption patterns of the sample of ALJAM employees he interviewd.[1] The indications are that, apart from house purchase, most of their surplus income was absorbed by the purchase of durable consumer goods. The labour force of bauxite and alumina enjoying a high rate of earnings, makes a substantial contribution to revenue through income tax and through indirect taxation.

Local Disbursements in the Bauxite and Alumina Enterprises

From the point of view of the present study it was essential to examine and to endeavour to distinguish between the contribution to the local economy by bauxite mining on the one hand and, on the other, the alumina enterprise inclusive of its mining activity. This meant, in more specific terms, to try to compare the local disbursements[2] in Jamaica per ton bauxite in bauxite mining with the local disbursements per ton bauxite processed locally into alumina, and to use for the calculations information which was available to the public both on activities in Jamaica and corresponding activities in the United States. The exercise to make these comparisons and the figures derived from it are based on the following sources: the Trade Reports (Table V.2), which provide quantities and values of bauxite and alumina exported over the years; the *National Accounts*, Income and Expenditure, Jamaica; *A National Plan for Jamaica 1957–67;* Ministry Paper No. 2, March 21, 1957; *Economic Survey, Jamaica 1960;* a breakdown of alumina costs in *Locational Factors influencing Recent Aluminum Expansion* by John V. Krutilla; similar estimates in an unpublished study: *The Bauxite Industry in Jamaica* by Peter M. Stern. The companies were approached and asked for supporting information which might throw light on the comparisons being made. They were sensitive in this whole general

1. Aaronson, Robert L., *op. cit.*
2. Hicks, J. R. and U.K. (*op. cit.*) stated: 'The bauxite companies . . . are in a sense external to the Jamaican economy. It is easier to think of the some-what peculiar effects which they have had on the economy of Jamaica if we mentally put a fence around them and think of the land which has been sold to the bauxite companies . . . as being outside Jamaica . . . If we look at the matter in this way the whole value of the bauxite export ceases to be a Jamaican export; what is exported from the Jamaican economy in the narrower sense is no more than the wages paid by the bauxite companies and a few purchases of other Jamaican products, together with the taxes which they pay to the Jamaican Government.'

area of allocation of costs and the type of information which they made available has added little to what was to be obtained from published sources.

A start was made with the export figures given in Table V.2, and the f.o.b. value per ton of bauxite and of alumina derived. In Table V.8 in the first column are shown the f.o.b. value per ton of bauxite, for the years 1954–61 – the total value of bauxite exports being divided by tons exported; in the second column, the value per ton of alumina; in the third column the value of alumina expressed not in terms of per ton alumina but of per ton bauxite. In 1960, 1 ton of bauxite was worth £2.625 (column (1)) and 1 ton of alumina was worth £25.01 (column (2)). This meant that 1 ton of bauxite as bauxite was worth £2.625 (column (1)) but that 1 ton of bauxite converted into alumina was, with value added, worth £10.12.

TABLE V.8   *F.O.B. Value of Jamaica's Bauxite and Alumina*

Year	(1) Value per ton Bauxite £	(2) Value per ton Alumina £	(3) Value of 1 ton Bauxite converted into Alumina[1] £
1954	1.786	23.38	8.35
1955	1.790	26.00	9.29
1956	1.786	28.03	11.06
1957	2.626	27.32	10.25
1958	2.625	24.48	9.91
1959	2.625	23.57	9.54
1960	2.625	25.01	10.12
1961	2.625	24.02	9.72

The sudden increase in the value of bauxite in 1957 was due to the new agreement made with the Jamaica Government which changed the notional price of bauxite. The new figure, it was agreed, was nearer than the old to what might be regarded as the market price of bauxite. The change in the notional price of bauxite did not affect the value of alumina because, while the price of bauxite

1. Conversion figures used are: 2.8 tons bauxite to 1 ton alumina for 1954–55; and 2.47 tons for 1956–61.

from 1956 to 1957 rose by about 50 per cent, the value of alumina fell by about 3 per cent.

The second step was to compute a break-down of the value of bauxite and to allocate charges to the several heads (Tables V.9 and V.9A). Although details of bauxite costs are available for 1960, the years 1957–58 were selected on the grounds that they were approximately the years for which the most recent alumina details (Table V.5) were available and for the purposes of comparison it was desirable that the years used as a basis for averaging costs should coincide as closely as possible. The value per ton of bauxite (£2.625) used was the average value per ton calculated from Table V.2 for the years 1957–58, the figures in Table V.2 being derived from the Government Trade Statistics.

TABLE V.9 *Estimated Breakdown of Value and of Local Disbursements per Ton Bauxite* (1957–1958) *in Jamaica*

	(1)	(2)	(3)	(4)
			Disbursements in Jamaica per ton Bauxite	
	Value per ton Bauxite			
	%	£	%	£
Wages and Salaries	8.062	0.212	7.558	0.198
Maintenance	5.374	0.141		
Labour			3.017	0.079
Material			0.778	0.020
Fuel				
Depreciation				
Normal	8.385	0.220	2.287	0.060
Accelerated (bauxite only)	4.180	0.110	0.523	0.014
Administration and Research	9.180	0.241	7.804	0.205
Cost of Material				
Transport	4.719	0.124	4.719	0.124
Net Cost of Agriculture	1.075	0.028	1.075	0.028
Insurance	0.175	0.005		
Interest	3.435	0.090		
Government Fees	3.958	0.104	3.958	0.104
Exploration	0.665	0.017	0.499	0.013
Miscellaneous				
Income Tax	20.317	0.533	20.317	0.533
Net Profit	30.475	0.800		
Total	100.000	2.625	52.535	1.378

TABLE V.9A *Estimated Breakdown of Value, Local Disbursements and Payments Abroad of Bauxite in Bauxite Enterprises in Jamaica*

	Total Value (£'000)				Local Disbursements (£'000)				Payments Abroad (£'000)			
	1958	1959	1960	1961	1958	1959	1960	1961	1958	1959	1960	1961
Wages and Salaries	1,017.4	889.8	879.4	1,054.7	950.2	831.0	821.3	985.1	67.2	58.8	58.1	69.6
Maintenance	676.7	591.8	584.9	701.5					201.7	176.3	174.2	209.0
Labour					475.0	415.5	410.7	492.5				
Material					379.1	331.6	327.7	393.0				
Fuel					95.9	83.9	83.0	99.5				
Depreciation												
Normal	1,583.6	1,385.0	1,386.9	1,641.7	355.1	310.6	307.0	368.1	1,228.5	1,074.4	1,061.9	1,273.6
Accelerated	1,055.7	923.3	912.6	1,094.5	287.9	251.8	248.9	298.5	767.8	671.5	663.7	796.0
(bauxite only)	527.9	461.7	456.3	547.2	67.2	58.8	58.1	69.6	460.7	402.9	398.2	477.6
Admininistration and Research	1,156.5	1,011.5	999.7	1,199.0	983.8	860.4	850.3	1,019.9	172.7	151.1	149.4	179.1
Cost of Material												
Transport	595.1	520.4	514.3	616.9	595.1	520.4	514.3	616.9				
Net Cost of Agriculture	134.4	117.5	116.1	139.3	134.4	117.5	116.1	139.3				
Insurance	24.0	21.0	20.7	25.0					24.0	21.0	20.7	25.0
Interest	431.9	377.7	373.3	447.7					431.9	377.7	373.3	447.7
Government Fees	499.1	436.5	431.4	517.4	499.1	436.5	431.4	517.4				
Exploration	81.6	71.3	70.5	84.5	62.4	54.6	53.9	64.7	19.2	16.7	16.6	19.8
Miscellaneous												
Income Tax	2,557.9	2,237.0	2,210.9	2,651.7	2,557.9	2,237.0	2,210.9	2,651.7				
Net Profit	3,839.2	3,357.6	3,318.4	3,980.0	3,839.2	3,357.6	3,318.4	3,980.0	3,839.2	3,357.6	3,318.4	3,980.0
Total	12,597.4	11,017.1	10,888.5	13,059.4	6,613.0	5,783.5	5,715.9	6,855.6	5,984.4	5,233.6	5,172.6	6,203.8

TABLE V.10 *Estimated Breakdown of Value and of Local Disbursements per Ton Alumina (inclusive of Alumina's Bauxite Activity) and per Ton Bauxite Converted (1956–1958) in Jamaica*

	(1) (2) Value (per ton) of Alumina		(3)	(4) (5) (6) Disbursements (per ton) in Jamaica		
	Per ton Alumina %	Per ton Alumina £	Per ton Bauxite converted £	Per ton Alumina %	Per ton Alumina £	Per ton Bauxite converted £
Wages and Salaries	9.205	2.432	.985	8.343	2.204	.892
Bauxite Wages and Salaries	1.978	.523	.212	1.855	.490	.198
Alumina Wages	4.270	1.128	.457	4.270	1.128	.457
Alumina Salaries	2.957	.781	.316	2.218	.586	.237
Maintenance	7.488	1.979	.801	5.298	1.400	.567
Labour	4.203	1.111	.450	4.203	1.110	.450
Material	3.285	.868	.351	1.095	.290	.117
Fuel	9.420	2.490	1.008			
Depreciation	17.330	4.580	1.855			
Normal	16.307	4.310	1.745	2.130	.563	.228
Accelerated (Bauxite only)	1.023	.270	.110	.128	.034	.014

TABLE V.10 Estimated Breakdown of Value and of Local Disbursements per Ton Alumina (inclusive of Alumina's Bauxite Activity) and per Ton Bauxite Converted (1956–1958) in Jamaica (continued)

Administration	5.816	1.536	.621	4.944	1.306	.528
Office Supplies	1.938	.512	.207	1.454	.384	.155
Travelling, etc.	1.939	.512	.207	1.551	.410	.166
Rent, etc.	1.939	.512	.207	1.939	.512	.207
Cost of Material	13.313	3.518	1.424	2.663	.704	.285
Transport	3.915	1.034	.419	3.915	1.034	.419
Net Cost of Agriculture	.265	.070	.028	.265	.070	.028
Insurance	1.866	.493	.200			
Interest	9.314	2.461	.996			
Government Fees	.973	.257	.104	.973	.257	.104
Exploration	.163	.043	.017	.122	.032	.013
Miscellaneous	2.000	.528	.214	1.000	.264	.107
	81.068			29.781		
Income Tax	7.573	2.001	.810	7.593	2.001	.810
Net Profit	11.359	3.001	1.215			
Total	100.000	26.423	10.697	37.354	9.869	3.995

The proportion of the value per ton of bauxite made up by wages and salaries and by other heads shown were based on the national account estimates (brought together in Table V.4). With the breakdown of the value per ton it became possible to attempt estimates of local disbursements by the bauxite companies. Local disbursements (by the bauxite companies) per ton of bauxite are shown in columns (3) and (4) (Table V.9). It is estimated that the bauxite companies disburse locally about 52 per cent of the value of bauxite and this amounted to about £1.378 per ton of bauxite out of a total value of £2.625 (Tables V.9 and V.9A).

The third step was to make a computation, corresponding to that done for the bauxite companies, for the alumina enterprise (Tables V.10 and V.10A). The average value per ton alumina 1956–1958 is £26.423. The detailed breakdown of this is shown in column (1) on a percentage basis and in column (2) on a value in sterling basis. Thus in the value of £26.423 per ton alumina, 9.205 per cent is estimated for wages and salaries and this is equivalent to £2.432 per ton alumina. In Table V.10A these proportions are combined with annual export figure to estimate total value, local disbursements, payments abroad for the year 1958–1961.

A major problem in allocating the value of alumina to the several heads was that Table V.5, which formed the basis for proportions, listed bauxite (item 4) as making up 42.45 per cent of the value of alumina in 1956–1958. This meant that the alumina enterprise in its books was valuing bauxite at about £4 12s 0d a ton compared with bauxite valued at about £2 12s 0d in the books of the bauxite enterprises. It seemed reasonable to infer from this that the alumina enterprise was including, under the head bauxite, charges not so included by the bauxite enterprises and that if one wanted to have meaningful comparison the two values of bauxite should be reconciled. The value of bauxite in one ton of alumina was obtained by multiplying the number of tons of bauxite per ton of alumina (assumed to be 2.47) by £2.625 (value per ton bauxite as calculated above). This amounted to £6.484 or 24.539 per cent of the value of alumina. The difference between 42.450 per cent and 24.539 per cent (respectively, the old and new proportionate values of bauxite) was then redistributed among the items and the redistribution done in such a way as to bring closer reconciliation between the figures of Table V.5 on the one hand and the Stern and Krutilla estimates on the other. An overall figure for bauxite is not included as one of the items making up the value of alumina in Table V.10.

E

TABLE V.10A   *Estimated Breakdown of Value, Local Disbursements and Payments Abroad of the Alumina Enterprise in Jamaica*

	Total Value (£'000)				Local Disbursements (£'000)				Payments Abroad (£'000)			
	1958	1959	1960	1961	1958	1959	1960	1961	1958	1959	1960	1961
Wages and Salaries	907.4	970.7	1,617.9	1,710.4	821.7	879.0	1,465.1	1,548.9	85.7	91.7	152.8	161.5
Maintenance	738.0	789.4	1,315.6	1,390.9	522.4	558.8	931.3	984.6	215.6	230.6	384.3	406.3
Labour	414.6	443.5	739.1	781.4	414.6	443.5	739.1	781.4				
Material	323.4	345.9	576.5	609.5	107.8	115.3	192.2	203.2	215.6	230.6	384.3	406.3
Fuel	928.7	993.4	1,655.6	1,750.3					928.7	993.4	1,655.6	1,750.3
Depreciation	1,709.0	1,828.1	3,046.8	3,221.0	223.0	238.5	397.5	420.2	1,486.0	1,589.6	2,649.3	2,800.8
Normal	1,607.7	1,719.7	2,866.2	3,030.0	210.1	224.7	374.5	395.9	1,397.6	1,495.0	2,491.7	2,634.1
Accelerated (bauxite only)	101.3	108.4	180.6	191.0	12.9	13.8	23.0	24.3	88.4	94.6	157.6	166.7
Administration and Research	572.1	612.0	1,020.0	1,078.2	486.4	520.4	867.3	916.7	85.7	91.6	152.7	161.5
Cost of Material	1,311.9	1,403.3	2,338.9	2,472.6	262.6	280.9	468.1	494.8	1,049.3	1,122.4	1,870.8	1,977.8
Transport	386.0	412.9	688.2	727.6	386.0	412.9	688.2	727.6				
Net Cost of Agriculture	25.8	27.6	46.0	48.6	25.8	27.6	46.0	48.6				
Insurance	184.3	197.1	328.5	347.3					184.3	197.1	328.5	347.3
Interest	917.6	981.6	1,636.0	1,729.5					917.6	981.6	1,636.0	1,729.5
Government Fees	95.8	102.5	170.8	180.6	95.8	102.5	170.8	180.6				
Exploration	15.6	16.7	28.0	29.5	12.0	12.8	21.4	22.6	3.6	3.9	6.6	6.9
Miscellaneous	197.2	210.9	351.5	371.6	98.6	105.4	175.7	185.8	98.6	105.5	175.8	185.8
Income Tax	746.3	798.3	1,330.4	1,406.5	746.3	798.3	1,330.4	1,406.5				
Net Profit	1,119.4	1,197.4	1,995.6	2,109.7					1,119.4	1,197.4	1,995.6	2,109.7
Total	9,855.1	10,541.9	17,569.8	18,574.3	3,680.6	3,937.1	6,561.8	6,936.9	6,174.5	6,604.8	11,008.0	11,637.4

Instead the bauxite items based on the allocations in Table V.9 are distributed in Table V.10 under the respective heads.

The proportion made up by wages and salaries is a little over 9 per cent in alumina (Table V.10) and a little over 8 per cent in bauxite (Table V.9). The items which show the most marked proportional differences relate to capital. The depreciation and interest charges amount to nearly 27 per cent of the value of alumina but only to about 16 per cent of the value of bauxite shipped by the bauxite companies. This is understandable in that it reflects the higher capitalization of the alumina enterprise.

On the basis of the computations in Table V.10 it was possible to proceed to the next step, the estimated disbursements in Jamaica of the alumina enterprise,[1] expressed in terms of local disbursements per ton alumina and the local disbursements per ton bauxite converted into alumina. The value per ton bauxite converted into alumina is derived by dividing the value per ton alumina by 2.47 (Table V.8). As mentioned above the costs of the bauxite activities of the alumina enterprise are included in the figures for value and local disbursements of alumina in Table V.10. It is estimated that the alumina enterprise disbursed in Jamaica £3.995 per ton bauxite converted into alumina while the bauxite companies disbursed £1.378 per ton bauxite shipped as bauxite.[2] The implications of this are shown in Table V.11. Up to 1959 the alumina shipments were relatively small and averaged about 1,000,000 tons of bauxite converted into alumina a year in 1957–1959, while the bauxite exported as bauxite was about four times that quantity. In 1960, however, the alumina enterprise stepped up its output and the quantity of bauxite converted into alumina in Jamaica increased by about 65 per cent. In terms of bauxite, the bauxite companies remained substantially larger than the alumina activities, mining over two and a half times as much bauxite in each of the two years 1960 and 1961. This meant

1. Throughout this study the phrase 'alumina enterprise in Jamaica' is used to include the bauxite mining activity of the alumina producing company, Alcan.
2. According to the estimates of Tables V.9 and V.10, the local disbursements per ton bauxite converted are three times the local disbursements per ton bauxite exported as bauxite. Mr J. F. Horwood, Managing Director of Alcan Jamaica, Limited, wrote (in *The Daily Gleaner*, Jamaica, January 7, 1963): 'The value of such bauxite (i.e. converted to alumina) to Jamaica is thereby increased some four-fold over bauxite shipped as such . . .' There is little doubt that the bauxite and alumina enterprises have access to much firmer figures than the estimates which – because of the inadequacy of the published material – this study has had to prepare. If one accepts the differential indicated by Mr Horwood it would mean that the benefits to the island of alumina conversion locally have been substantially underestimated in this study.

that in each of the years 1960 and 1961 Jamaica bauxite companies together exported about 3 million tons more bauxite than were used for local conversion into alumina but in each of those years disbursed in the Jamaica economy an average of nearly £0.5 million less than did the alumina enterprise.

TABLE V.11 *Estimated Local Disbursements of Bauxite and Alumina[1] in Jamaica*

Year	Local Disbursements of Total Bauxite Exported at £1.378 per ton bauxite £'000	Local Disbursements of Total Alumina Exported at £3.995 per ton bauxite converted £'000
1956	3,548.4	2,042.6
1957	5,017.3	4,302.2
1958	6,613.0	3,680.6
1959	5,783.5	3,937.1
1960	5,715.9	6,561.8
1961	6,855.6	6,936.9

The last columns of Tables V.9 and V.10 show wherein the main differences lay. For every ton of bauxite handled the alumina enterprise disbursed locally in wages nearly 18s, the bauxite companies nearly 4s. For maintenance, alumina disbursed locally about 11s a ton of bauxite, bauxite nearly 2s. For administration alumina disbursed locally about 10s a ton of bauxite, bauxite over 4s. For transportation alumina disbursed locally over 8s a ton of bauxite, bauxite about 2s 6d. In income tax alumina paid locally over 16s a ton of bauxite, the bauxite companies paid nearly 11s and the outlook was that the income tax payments from the alumina enterprise should rise even if there should be no increase in output. For the years being considered here for alumina, 1956–58, there were recently incurred high capital charges for a new alumina plant. In consequence the depreciation allowance was high,[2] amounting to

1. Conversion figure used is 2.47 tons bauxite to 1 ton alumina, this being the average for 1957–58.
2. Compared with the depreciation allowance in alumina of 17 per cent, that in the mining companies was 12 per cent.

about 17 per cent of the value of a ton of alumina (i.e. about £4 12s
a ton of alumina, equivalent to about 38s a ton of bauxite converted). Because of the nature of accelerated allowances their value
must necessarily decline relatively rapidly. This may seem of little
concern to this exercise directly, since in any event only a small
proportion of depreciation allowance is allocated to local disbursement. But as the allowance becomes smaller the income tax payments in Jamaica, other things being equal, will become higher. To
this extent, therefore, the outlook is that, in Jamaica, alumina,
relative to bauxite exported, should make higher payments in
income tax than the estimates based on 1956–58 indicate.

In Table V.11A are shown the figures for the combined bauxite
and alumina enterprises – total value, local disbursements and payments abroad for the years 1958–61.

It was decided as a further step to undertake an exercise of a
hypothetical nature and to assume that the exporters of bauxite
had been persuaded to convert varying proportions of their exports
into alumina locally. Based on these assumptions calculations were
then made to determine what such changes would have meant for
the Jamaica economy. In Table V.12 are estimates of the order of
local disbursements in Jamaica if the bauxite enterprises exporting
their bauxite as bauxite could have been persuaded to process
locally varying proportions of their Jamaica mined bauxite into
alumina. Thus in the first column the annual exports of bauxite
which are given in the Trade Statistics are listed. In the second
column the local disbursements from these exports are given on the
basis of £1.378 per ton of bauxite. There are then three sets of
further assumptions made:

*That 75 per cent of bauxite companies' output was converted
locally:* The assumption here is that only 25 per cent of each year's
bauxite output actually had been exported and that the other 75
per cent of the bauxite had been converted into alumina locally.
In column (3) (Table V.12) figures are given, on the basis of £1.378
per ton of bauxite, for disbursements locally of this 25 per cent of
the bauxite output. Thus in 1958, 25 per cent of 4,799,000 tons
(bauxite actually exported) at £1.378 a ton would amount to local
disbursements of £1,653,600. The other 75 per cent of the bauxite
in that year, it is assumed, was converted into alumina and at
£3.995 per ton bauxite converted would amount to local disbursements of £14,378,000. In column (5) the total local disbursements

TABLE V.11A Estimated Breakdown of Value, Local Disbursements and Payments Abroad of Combined Bauxite and Alumina Enterprises in Jamaica

	Total Value (£'000)				Local Disbursements (£'000)				Payments Abroad (£'000)			
	1958	1959	1960	1961	1958	1959	1960	1961	1958	1959	1960	1961
Wages and Salaries	1,924.8	1,860.5	2,497.3	2,765.1	1,771.9	1,710.0	2,286.4	2,534.0	152.9	150.5	210.9	231.1
Maintenance	1,414.7	1,381.2	1,900.5	2,092.4	997.4	974.3	1,342.0	1,477.1	417.3	406.9	558.5	615.3
Fuel	928.7	993.4	1,655.6	1,750.3					928.7	993.4	1,655.6	1,750.3
Depreciation Normal	2,663.4	2,643.0	3,778.8	4,124.5	498.0	476.5	623.4	694.4	2,165.4	2,166.5	3,155.4	3,430.1
Accelerated (bauxite only)	629.2	570.1	636.9	738.2	80.1	72.6	81.1	93.9	549.1	497.5	555.8	644.3
Administration and Research	1,728.6	1,623.5	2,019.7	2,277.2	1,470.2	1,380.8	1,717.6	1,936.6	258.4	242.7	302.1	340.6
Cost of Material	1,311.9	1,403.3	2,338.9	2,472.6	262.6	280.9	468.1	494.8	1,049.3	1,122.4	1,870.8	1,977.8
Transport	981.1	933.3	1,202.5	1,344.5	981.1	933.3	1,202.5	1,344.5				
Net Cost of Agriculture	160.2	145.1	162.1	187.9	160.2	145.1	162.1	187.9				
Insurance	208.3	218.1	349.2	372.3					208.3	218.1	349.2	372.3
Interest	1,349.5	1,359.3	2,009.3	2,177.2					1,349.5	1,359.3	2,009.3	2,177.2
Government Fees	594.9	539.0	602.2	698.0	594.9	539.0	602.2	698.0				
Exploration	97.2	88.0	98.5	114.0	74.4	67.4	75.3	87.3	22.8	20.6	23.2	26.7
Miscellaneous	197.2	210.9	351.5	371.6	98.6	105.4	175.7	185.8	98.6	105.5	175.8	185.8
Income Tax	3,304.2	3,035.3	3,541.3	4,058.2	3,304.2	3,035.3	3,541.3	4,058.2				
Net Profit	4,958.6	4,555.0	5,314.0	6,089.7					4,958.6	4,555.0	5,314.0	6,089.7
Total	22,452.5	21,559.0	28,458.3	31,633.7	10,293.6	9,720.6	12,277.7	13,792.5	12,158.9	11,838.4	16,180.6	17,841.2

TABLE V.12 Estimated Local Disbursements if 75%, 50% or 25% Bauxite Output Converted into Alumina[1] in Jamaica

Year	(1) Total Annual Bauxite Exports[2] '000 tons	(2) Disbursements if: 100% Bauxite Exported[3] £'000	(3) 25% Bauxite Exported[4] £'000	(4) 75% Bauxite Converted £'000	(5) Col. (3) plus Col. (4) £'000	(6) Disbursements if: 50% Bauxite Exported £'000	(7) 50% Bauxite Converted £'000	(8) Col. (6) plus Col. (7) £'000	(9) Disbursements if: 75% Bauxite Exported £'000	(10) 25% Bauxite Converted £'000	(11) Col. (9) plus Col. (10) £'000
1956	2,575	3,548.4	887.2	7,715.1	8,602.3	1,774.2	5,143.6	6,917.8	2,661.2	2,572.0	5,233.2
1957	3,641	5,017.3	1,254.4	10,909.1	12,163.5	2,508.6	7,272.9	9,781.5	3,762.9	3,636.6	7,399.5
1958	4,799	6,613.0	1,653.6	14,378.0	16,031.6	3,306.5	9,586.0	12,892.5	4,959.4	4,794.0	9,753.4
1959	4,197	5,783.5	1,445.9	12,575.1	14,021.0	2,891.7	8,383.5	11,275.2	4,337.5	4,192.0	8,529.5
1960	4,148	5,715.9	1,428.9	12,428.4	13,857.3	2,858.0	8,285.6	11,143.6	4,287.0	4,142.8	8,429.8
1961	4,975	6,855.6	1,714.0	14,906.1	16,620.1	3,427.8	9,937.6	13,365.4	5,141.6	4,969.0	10,110.6

1. Conversion figure used is 2.47 tons bauxite to 1 ton alumina this being the average of 1957–58.
2. Assumption is that in Column (1) the export of bauxite companies is the same as their output.
3. Assumption is that all bauxite in Column (1) is exported.
4. Assumption is that 25 per cent bauxite in Column (1) is exported and that 75 per cent bauxite in Column (1) is converted locally into alumina.

(based on the assumption that 75 per cent bauxite output was converted locally and 25 per cent exported as bauxite) are shown, the figures being arrived at by adding columns (3) and (4).

That 50 *per cent of bauxite companies' output was converted locally:* In columns (6) and (7) the estimates are shown for local disbursements based on conversions locally of 50 per cent of bauxite output. As before the computations are based on local disbursements of £1.378 per ton bauxite exported and of £3.995 per ton bauxite converted. Column (8) shows the total.

That 25 *per cent of bauxite companies' output was converted locally:* In columns (9) and (10) estimates are shown for local disbursements based on the conversion of 25 per cent of the bauxite output into alumina and on the exports of the difference (or 75 per cent of bauxite output). Column (11) gives the total for the two columns.

In Table V.13 the order of increase in local disbursements is shown: when the assumptions of Table V.12 are implemented, that is, with varying proportions of the bauxite companies' output being

TABLE V.13   *Estimated Increases in Local Disbursements if* 75%, 50% *or* 25% *Bauxite Companies' Output Converted into Alumina in Jamaica*

Year	(1) 25% exported 75% converted £'000	(2) 50% exported 50% converted £'000	(3) 75% exported 25% converted £'000
1956	5,053.9	3,369.4	1,684.8
1957	7,146.2	4,764.2	2,382.2
1958	9,418.6	6,279.5	3,140.4
1959	8,237.5	5,491.7	2,746.0
1960	8,141.4	5,427.7	2,713.9
1961	9.764.5	6,509.8	3,255.0

converted into alumina locally. Thus the first column of Table V.13 is obtained by subtracting column (2) of Table V.12 from column (5) of Table V.12 and shows the increase that would be obtained if

75 per cent of bauxite output were converted locally. Column (2) of Table V.13 is obtained by subtracting column (2) of Table V.12 from column (8) of Table V.12. A corresponding subtraction was done for the third column of Table V.13. The estimates indicate that if 75 per cent of the bauxite exported had been converted into alumina locally the increase in disbursements within the island would have been of the order of £9.4 million in 1958, £8.2 million in 1959, £8.1 million in 1960 and £9.8 million in 1961. If 50 per cent of the annual bauxite exports had been converted locally into alumina, the increase in disbursements within the island would have been of the order of £6.3 million in 1958, £5.5 million in 1959, £5.4 million in 1960 and £6.5 million in 1961. If 25 per cent of the annual bauxite exports had been converted locally into alumina the increase in disbursements within the island would have been of the order of £3.1 million in 1958, £2.7 million in 1959, £2.7 million in 1960 and £3.3 million in 1961. It might be well to restate this in terms of company activities. The conclusion from the estimates is that if in 1958 the United States industrial groups had been persuaded to reduce their exports of bauxite and to convert 75 per cent of it into alumina locally, payments in the local economy would have been about £9.8 million higher. Since the Gross Domestic Product was £207 million, there would have been an increase of 4.7 per cent of the GDP even if one ignored the multiplier effect.

The increases in local disbursements are shown (Table V.13A) allocated to certain broad heads. Thus if there had been a conversion locally to alumina of 75 per cent of bauxite output in 1961, the increase in the wages and salaries item paid within the island would have amounted to £2.59 million and the increase in income tax (to the Jamaica Government) to £1.03 million. If there had been a conversion to alumina of 50 per cent of bauxite exports in 1960 the increase in the wages and salaries item would have been £1.44 million and the increase in income tax received by the Jamaica Government would have been £0.57 million. If there had been a conversion to alumina of 25 per cent of bauxite exports in 1958, the increase in the wages and salaries item paid within the island would have been £0.83 million and the increase in income tax paid locally would have been £0.33 million.

There is in Table V.14 a breakdown showing the distribution under several heads of the local disbursements made by the conversion into alumina of varying proportions of the bauxite companies' output. In each of the first three columns the assumption

TABLE V.13A Estimated Breakdown of Increases in Local Disbursements if 75% 50% or 25% Bauxite Companies' Output Converted into Alumina in Jamaica

	25% exported 75% converted			50% exported 50% converted			75% exported 25% converted		
	1958	1960	1961	1958	1960	1961	1958	1960	1961
	£'000	£'000	£'000	£'000	£'000	£'000	£'000	£'000	£'000
Wages and Salaries	2,497.7	2,159.0	2,589.5	1,665.3	1,439.4	1,726.2	832.8	719.7	863.2
Maintenance									
Labour	1,684.4	1,455.8	1,746.3	1,123.1	970.5	1,164.2	561.6	485.3	582.1
Material	1,335.2	1,154.1	1,384.3	890.3	769.4	922.9	445.2	384.8	461.5
Fuel	349.2	301.7	362.0	232.8	201.1	241.3	116.4	100.5	120.6
Depreciation									
Normal	604.7	522.6	626.8	403.2	348.4	418.0	201.6	174.2	209.0
Accelerated									
Administration and Research	1,162.4	1,004.9	1,205.2	775.0	670.0	803.4	387.6	335.0	401.7
Cost of Material	1,025.7	886.6	1,063.4	683.9	591.1	708.9	342.0	295.5	354.5
Transport	1,061.7	917.8	1,100.7	707.8	611.9	733.9	354.0	306.0	367.0
Net Cost of Agriculture									
Insurance									
Interest									
Government Fees									
Exploration									
Miscellaneous	385.1	333.0	399.2	256.7	222.0	266.2	128.4	111.0	133.1
Income Tax	996.9	861.8	1,033.5	664.6	574.4	689.0	332.4	287.3	344.5
Net Profit									
Total	9,418.6	8,141.5	9,764.6	6,279.6	5,427.7	6,509.8	3,140.4	2,714.0	3,255.1

TABLE V.14 *Estimated Breakdown of Local Disbursements if 75%, 50% or 25% Bauxite Companies' Output Converted into Alumina in Jamaica*

	25% exported 75% converted[1]			50% exported 50% converted			75% exported 25% converted		
	1958	1960	1961	1958	1960	1961	1958	1960	1961
	£'000	£'000	£'000	£'000	£'000	£'000	£'000	£'000	£'000
Wages and Salaries	3,447.9	2,980.3	3,574.6	2,615.5	2,260.7	2,711.3	1,783.0	1,541.0	1,848.3
Bauxite Wages and Salaries									
Alumina Wages									
Alumina Salaries									
Maintenance	2,159.4	1,866.5	2,238.8	1,598.1	1,381.2	1,656.7	1,036.6	896.0	1,074.6
Labour	1,714.3	1,481.8	1,777.3	1,269.4	1,097.1	1,315.9	824.3	712.5	854.5
Material	445.1	384.7	461.5	328.7	284.1	340.8	212.3	183.5	220.1
Fuel									
Depreciation									
Normal	892.6	771.5	925.3	691.1	597.3	716.5	489.5	423.1	507.5
Accelerated (Bauxite only)	67.2	58.1	69.6	67.2	58.0	69.6	67.2	58.1	69.6

TABLE V.14 *Estimated Breakdown of Local Disbursements if 75%, 50% or 25% Bauxite Companies' Output Converted into Alumina in Jamaica* (continued)

Administration Office Supplies Travelling Rent, etc.	2,146.2	1,855.2	2,225.1	1,758.8	1,520.3	1,823.3	1,371.4	1,185.3	1,421.6
Cost of Material	1,025.7	886.6	1,063.4	683.9	591.1	708.9	342.0	295.5	354.5
Transport	1,656.8	1,432.1	1,717.6	1,302.9	1,126.2	1,350.8	949.1	820.3	983.9
Net Cost of Agriculture	134.4	116.2	139.3	134.4	116.2	139.4	134.4	116.2	139.3
Insurance Interest									
Government Fees	499.1	431.2	517.4	499.1	431.2	517.4	499.1	431.2	517.4
Exploration	62.4	53.9	64.7	62.4	54.0	64.6	62.4	53.9	64.7
Miscellaneous	385.1	333.0	399.2	256.7	222.0	266.2	128.4	111.0	133.1
Income Tax Net Profit	3,554.8	3,072.7	3,685.2	3,222.5	2,785.3	3,340.7	2,890.3	2,498.2	2,996.2
Total	16,031.6	13,857.3	16,620.2	12,892.5	11,143.5	13,365.4	9,753.4	8,429.8	10,110.7

1. Assumption being that when 75 per cent bauxite output is converted locally into alumina the balance (i.e. 25 per cent of output of bauxite) is exported.

is that 75 per cent of bauxite output is converted into alumina (with local disbursements of £3.995 a ton) and the balance (i.e. 25 per cent) exported (with local disbursements of £1.378 a ton).

In Tables V.12, V.13, V.13A and V.14 are estimates of local disbursements and increases which would accrue if the bauxite companies were persuaded to convert (in Jamaica) varying proportions of their bauxite output. That is, while above the results of utilizing (in varying degrees) for Jamaican alumina production the bauxite exported as bauxite have been considered, it is now intended to show what the results would be to the local economy if certain percentage increases in alumina output had taken place, and how much bauxite it would then have been necessary to export in order to obtain the same benefits as were actually obtained from bauxite-alumina. Obviously, if alumina output had been larger, either the benefits from local disbursements would have been larger, as indicated above, or less bauxite would have been mined to provide the same level of local disbursements. The estimates in Table V.13 accordingly show what would be the implications for the economy if the annual output of the alumina enterprise were increased by varying proportions. This information would be relevant if the island decided to depend increasingly on its alumina rather than on its bauxite enterprise.

In Table V.15 the operations of the bauxite companies are not included. The calculations are based on the alumina enterprise and are intended to show what would be the implications for the Jamaican economy if there were given increases in output of the alumina enterprise. The estimates show what would accrue in the form of local disbursements if the alumina enterprise increased its output by 25 per cent (column (2)), 50 per cent (column (3)), 75 per cent (column (4)), 100 per cent (column (5)) and 150 per cent (column (6)). Alumina, if it increased its 1961 output by 100 per cent (i.e. if it doubled its 1961 output), would make disbursements in the island slightly more than those of the alumina and the bauxite enterprises totalled in that year (Tables V.11 and V.15). If output of alumina were increased by 50 per cent of current output the local disbursements in 1961 would have amounted approximately to £10.5 million as against £13.8 million for both the alumina and bauxite enterprises in that year. This would be a difference (deficit) of £3.3 million. There would however always be a demand for some unprocessed bauxite, and if one assumed that a figure approximating 50 per cent of the 1961 bauxite exports

TABLE V.15   *Estimated Local Disbursements with Expansion in Production of the Alumina Enterprise in Jamaica*

Year	(1) Local Disbursements with current Alumina Exports	(2)	(3)	(4)	(5)	(6)
		Local Disbursements if Alumina Enterprise increased its production by:				
		25%	50%	75%	100%	150%
	£'000	£'000	£'000	£'000	£'000	£'000
1958	3,680.6	4,600.6	5,521.1	6,440.7	7,361.2	9,201.3
1959	3,937.1	4,921.4	5,905.8	6,889.8	7,874.1	9,842.6
1960	6,561.8	8,202.1	9,842.9	11,483.2	13,123.6	16,403.9
1961	6,936.9	8,671.1	10,405.4	12,139.6	13,873.8	17,342.3

continued to go abroad these bauxite exports would account for local disbursements of about £3.4 million. This would bring the total local disbursements to approximately the same as the £3.3 million deficit referred to above. The conclusion from all this is that if the 1961 alumina output were to be increased by only 50 per cent Jamaica would have to continue exporting about half of the bauxite exported in 1961 if her local disbursement from this sector were not to fall. This means that Jamaica would need to export some 2.5 million tons of bauxite as bauxite and that she would still be the second largest bauxite exporter in the world, surpassed only by Surinam whose plans are well advanced for alumina and aluminium processing locally. Jamaica would therefore need to increase her alumina output by more than 50 per cent.

An increase of 75 per cent of the alumina capacity would lead to total local disbursements (Table V.15) of about £12.1 million as against the total 1961 disbursements of £13.8 million. This would be a difference (deficit) of £1.7 million. Jamaica is unlikely to wish to export less than 25 per cent of present bauxite exports and 25 per cent of bauxite exports would yield £1.7 million in local disbursements. The community would therefore be no better off, unless substantial exports of bauxite as bauxite continued. It can be seen (Table V.15) that doubling the present alumina output would still leave much to be desired and that real gains to the economy are to be found only when the alumina output of 1961 were increased by 150 per cent or that the new output should be not less than two and a half times the 1961 output. This increase would be a major task but should not be too formidable since Jamaica's alumina exports in 1961 increased by more than 100 per cent over (i.e. more than double) those of 1957, and this was by one company only.

In Table V.16 the question is looked at not in money terms but from the point of view of the island's mineral resources. The figures show what would be the demands on the ore deposits if the island shifted a good deal of its productive effort from the export of bauxite to the export of alumina. If the island were producing enough alumina so that it were receiving in local disbursements from alumina (Table V.15) approximately the same amount as was received in 1961 from both its bauxite and alumina enterprises together (Table V.11), the consumption in the alumina enterprise would be about 3.5 million tons of bauxite (Table V.16). In 1961 the bauxite plus alumina exports expressed in terms of bauxite were

TABLE V.16 *Estimated Demand for Bauxite with Expansion in Production of the Alumina Enterprise in Jamaica*

Year	(1) Annual Bauxite Exports '000 tons	(2) 100% Annual Alumina Exports[1] Expressed in Tons Bauxite[2] '000 tons	(3) Total Output Tons Bauxite '000 tons	Bauxite contained in Alumina if Production of existing Alumina Enterprise increased by:				
				(4) 25%[3] '000 tons	(5) 50% '000 tons	(6) 75% '000 tons	(7) 100% '000 tons	(8) 150% '000 tons
1954	1,728	347.2	2,075.2					
1955	2,172	515.2	2,687.2					
1956	2,575	511.3	3,086.3					
1957	3,641	1,076.9	4,717.9					
1958	4,799	921.3	5,700.3	1,151.6	1,382.0	1,612.2	1,842.6	2,303.2
1959	4,197	985.5	5,182.5	1,231.9	1,478.3	1,724.6	1,971.0	2,463.7
1960	4,148	1,642.5	5,790.5	2,053.1	2,463.8	2,874.4	3,285.0	4,106.2
1961	4,975	1,736.4	6,711.4	2,170.5	2,604.6	3,038.7	3,472.8	4,341.0

1. Exports assumed to be equal to production.
2. Conversion figures used are 2.8 tons bauxite to 1 ton alumina for 1954–55 and 2.47 tons bauxite to 1 ton alumina for 1956–61.
3. I.e., 125 per cent of Column (2), with corresponding changes in Columns (5), (6), (7) and (8).

about 6.7 million tons of bauxite. The difference amounted to 3.2 million tons of bauxite. This meant that Jamaica, with adequate emphasis on alumina in 1961, would, as far as income was concerned, have been just as well off if she had depleted her deposits of bauxite by 3.2 million tons less. One could express this differently by saying that Jamaica without being any worse off in terms of income could have, for the year 1961 alone, been 3.2 million tons of bauxite better off. One sees this in perspective if one remembers that there were only two other countries in the world whose total output of bauxite in either 1960 or 1961 was as much as 3 million tons.

	Production of Bauxite ('000 tons)	
	1960	1961
British Guiana	2,478	2,374
Surinam	3,400	3,351
U.S.S.R.	3,445	4,000
Jamaica	5,745	6,663

Next to Jamaica the world's largest producers of bauxite were: U.S.S.R., 3.4 million tons; Surinam, 3.4 million tons; British Guiana, 2.5 million tons; France, 2 million tons.

A major proposal arising out of the discussions which have gone before is that Jamaica increase its alumina conversion at the expense of bauxite exports. It has also been suggested that expansion in capacity, of the order envisaged, might involve about £32 million capital. This figure is predicated on the assumption that the two existing alumina plants in Jamaica could be expanded and that in consequence the capital expenditure required would be less than if the only choice was for expanded capacity to rely solely on new plants which would have to be built 'from the ground up'.

Jamaica has two alumina plants, the larger of which has a capacity of 480 thousand tons. The main plants of the four main producers in North America are about twice that size (Table V.17.) Since, as has been argued earlier, the conversion of bauxite to alumina is essentially a chemical process and enjoys economies of large-scale production this larger size is understandable. It would therefore be feasible to double the capacity of Jamaica's plant of 480 thousand tons with investment far less than would be required if a new plant were to be erected. On the assumption that bauxite deposits with low transport charges are available, then the doubling of capacity would, other things being equal, increase the economic efficiency of the plant. The second alumina plant has a capacity of 240 thousand tons and in a country with the largest bauxite production in the world is small indeed. One even wonders why a second plant should have been built at all when the plant first erected was by comparable standards well below the going size. Had the capacity of the earlier alumina plant been doubled it would have still been smaller than

TABLE V.17   *Capacity of Alumina Plants in North America and the Caribbean,* 1961

Company	Location	Capacity ('000 tons)			
		Plant 1	Plant 2	Plant 3	Plant 4
Alcoa	United States	880	375	335	closed
Reynolds	United States	716	782	closed	
Kaiser	United States	759	384		
Ormet	United States	322			
Alcan	Canada	1,140			
Alcan	Jamaica	480	240		
Alcan	British Guiana	220			

Alcoa's plant (at Mobile, Alabama), Aluminium Limited's plant (at Arvida) and only a little larger than Reynolds' two plants (at Hurricane Creek, Arkansas, and Corpus Christi) and Kaiser's plant (at Baton Rouge, Louisiana). The considerations which might have led to the erection of a second plant by Alcan – and such a small plant at that – might include one or more of the following:

(i) The decisions of Aluminium Limited to erect a second plant in Jamaica were taken in 1956 or earlier. The Russian episode described above was in its earliest stages and had not yet assumed the proportions which later induced Aluminium Limited to fear an eventual disruption of the United Kingdom market. Reynolds had not yet undertaken its invasion of Western Europe, nor had of course either Alcoa or Kaiser. The recession in the United States had not yet made itself felt and the international market for Aluminium Limited's aluminium and alumina looked buoyant. Aluminium Limited might, then, in the mid-1950s well have found it attractive to start two modestly sized plants both of which could later and easily be expanded in capacity. Such expansion might one day meet the needs of the market on the one hand and enjoy the economies of scale on the other. If this was the consideration, or one of the considerations, Aluminium Limited would be able, if willing, to expand capacity in one or both plants substantially with, relatively, modest investment charges.

(ii) A second consideration might have been internal transport costs. Jamaica is a hilly island. The second plant has been so located as to handle a block of bauxite deposits separated by mountainous terrain from the site of the earlier plant. The second plant secures supplies from an area where Alcan and Reynolds have the main holdings while the earlier plant is situated in a region where Alcan and Kaiser have the main holdings.

(iii) A third consideration might have been that Aluminium Limited had enough inside information to have foreseen the possible later developments in Guinea and the President's decision to terminate the company's mining rights. With disruption of supplies from that source the company may have prudently and understandably decided to place itself strategically to expand alumina capacity in Jamaica.

(iv) The Company might have been sensitive to the possible charge that it was holding bauxite lands in the Ewarton area without bringing any benefits to that area. Other companies were known to be prospecting. If any such prospector failed to find good deposits (which were not yet taken up) political pressure might eventually lead to proposals that holdings not being developed might be leased to newcomers who were prepared to develop.

(v) Alcan's older plant at Kirkvine had been expanded once and the construction work had had an unsettling effect on workers in the plant. In addition, further new construction work there would involve finding quarters for new workers in an area with high living costs.

There are two conclusions from these considerations. One is that the existing plants can be expanded economically. The proportions would depend on the extent to which collaboration could be secured between the several companies. The second conclusion is that if expansion occurred and if collaboration between the companies were secured the two existing alumina plants being so strategically located could service two of the main ore-bearing blocks in the island. While there are obvious advantages to this kind of collaboration, it is highly improbable that companies would be prepared to rationalize facilities along lines such as we have discussed but the possibilities do deserve even passing reference. The Jamaica Government, it would seem, could advisedly use its influence to secure enough outlet for Aluminium Limited's increased output of alumina as a necessary pre-requisite to that company's raising its two alumina plants up to the capacity of, say, 700 to 800 thousand tons each. If the total capacity of the two existing plants were thus brought to 1.4 to 1.6 million tons capacity, additional plant or plants would need to have supplementary capacity of about 450 thousand tons to bring the island's output of alumina to about 1.9 million tons. The figure of 1.9 million tons alumina capacity would be the requirement if 75 per cent of the 1960[1] bauxite exports were to be converted locally. On the basis of 1960 figures, such an increase in capacity would, if achieved, mean an increase in local disbursements of some £8.1 million a year (Table V.13A) and in 1961 an increase of $9\frac{3}{4}$ million a year.

The capital involved in the expanded capacity is estimated at about £16 million for machinery and equipment for the new additional plant and another £16 million for the expansion of the two existing plants. This assumes that Alcan could be persuaded to expand its existing plants and that new plants would be built to meet only residual capacity of 450 thousand tons. If this arrangement were not achieved the capital requirement would be considerably greater.

Balance of Payments

It is evident that the expansion of alumina with its heavy overseas capital requirements will have implications for the receipts and payments of the island from and to the rest of the world. It is customary to separate into two broad categories the items which make up such receipts and payments. One broad category concerns the receipts and payments relating to goods and services and is

1. 75 per cent of bauxite exports in 1960 would be 3,111,000 tons (bauxite). This would be equivalent to 1,250,000 tons of alumina. Existing capacity in 1960 was 720,000 tons with production of 665,000 tons. If existing capacity were expanded to 1,500,000 tons (and the plants would then be no larger than plants owned by each of the large producers in North America), the additional capacity in new local plant to be built would be 450,000 tons.

reflected in the Current Account. In the Current Account are the receipts for goods exported and payments for goods imported. This balance of trade, or Visible Trade, gives a first approximation of the island's external position. Invisible Trade in this Sector Account includes returns to factors of production. A third section of the Current Account deals with unilateral transfers and includes remittances.

The second broad category concerns the Capital Account, which is concerned with two things. One is the autonomous movement of savings from one country to another. The second is how the over-all balance of goods, services and autonomous capital movements is financed. This latter aspect of the capital account can be termed accommodating and would normally be absent from the accounts which deal with direct investment in a territory by an overseas concern. If Jamaica is to expand alumina capacity this would imply increasing her imports. Other things remaining equal, this would have a tendency towards a current account deficit. This can be met either by increasing exports and/or an increased capital inflow. In the case of alumina such capital inflow might be expected to take the form, as in the past, of direct investment of overseas industrial groups.

The figures published by the Jamaica Department of Statistics have been rearranged (Table V.18) to place the island's balance of payments statement with a method of presentation approximately similar to that used in Tables V.19–V.22 for the sector balance of payments.

Exports and imports for the whole economy have grown rapidly in recent years but the period covered shows imports in excess of exports (Table V.18). This has been the characteristic situation. Not since 1922 has the value of the island's exports exceeded that of imports and the deficit on Visible Trade increased from £6 million in 1954 to £22 million in 1959. Not only has there been this deficit but the trend has been for it to increase, until about 1959. The substantial deficit persisted even after the revaluation in 1957 of the island's bauxite exports. As far as invisibles are concerned Jamaica pays to the rest of the world just about the same as she receives, but on the whole and especially in recent years, receipts have been slightly in excess. Unilateral transfers have been a large contributor and was especially so in 1960, the year selected below as a basis for further discussion. To meet the requirements of this situation Jamaica has had fairly heavy net capital inflows – from C.D. & W., from the bauxite and alumina industrial groups and from the running down of assets abroad. For each year shown mining has been the sector which has been the largest recipient.

The items in the sectoral account were arranged in Tables V.19, V.20 and V.21 to show the transactions with the rest of the world

TABLE V.18   *Jamaica's Balance of Payments: Summary of Current and Capital Accounts*[1]

	1957 £'000,000	1958 £'000,000	1959 £'000,000	1960 £'000,000	1961 £'000,000
Current					
a. **Visible**					
Imports	66.8	64.7	69.2	77.6	75.5
Exports	50.4	48.0	46.9	58.8	63.6
Balance	− 16.4	− 16.7	− 22.3	− 18.8	− 11.9
b. **Invisible**					
Net	− 0.3	0.8	0.8	1.0	0.6
Balance on Visible and Invisible	− 16.7	− 15.9	− 21.5	− 17.8	− 11.3
Unilateral Transfers	5.1	5.5	5.2	7.2	6.9
Total Current	− 11.6	− 10.4	− 16.3	− 10.6	− 4.4
Capital					
Net inflow (Mining)	6.8	3.1	1.4	3.0	
Other	8.5	7.4	7.2	5.4	
Total Capital	15.3	10.5	8.6	8.4	

respectively for the bauxite enterprises, for the alumina enterprises and for the combined enterprises. There was a revision in price of bauxite in 1957 and this much inflated the value of exports (Table V.19). Detailed balance of payments figures are not available prior to 1958 but this was the first full year in which the new and high

1. Francis, O. C. and Clarke, E. St A. *Balance of Payments Statistics*, Department of Statistics, Jamaica, 1962.

price for bauxite was in operation. The characteristic of the bauxite figures is a high positive cumulative balance on current account. The rise in price of bauxite is understandably associated with a

TABLE V.19   *Schedule of Payments Abroad of the Bauxite Enterprise[1] in Jamaica*

	1958 £'000	1959 £'000	1960 £'000	1961 £'000
On Current Account				
a. **Visible**				
Exports	12,597.4	11,017.1	10,888.5	13,059.4
Imports				
Maintenance	− 201.7	− 176.3	− 174.3	− 209.0
Fuel				
Cost of Material				
Machinery and				
Equipment	− 71.5	− 91.0	− 247.6	
Imports – Total	− 273.2	− 267.3	− 421.9	− 209.0
Balance	12,324.2	10,749.8	10,466.6	12,850.4
b. **Invisible**				
Transportation				
Insurance	− 24.0	− 21.0	− 20.7	−25.0
Net Profit	− 3,839.2	− 3,357.6	− 3,318.4	− 3,980.0
Interest	− 431.9	− 377.7	− 373.3	− 447.7
Wages and Salaries	− 67.2	− 58.8	− 58.1	− 69.6
Administration and				
Research	− 172.7	− 151.1	− 149.4	− 179.1
Exploration	− 19.2	− 16.7	− 16.6	− 19.8
Miscellaneous				
Invisible – Total	− 4,554.2	− 3,982.9	− 3,936.5	− 4,721.2
Current Account				
Cumulative Balance	7,770.0	6,766.9	6,530.1	8,129.2
On Capital Account				
Net Capital Inflow	909.0	202.0	1,391.0	420.0

1. On basis of 1957–58 prices. *See* Table V.9A.

high level of profits paid to the rest of the world. Thus in the years 1958 and 1959 when the cumulative balances on Current Account in alumina (Table V.20) were low, profits (sent abroad) were, understandably, below profits (sent abroad) in bauxite. But even

TABLE V.20   *Schedule of Payments Abroad of the Alumina Enterprise[1] in Jamaica*

	1958 £'000	1959 £'000	1960 £'000	1961 £'000
On Current Account				
a. **Visible**				
Exports	9,855.1	10,541.9	17,569.8	18,574.3
Imports				
Maintenance	− 215.6	− 230.6	− 384.3	− 406.3
Fuel	− 928.7	− 993.4	− 1,655.6	− 1,750.3
Cost of Material	− 1,049.3	− 1,122.5	− 1,870.9	− 1,977.7
Machinery and				
Equipment	− 1,692.0	− 334.1	− 238.6	− 254.1
Imports – Total	− 3,885.6	− 2,680.6	− 4,149.4	− 4,388.4
Balance	5,969.5	7,861.3	13,420.4	14,185.9
b. **Invisible**				
Transportation				
Insurance	− 184.3	− 197.1	− 328.5	− 347.3
Net Profit	− 1,119.4	− 1,197.4	− 1,995.6	− 2,109.7
Interest	− 917.6	− 981.6	− 1,636.0	− 1,729.5
Wages and Salaries	− 85.7	− 91.6	− 152.8	− 161.5
Administration and				
Research	− 85.7	− 91.6	− 152.5	− 161.5
Exploration	− 3.6	− 4.0	− 6.6	− 6.9
Miscellaneous	− 98.6	− 105.5	− 175.8	− 185.8
Invisible – Total	− 2,494.9	− 2,668.8	− 4,447.8	− 4,702.2
Current Account				
Cumulative Balance	3,474.6	5,192.5	8,972.6	9,483.7
On Capital Account				
Net Capital Inflow	4,000.0	1,600.0	1,600.0	580.0

1. On basis of 1956–58 prices. *See* Table V.10A.

in 1960 when the cumulative balance on current account was higher in alumina (Table V.20) than in bauxite (Table V.19) the profits (sent abroad) were lower in the alumina enterprise than in the bauxite enterprise (Table V.20A).

TABLE V.20A   *Jamaica Bauxite and Alumina Enterprises:*
Cumulative Balance and Profits sent Abroad

| | Cumulative Balance (Excess of Value of exports over Value of payments abroad) | | Profits sent abroad | |
Year	Bauxite £'000,000	Alumina £'000,000	Bauxite £'000,000	Alumina £'000,000
1958	7.8	3.5	3.8	1.1
1959	6.8	5.2	3.4	1.2
1960	6.5	9.0	3.3	2.0
1961	8.1	9.5	4.0	2.1

The total of wages and salaries sent abroad by the alumina enterprise (through the household sector) is substantially higher than in the bauxite enterprises (Tables V.10A and V.9A) and this is to be expected since in the alumina enterprise the number of technicians and personnel in the higher administrative posts is greater than in bauxite. As may also be expected the interest charges (sent abroad) are much higher in alumina than in bauxite.

The combined table (Table V.21) shows how major is the positive contribution of the sector to the balance of payments. As has been mentioned above the sector has been the main recipient of capital inflows but the positive balance on current account is considerably greater.

An exercise (in Table V.22) was undertaken to determine on the basis of the 1960 export of the bauxite companies (Table V.16) what would be the implications for the balance of payments if 75 per cent of that bauxite were converted into alumina. The assumption is that four years would be required before there would be any increase in alumina output. (This is an unduly conservative assumption since expansion of the capacity of the existing plants could

certainly achieve some increased output before the expiry of a four-
year period). It is also assumed that there would be an expenditure
on machinery and equipment amounting to £8 million in each of

TABLE V.21   *Schedule of Payments Abroad of the Bauxite and
the Alumina Enterprises in Jamaica*[1]

	1958 £'000	1959 £'000	1960 £'000	1961 £'000
On Current Account				
a. **Visible**				
Exports	22,452.5	21,599.0	28,458.3	31,633.7
Imports				
Maintenance	− 417.3	− 406.9	− 558.6	− 615.3
Fuel	− 928.7	− 993.4	− 1,655.6	− 1,750.3
Cost of Material	− 1,049.3	− 1,122.5	− 1,870.9	− 1,977.7
Machinery and				
Equipment	− 1,763.5	− 425.1	− 486.2	− 254.1
Imports – Total	− 4,158.8	− 2,947.9	− 4,571.3	− 4,597.4
Balance	18,293.7	18,611.1	23,887.0	27,036.3
b. **Invisible**				
Transportation				
Insurance	− 208.3	− 218.1	− 349.2	− 372.3
Net Profit	− 4,958.6	− 4,555.0	− 5,314.0	− 6,089.7
Interest	− 1,349.5	− 1,359.3	− 2,009.3	− 2,177.2
Wages and Salaries	− 152.9	− 150.4	− 210.9	− 231.1
Administration and				
Research	− 258.4	− 242.7	− 301.9	− 340.6
Exploration	− 21.8	− 20.7	− 23.2	− 26.7
Miscellaneous	− 98.6	− 105.5	− 175.8	− 185.8
Invisible – Total	− 7,048.1	− 6,651.7	− 8,384.3	− 9,423.4
Current Account				
Cumulative Balance	11,245.6	11,959.4	15,502.7	17,612.9
On Capital Account				
Net Capital Inflow	3,091.0	1,398.0	2,991.0	1,000.0

1. *See* Table V.11A.

four years and that 65 per cent of this would be imported, with 35 per cent being spent on installation and related local expenditure. The capital inflow was estimated on the basis of the figures in the *Annual Report*[1] of 1961 of Aluminium Limited where a consolidated

TABLE V.22   *Schedule of Payments Abroad if 75 per cent Bauxite Companies' Output Converted and 25 per cent Exported*

	For the four years of expansion based on production figures for 1960 and average cost figure for 1956–58 £'000	In fifth year when assumption is that 75% bauxite output is converted and 25% exported £'000
On Current Account		
a. **Visible**		
Exports	28,458.3	36,000.5
Imports		
Maintenance	− 557.0	− 771.6
Fuel	− 1,655.6	− 3,135.9
Cost of Material	− 1,870.9	− 3,543.4
Machinery and Equipment	− 5,200.0	
Imports – Total	− 9,283.5	− 7,450.9
Balance	19,174.8	28,549.6
b. **Invisible**		
Transportation		
Insurance	− 349.2	− 627.4
Net Profit	− 5,314.0	− 4,609.5
Interest	− 2,009.3	− 3,191.9
Wages and Salaries	− 210.9	− 303.8
Administration and Research	− 301.9	− 326.7
Exploration	− 23.2	− 16.6
Miscellaneous	− 175.8	− 332.9
Invisible – Total	− 8,384.3	− 9,408.8
Current Account		
Cumulative Balance	10,790.5	19,140.8
On Capital Account		
Net Capital Inflow	8,000.0	

1. Aluminium Limited. *Annual Report* 1961, p. 26.

statement shows that, in 1960, income, after income taxes, amounted
to \$43.0 million and that dividends amounted to \$3.9 million on
preferred shares, plus \$20.7 million on equity dividends. Profits
were therefore allocated in the rough proportion of 57 per cent
distributed and 43 per cent undistributed. The income after taxes for
the combined enterprise in Jamaica (Table V.22) amounted to
£5.3 million and if one assumes the proportion of undistributed
profits to be 43 per cent one gets a figure of £2.3 million for undistributed profits by the sector in 1960. On this basis the net
capital inflow could therefore be £8 million less £2.3 million (or
£5.7 million) for four years.

This adds to the deficit on current and capital account and would
have to be looked at in that context. According to these estimates
the adverse balance would rise by £2.8 million for four years, but
the fifth year would wipe out £8.3 million of this £11.2 million.
Thus the operation would be worth while in itself especially since
(as stated above) not all of the four years would show £2.8 million
deficit increase. The problem posed here is similar to that in most
under-developed economies: the price which has to be paid for
high capital inflows and the constraint which the balance of payments imposes. It is evident that the increased output of alumina
would justify heavy investment even largely from external sources.
In year five, when expansion has been achieved and the equivalent
of 75 per cent of 1960s bauxite output was being converted locally
into alumina, the cumulative balance on the current account in
the sector would be about £19 million a year.

6 Technology and Innovation

There is no intention here to attempt a technical discussion of the chemical and related aspects of the various processes in the industry. Rather is it the purpose to describe briefly what the processes are and then from that starting point to consider implications for development in the future. While for some purposes it may be best to consider technology in a general context, such is the orientation of this whole discussion that the implications for development are appraised mainly in regard to possible relevance for the Caribbean.

The Processes involved in the Production of Aluminium[1]

The Bauxite Stage

Bauxite, the ore which is the basis for most commercially produced aluminium, contains aluminium oxide as well as other oxides (e.g. silica, iron oxide, titanium oxide). In areas like the Caribbean the bauxite deposits are in the trihydrate group. In general the ore is crushed, washed to remove some of the impurities and dried in heated revolving drums. This operation causes a gain of about 50 per cent in the yield of ore transported. Often where the deposits are nearer the processing plants there is no drying.

The Alumina Stage

The chief requirements in the production of alumina are bauxite, caustic soda, filter cloth, starch, water, heat. The method of production used generally on a commercial scale is based on the Bayer process and this basically is: ground bauxite is digested in hot caustic solution; the alumina is dissolved and the impurities separated in 'red mud'; the sodium aluminate solution and mud are then separated by filtration, or settling, or both, and the residue is washed to raise the recovery; the clear solution is cooled and pumped and 'seeded' with hydrated alumina to precipitate hydrated alumina from the solution; the precipitate is washed and calcined

1. Dumas, André. 'L'Aluminium et le progrès technique', *Revue de l'Aluminium*, No. 282.

to produce aluminium oxide or alumina; the spent sodium aluminate solution is evaporated down. The Bayer process may be modified in several ways. The European Bayer process is used for the mono-hydrate ores. The American Bayer for high-grade bauxites with ores chiefly of the trihydrate type. The Combination process is used for lower grade (high silica) trihydrate ores.

Anaconda in the United States consider their experiments far advanced for the production of alumina from clays which have a lower aluminium oxide content than bauxite. They had erected a pilot plant for the trials and considered the results would as early as 1957, if necessary, justify commercial operation.

One of the notable developments is reported from Russia where the available bauxite deposits are considerable but not enough to ensure the massive expansion which is planned. In consequence the U.S.S.R. industry has been exploiting the substitution for bauxite of another ore, nepheline, which occurs in abundance within the country. Nepheline is an aluminous clay with roughly the following composition: aluminium oxide, 30 per cent; potash and soda, 20 per cent; silica, 43 per cent; residual substances, 7 per cent. While the alumina content is low the U.S.S.R. technologists claim that the process has the advantage of yielding profitable by-products to alumina. The ore is processed with limestone which yields a good raw material for a type of Portland cement, sodium and potassium which are used in the fertilizer industry. The profit from these by-products, the Russians claim, justify the process although it is more complex than the more usual extraction of alumina from bauxite.

Olin Mathieson[1] are reported to be experimenting with a process which by-passes both bauxite and the normal alumina process and involves recovering aluminium from clay. The process is based on separation via aluminium sulphate. The clay is calcined to remove the silica and then treated with sulphuric acid and this converts the aluminium oxide into aluminium sulphate, ferrous sulphate being also formed. Then the aluminium sulphate is calcined to remove the sulphurous gases leaving aluminium oxide behind. An advantage claimed is that there is an important by-product which can be used in the building industry. The process is conceived to be potentially as economical as recovery from bauxite and the company was reputed in 1961 to have plans in hand for investment of half a million dollars for a pilot plant to evaluate the commercial possibilities.

1. *Light Metals* (London), May 1961, p. 120.

Aluminium Limited are experimenting with a sub-halide process of aluminium production, the Gros process, which would eliminate the alumina phase. They and their associates in Japan are those doing most work and experimentation with the process and the details of the process are supposed to be still secret. The bauxite is reduced in an electric furnace. There is reaction with one of the sub-halides or halogen family (the chlorine, fluorine family) resulting in the elimination of an intermediate alumina phase. There is no saving in electric power required but the economies introduced have encouraged Aluminium Limited to consider it justified to erect a 5,000 to 7,000 ton a year pilot plant.

Kaiser and British Aluminium are said to have worked out a variant of the sub-halide process in which alumina is produced in normal fashion and the sub-halide used in the smelter with notable improvement in efficiency. Gains in production of as high as 37 per cent are claimed. The public does not know whether or not this process was evolved before British Aluminium and Reynolds were associated and what is Reynolds' status in regard to these developments.

Pechiney has a process in which it has had enough confidence to establish a 5,000 ton pilot plant. The Pechiney process does not eliminate an intermediate stage of aluminium oxide but claims savings in regard to investment. There are two stages in the process: (a) the production, in an electric furnace, of corundum by selective reduction of bauxite when impurities are removed; (b) reduction of the corundum in an electric furnace in the presence of carbon and the separation of aluminium from carbide. Corundum is also an aluminium oxide, and while the chemical composition is the same as that of alumina the physical structure is different.

There are thus two major lines of development which have implications not only for the trade lines connecting bauxite-alumina supplies with the aluminium production complex but, more fundamentally for the traditional method of deriving aluminium from bauxite and/or alumina. One is an increase in the intensification of geological surveys to discover deposits and improvements in the techniques of discovery of such deposits. There is in consequence at present, knowledge of far greater bauxite reserves than there was a decade ago. Then Jamaica's 500 million tons were the largest recorded deposits. Now both Guinea and Australia are reputed to have deposits 3–4 times the size of Jamaica's.

The other line of development is the improvement in technology which might have one of several effects. One result might be to make economic the extraction of alumina from clays other than bauxite. Another might be to introduce innovations in the traditional method of production of aluminium oxide. Another might be to introduce innovations in the processes in the smelter, so as to modify not only the traditional method of production of, but even the elimination of the need for, alumina. Developments in either of these directions could profoundly modify the distribution and location of ore and aluminium oxide facilities in the industry.

Technology and innovation have also brought improvements to the traditional bauxite-alumina-aluminium process. One of the chief of these is the reduction in thermal energy required in alumina production. For every ton of alumina produced the requirements in steam were: 14 tons in 1944, 5.8 in 1950, 4.7 in 1955 and 2.4 in 1960. This means that the steam requirements at the end of the War were nearly six times what they were in 1960, that the requirements in 1955 were nearly double what they were five years later.

There were many signs that the world industry was prepared for the present to back the improvements in the traditional methods of production rather than radical departures. There was much major expansion taking place in 1962 based overwhelmingly on the traditional methods. These major expansion schemes included: Alcoa's alumina reduction plant and alumina plant in Kwinana, Australia; Consolidated Zinc (with Kaiser as an associate) investing £100 million in smelting facilities in New Zealand; Kaiser and associates investment of £100 million in bauxite mining facilities and an alumina plant at Weipa in North Queensland, Australia.

The Aluminium Stage

In normal industrial use the method of producing aluminium is based on the electrolysis of an alumina solution in molten cryolite. The reduction is done in a series of electrolytic cells called potlines. The potlines are steel boxes lined with carbon which acts both as the cathode and as a container for the molten electrolyte. Carbon anodes dip into the potlines from above and direct current passing between the anode and cathode reduces the aluminium oxide and the metal sinks to the bottom of the cell.

There are two lines of technological advance which receive much attention in research being carried on by the industry. One relates to the reduction of costs of supply of electric power. While hydro-electric power has in the past been the most economical method, competitive demand for and limited supplies of such power have encouraged the industry to look for alternative sources of electricity. Due to technological change both gas and coal are now supplying electricity for commercial production. Atomic power as a source is not yet feasible but the time is not as far off as seemed likely not long ago. In a report[1] published by OECD under the heading of 'Forecasts 1961–66' this statement appears:

> 'Many experts believe . . . that nuclear energy will become competitive for base load requirements by about 1970. In certain cases nuclear power production may be competitive before 1970.'

The other main line of direction of research relates to the electro-chemical equipment and methods used in producing aluminium. Some of these have been referred to above and receive much attention in the technical journals.

Technological Change and Implications for Development

The countries involved may be divided into two groups as far as participation in the industry is concerned. The one group would be composed of those countries which have the conditions conducive to aluminium production and would have power resources with or without deposits of the ore. If such countries do not have the ore they may import it (as is done in Norway, Japan or India), convert it into aluminium, consume some and export the remainder. Some countries have the power resources as well as the ore and the most notable example of these would be West Africa and Australia. There are some territories which have deposits of the ore and which for the immediate future seem to have no prospects of taking their enterprises to the aluminium stage. It is in this group that much of the Caribbean Commonwealth falls and it is primarily this sort of question which is to be asked: what tech-nological processes should one endeavour to explore if the object is to increase the contribution of the bauxite-alumina enterprise to the economic growth of communities like those of the Common-wealth Caribbean? In trying to answer this question there are four

1. OECD, *The Electricity Supply Industry in Europe*, 12th Enquiry, p. 32.

assumptions which can be made. One assumption is that the labour is available and can be taught the necessary skills. It is now recognized that unskilled labour can be taught many of the skills and disciplines requisite for participating in secondary industry. At the level of professional workers – e.g. engineers, chemists, accountants – the West Indies could benefit from more trained personnel but there is now a University with provision for training engineers, chemists, chemical engineers. In addition many students go abroad for training, especially to North America and to the United Kingdom. In 1960 the number of students in Higher Education was 5,435, of whom 544 were studying engineering and 1,011 the natural sciences.[1] In addition to the trained nationals available for professional and administrative posts there are complementary supplies obtainable through technical assistance from either the public or the private sector of the more advanced communities.

A second assumption, and related to the first, is that in the public and/or private sector there are the will and the means of an entrepreneurial group to take risks in the context of much uncertainty; to evaluate the profits from such risks in terms not only of internal but also external economies, in not only the short but the long run; to secure the distribution outlets which often prove the limiting factor for success of an enterprise. These are achievements which (for undertakings such as one is here discussing) may be beyond the attainment of an entrepreneurial group which does not obtain the vigorous collaboration of the Government.

A third assumption, that adequate capital is available,[2] is largely dependent on the second assumption. The availability of capital for undertakings similar to those under consideration will in large measure depend on the collaboration of the entrepreneurial team whose responsibilities and composition have been sketchily outlined under the second assumption. The pattern, now being universally set for such enterprises, is that the managerial skill and capital are provided by a consortium including the Government, local interests and interests from abroad.

The fourth assumption is that one limits oneself primarily to the consideration of the type of risk which has resulted in profit to

1. Manktelow, R., White, H. McD., Mills, G. E. *The West Indies Staffing Problems*, Federal House, Trinidad, 1962.
2. *The Economist*, in its issue of August 4, 1962, p. 469, discussing financing for development, wrote: 'The CDFC (Commonwealth Development Finance Corporation) languishes with impressive backers and good management but a dearth of projects.'

F

territoiies with endowments comparable to those of the Commonwealth Caribbean.

The assumptions are a prerequisite for the following projects which, regarded from the point of view of technology, are suggested as worthy of consideration.

Conversion of Bauxite into Alumina

On technological grounds there is no problem in converting bauxite into alumina in the Commonwealth Caribbean and in communities like the Caribbean. The figures presented elsewhere in this study show that to an economy there are advantages in converting, locally, its bauxite into alumina. It may well happen that with an industry that is as vertically integrated as aluminium and which is as market oriented as is a basic metal, the management of the industrial group may decide that it is more expedient for their overall interests to locate their alumina plants at some point other than near the bauxite deposits. Unless the local government and interests aie sufficiently adroit in their negotiations, the decision may therefore be taken not to convert alumina in the country possessing the ore. The answer to this is that – as it is probably, in the final analysis, a question of bargaining – the local government and local interests should not grow weary in vigilance or resourcefulness in exploring ways and means of ensuring that the gains are not denied their community. The local government and the local interests, if in doubt as to how resolute they should be, ought to note the developments in the industry throughout the world today. The policy of Governments – whether in Indonesia, in Australia, in Ghana, in Guinea or in Surinam – is much more sophisticated in the 1960s than was the case a decade or two ago: they make it a condition that in the country of origin the processing is taken at least to the alumina stage. The conclusion is that any community which has sizeable deposits of bauxite and does not enjoy the advantages of its conversion into alumina should carefully consider whether the conditions of the second assumption have been met.

Exploitation of Different Uses of Alumina

Experience is that, in an area like the Commonwealth Caribbean, alumina is produced only by an organization having large capital resources and requiring it primarily in the manufacture of aluminium.

If the firm is as vertically integrated as is the case in aluminium, it can happen that the production of alumina is aimed so purposefully at meeting the firm's own needs that there is no pressure on managerial policy to produce excess supplies or to set up the organization necessary to sell any such excess supplies. It can often be that excess of supplies is a good incentive for expanded markets.[1]

One has spoken thus far in terms of alumina for reduction to aluminium. This is understandable since in the United States about 95 per cent of alumina is used for this purpose, but there is a demand for alumina for other uses. Firms like Giulini[2] in West Germany, Kaiser and Alcoa in the United States and Mitsubishi Chemical Industries in Japan are not interested in alumina only as a base for aluminium but in its use in the chemical industry and

---

1. The writer came upon an incident which illustrates the point. A firm in Europe made application to Alcan for the purchase of alumina in 1961. Alcan made the sale, shipping alumina direct from Jamaica to the firm on the Continent. When the alumina arrived in Europe the firm discovered that the alumina was, in chemical composition, all the specifications called for, but not of the physical consistency which the firm had anticipated or had been in the habit of handling. The type of alumina expected was one of higher calcination with some of the ordinary alumina converted partly into a corundum-like form. The question which one asks is: would Alcan be prepared to perform the higher calcination? It would probably be unwilling if it meant substantial change in its technology and/or added capital charges. The implications might, however, be wider from the point of view of Jamaica. Suppose there was available some of this type of alumina and suppose there were facilities for aggressive marketing, is there a possibility that Jamaica's output of alumina could increase with advantage to Jamaica? Would it be in Jamaica's interest to try to encourage this wider demand for Alcan's alumina and if necessary to enter into negotiation with Alcan in order to make this increased production attractive to Alcan?

One might raise a second and different but related query about the supplies of alumina in the 1950s to the Harvey smelters on the West Coast of America. One wonders whether, if a really aggressive effort were made to widen the demand, Jamaica's alumina (on ships leaving Jamaica going through the Panama Canal to smelters at Kitimat on the West Coast of Canada and so passing Harvey's door-step, on the West Coast of America) could not have effectively competed with the Japanese alumina supplied to Harvey. It may not have suited Alcan's interests or commitments to do this but would it not have been worth-while from Jamaica's point of view to grasp this opportunity to widen her participation in world trade in alumina?

2. Giulini, Ludwigshafen, Germany, has published a booklet *Our Alumina Products*. In the foreword to this booklet the firm explains how aluminium sulphate is one of their main products and that it is made from alumina. The booklet then goes on to list the chemical products which they derive from alumina and to indicate the chief uses for which the firm markets these products. The products listed are a few which this firm and others are exploiting in the use of alumina as a base for a light chemical industry.

as a basis for other products. Some of these products and their uses are:

a. *Hydrated aluminas* for glass and porcelain industries; for manufacture of alumina salts; for brake linings; as filters for rubber and plastics; as bulk filler for paints; in talcum powder and dentifrices; in manufacture of lithographic ink.

b. *Calcined aluminas* in manufacture of aluminium; for refractory brick and fine clays; as dehydration catalysts; for insulators; for polishing.

c. *Aluminium sulphate* for water purification; in textile dyeing; manufacture of white paper; in manufacture of aluminium compounds; in fire-proofing.

These products are not likely to be manufactured in isolation and will probably make their appearance only as part of a larger complex. Perhaps one way to create such a complex is to recognize that alumina could be a good starting point.

Introduction of Caustic Soda[1] Production

Caustic soda is used in the production of alumina. In general caustic soda is produced industrially by one of two methods: (*a*) the lime-soda process; (*b*) the electrolysis of brine. In the one, the chemical process, a solution of soda ash is treated with slaked lime. This yields a precipitate calcium carbonate and an aqueous solution of caustic soda. The insoluble calcium carbonate is removed and the solution concentrated down to produce the grade of caustic soda which is desired.

In the second, the electrolytic process, an electric current in mercury or diaphragm-type cells is passed through a solution of salt (sodium chloride). The current decomposes the sodium chloride to form a weak caustic soda solution, with hydrogen gas forming at the cathode and chlorine at the anode as co-products. It is from this source that practically all of the chlorine in industrial use is derived. No firm figures are available on the proportions of caustic soda produced by the two different methods, but it is probable that about 75 per cent is by the electrolytic process. Thus in the United States in 1954 electrolysis accounted for over 85 per cent

1. The writer acknowledges his reliance on notes prepared by The Economist Intelligence Unit relating to the economic aspects of the location of the industry. The responsibility for the conclusions drawn are, of course, the writer's.

of the caustic soda consumed in that country and it is probable that by 1970 the lime-soda process will have become obsolete.

The preference for the electrolytic process has been growing throughout the world to a large extent because of the chlorine produced. Chlorine plays an increasing part in the 'second chemical revolution' resulting from developments in the field of organic heavy materials, many of which contain chlorine or have involved chlorine in their manufacture. Since caustic soda and chlorine are produced in a ratio of almost one to one in the electrolytic process and since the demand for chlorine is growing faster than the demand for caustic soda, the economic viability of the chemical process should become progressively endangered and here this discussion restricts itself to the feasibility of the production of caustic soda by the electrolytic process.

Salt, being the basis of the caustic soda and chlorine industry, must be available, and this is a primary consideration. In the United Kingdom the large caustic soda plants have traditionally been located near the salt deposits. There are, however, caustic soda plants (e.g. in North England and in South Wales) where close proximity to salt deposits has not been the limiting factor. The pattern of location in France is similar to that which obtains generally in England, the operations being carried on near the salt fields. In West Germany the pattern is somewhat different and many important caustic soda plants are in areas which are considerable distances from salt fields. Rock salt, from the salt fields at Heilbron and Borth, is conveyed by rail and barge to the principal electrolytic plants. On the other hand in East Germany the main electrolytic installations are close to the salt sources. In the United States the traditional pattern of location has been determined by the proximity to salt deposits but recently other considerations have led to divergence from this pattern and to centres of consumption having an increasing influence on the location of electrolytic plants.

Another important factor influencing the location of electrolytic plants is the supply of cheap and regular supplies of electricity.[1]

1. The ideal of course is the presence of cheap electric power in conjunction with salt deposits. Increasingly, however, considerations of the market have modified the attitude towards this supplies-orientation and have grown to exert an influence on location. Complicating the question of supplies *vs* market influences are such questions as economies of scale and external economies which play a particularly important part in chemical industries and which make profitable an export trade from centres such as the United Kingdom and the United States.

Between 2,500 and 4,000 kWh. produce 1 ton of chlorine and 1.13 tons of caustic soda. If the energy per ton is taken as 3,500 kWh., an electrolytic plant producing 5.8 tons of chlorine an hour (or about 140 tons a day or 50,000 tons a year) would require generating equipment to deliver, per hour, 3,500 × 5.8 or 20,300 kWh., the equivalent of 27,200 horse power. An indication of the comparative consumption is that such a plant would be adequate for an average modern town of 40,000 people.[1] While a smaller caustic soda plant would require a smaller generating plant it would not be proportionately so and an optimum-sized plant is not usually regarded as much under 100 tons a day.

Water is another factor which must be considered in location since the chlor-alkali industry is a large consumer of water.

The chlor-alkali plant does not employ directly a large number of people. One plant in the United States producing 220 tons of chlorine a day employs less than 200 people including office and technical personnel needed for the three shifts which the plant operates. The demand for labour can be evaluated only if the

TABLE VI.1   *Demand for Caustic Soda and Chlorine in United States[2], 1956*

Caustic Soda	% Total	Chlorine	% Total
Chemicals	30.6	Solvents	20
Rayon and Film	18.1	Plastics and Fibres	12
Petroleum refining	8.4	Pesticides and Herbicides	12
Pulp and Paper	7.7	Pulp and Paper	11
Lye and Cleansers	5.8	Automotive fluids	11
Textiles	5.3	Refrigerants and Propellants	8.5
Soap	5.0	Disinfectants and Sanitation	4
Metal processing	2.5	Textiles	3
Vegetable oils	1.4	Other Chemicals	15.5
Reclaimed rubber	1.4	Miscellaneous	3
Miscellaneous and Export	13.8		
Total	100	**Total**	100

1. Another type of comparison is that the Caribbean Cement Company, Jamaica, has built for itself a plant to generate the power it needs. In the United Kingdom about half the electricity used in electrolysis is privately generated.
2. The pattern of consumption in the United Kingdom is largely similar.

indirect as well as the direct activities are also brought into the picture. While quantitatively the demand for labour is low, qualitatively it is high since an adequate cadre of professionally trained chemists and engineers supported by well-trained technicians is essential.

The pattern in the use of chemicals can often undergo rapid change but in 1956 the uses shown (Table VI.1) reflect the purposes for which chlorine and caustic soda were demanded in both the United States and the United Kingdom.

In the United Kingdom between 1950 and 1957 the index of production showed a rise of 27 points for caustic soda compared with 40 points for chlorine. In the United States for the same period the index of production rose 55 points for caustic soda and 65 points for chlorine. Demand is likely to increase especially in refrigerant and propellant manufacture; plastics and resins; chlorinated solvents; pulp and paper; insecticides and herbicides; water chlorination and waste disposal.

The outlook for caustic soda is less encouraging, with increasing evidence of excess capacity.[1] Competition from new fibres is threatening rayon which provides one of the main outlets for caustic soda. There is a modest demand in soap manufacture (which with textiles once provided the major outlets) but this is likely to decline even further as detergents replace soaps. Thus in the United States soap constituted 90 per cent of all detergent and soap sales in 1947 but only 30 per cent in 1956. As industrialization in some of the newer countries expands, the demand for caustic soda should find new markets but the immediate outlook is not promising.

Hydrogen is produced as a by-product of the electrolytic process in the ratio of 0.028 tons of hydrogen to 1 ton of chlorine. The chief demands for the gas are for the production of hydrochloric acid; for ammonia and nitrogen (by combustion with air); hydrogenation and synthesis; in the generation of steam; for absorption-type refrigerators. There is a large demand for the gas which is generally compressed into cylinders for transport to small consumers. The outlook for hydrogen is good. As far as market

1. During the summer of 1962 the writer visited one of the large industrial firms in West Germany in the chemical industry, and was told that caustic soda was very much in excess supply but that so active was the demand for chlorine that production of caustic continued unabated. The principal of the firm added: 'We should be able to get you a price for caustic soda almost certainly below the price that you are now being quoted.'

considerations are concerned, the chief problem arises because of the differing rates of consumption of the two jointly manufactured products, caustic soda and chlorine. An increasing demand for chlorine has resulted from an expansion in recent years of the organic heavy chemical industry. The increase in output of chlorine has led to the production of caustic soda in larger quantities than the demand calls for. This has been most noticeable in the United States where the annual rate in growth of demand for chlorine has been about 11 per cent as against corresponding 7–8 per cent for caustic soda. One effect of this is that chlor-alkali producers in countries like the United States and the United Kingdom are aggressively exploring opportunities on export markets for their caustic soda.

The United States producers are an important element in decisions about future policy on world markets since they possess some 55 per cent of the world's capacity of chlorine and caustic soda. It is of course possible that they might influence the market by taking precisely the opposite line of action which has up to the present existed – the expansion of chlor-alkali plants to meet the need for chlorine. The producers are aware that their profits are influenced by the sale of both caustic soda and chlorine. They could conceivably decide to import the chlorine they want in order to stabilize the caustic soda market and produce only the quantities of soda which the market would absorb. If this were so a profitable outlet could be found on the United States markets for some imports of chlorine. This would certainly mean that it would be unwise on economic grounds to embark on chlor-alkali production by electrolysis unless there were an assured domestic market for caustic soda.

It is clear from the above discussion that unless the overseas market contacts were extremely strong, it could be hazardous for a territory like Jamaica to embark on such a major undertaking as a chlor-alkali plant. Jamaica has a relatively small population and consequently a limited domestic demand for the productions of a chemical industry. One of the products in question is in excess supply from the countries which are already economically developed and while there is a good demand for the other, the process is one of joint supply. Such are the rigidities of the chemistry involved that a plant which produced a certain quantity of marketable chlorine must produce even more of caustic soda. The first step would therefore be to examine the possible outlets which the territory would find for caustic soda.

The demand in Jamaica (Table VI.2) would absorb the output of caustic soda of a plant of economic size. The domestic demand comes mainly from the alumina industry and an increased production of alumina in Jamaica should make the chlor-alkali plant even more viable. If therefore it were decided to establish a chlor-alkali plant in Jamaica one of the results which should flow from such a decision would be the inducement of increased conversion in Jamaica of bauxite into alumina. This inducement seen in reverse, the writer believes, was one of the factors discouraging United States

TABLE VI.2   *Caustic Soda Imports[1] into Jamaica*

Year	All Sources Tons '000	All Sources £ '000	United Kingdom Tons '000	United Kingdom £ '000	United Kingdom %	United States Tons '000	United States £ '000	United States %
1958	58	884	35	509	60	23	365	39
1959	43	792	30	522	69	13	268	30
1960	44	1,011	31	727	71	13	283	29
1961	41	993	40	975	98	0.4	12	1

aluminium companies from locating their alumina plants abroad. An oil refinery was planned for erection in Jamaica and should increase the domestic demands for caustic soda. In the United States such refineries provide one of the main outlets for caustic soda.

If a chlor-alkali plant were established in Jamaica, the chlorine would presumably at first be exported, but the main contribution of chlor-alkali production to a broad expansion of the economy would be if it became the basis for a chemical industry complex.

On the supply side the two major factors for consideration, as mentioned elsewhere, would be salt and electric power. Jamaica at present produces no salt. It may well be that further exploration may one day correct this, since the analysis of the water of springs (in the Portland Ridge and the Salt River) has shown salt to be

1. The average imports of caustic soda for the two years 1960 and 1961 were 42.5 thousand tons with a value of just over £1 million a year. From 1958 to 1960 the United Kingdom supplied about two-thirds of these needs with the United States supplying practically all of the remainder. In 1961 the trade swung even more overwhelmingly in favour of Britain who supplied over 98 per cent of the total imports.

present in these springs and that the composition was different from that of sea water. This could conceivably indicate that there were salt deposits underground and exploration should be encouraged by the presence of salt domes in near-by Cuba and the Gulf Coast area. Conceivably also on the dry south coast of the island production of salt by solar evaporation should be feasible.[1] This, however, is in the realm of possibility only and has little relevance for supplies of salt in the immediate future.

At the present time Jamaica's supplies of salt come from one of its associated territories, the Turks Islands. The salt from this source is about 98.5 per cent purity but has thus far maintained a sustained supply of not more than about 60,000 tons a year. Since 1.7 tons of salt are required for 1 ton of caustic soda, a production of 50,000 tons of caustic soda would call for 85,000 to 100,000 tons of salt. The potential of the Turks Islands is estimated at about 90,000 tons a year[2] and for this to be obtained there will have to be capital expenditure on equipment for making more extensive ponds to accelerate evaporation. Additional supplies of salt if the need arose could come from Inagua or St Kitts. Imaginative use of the ships of the aluminium companies returning empty to Jamaica should reduce costs. The securing of supplies of salt from overseas should prove feasible since one of the chemical companies with a plant located in Georgia (U.S.) imports its supplies from one of the West Indian islands.

There are indications that there could be economies of scale if the volume of salt shipped from the Turks Islands were increased and that the most economical method of transport would be by towed barges. With such an arrangement salt could probably be delivered f.o.b. at fifteen shillings a ton and shipping and unloading charges would probably raise the price of salt at the wharf in Jamaica to about twenty shillings a ton. It would be feasible to use salt (which averages about 2 per cent impurities) at this price for electrolysis.

In regard to electric power, Jamaica has only limited hydro-electric resources and such is the demand that the cost of power from this source is not cheap. Nor have there yet been discovered any supplies of gas, coal or oil, so that her source of power is

1. Production of salt by solar evaporation in ponds on the dry South Coast of Jamaica was a well established practice in the seventeenth century. There is still evidence of these artificial ponds.
2. Underwood, A. J. V. *Report to Secretary of State for the Colonies.*

imported oil which is the source of power for cement manufacture and other industries including, of course, bauxite and alumina. One method of reducing the cost of power would be to have the chlor-alkali plant associated with an alumina plant. Kaiser have in operation on the Gulf Coast a chlor-plant which is associated with their alumina plant there. Steam is generated and the high pressure steam is used for the production of electricity. The low pressure steam is then used for the alumina plant for heating. In the light of Jamaica's substantial consumption of caustic soda one of the large international chemical firms could conceivably be interested in participating in the setting up of a plant in the Island, provided the undertaking was made reasonably attractive. One would have to ensure that the local processing of alumina was not penalized by local manufacture of caustic soda. On the other hand one would have necessarily to examine import prices critically to ensure that prices quoted were not part of a dumping policy to kill the local caustic soda enterprise. For one of the large international chemical firms, the attraction, of establishing a chlor-alkali plant in Jamaica, would be that the major headache of finding a market for the caustic soda would be gone and in addition the firm would add to its supplies of much sought-after chlorine.

A happy solution would, of course, be that the firm setting up the caustic soda plant was also engaged in alumina processing.

Part III
Summary and Conclusions

7 Summary, Conclusions and Some Implications for Policy

This study began with an examination of certain aspects of location in the North American aluminium industry with special reference to the influences on and by the Commonwealth Caribbean. The Caribbean enterprises are a part, and an important part, of a larger complex and it is possible to assess the present and the future trends which relate to developments in the Commonwealth Caribbean primarily by examining the influences which the developments in aluminium in North America and Europe are exerting. The material presented in this study has been centred around the following six fields of discussion:

policy of the North American industrial groups in relation to the location of alumina plants and the implications of this policy especially for the Commonwealth Caribbean;

changes in international trade heralded by, if not associated with, the Soviet aluminium episode and the Reynolds-Alcoa-British Aluminium episode;

expansion into export markets and particularly the United Kingdom market in the late 1950s and 1960s, by the United States industrial groups;

some implications for both aluminium and alumina of the birth and evolution of the European Free Trade Association and the European Economic Community;

comparative contributions to the Jamaican economy of the bauxite-alumina enterprises, with an attempt made to present local disbursements of the bauxite companies separately from those of the alumina processing activity, the alumina activity being inclusive of its associated mining operation;

some recent and potential technological developments and their implications in special regard to the Commonwealth Caribbean enterprises.

The present chapter with summary and conclusions brings together the chief implications which emerge from the study, and which relate to policy.

Early and Orderly Developments in the Industry

In 1960 the Commonwealth Caribbean's production of bauxite was four times that of North America, nearly twice that of Europe (excluding the Soviet allied Bloc), over a third of the production of the Western world and about 30 per cent of the world total. Jamaica is the highest producer not only in the Caribbean but in the world and the output of the U.S.S.R., the world's next highest producer, was in 1960 only 60 per cent that of Jamaica. Jamaica is singled out and examined specifically not only because of the large size of its enterprise. The case of Jamaica is dealt with in this manner since it typifies and makes manageable an appraisal of the considerations affecting the bauxite-alumina-aluminium complex in the Commonwealth Caribbean. The deposits of Jamaica are exploited primarily by two aluminium groups: a Canadian company which processes the ore into alumina in Jamaica; an American group which do not. The American group mine between two and three times as much ore as the Canadian company. In the period 1952–60 Jamaica produced about 31 million tons of bauxite, but converted in Jamaica only about 19 per cent of this into alumina. Hence it was clear that over 80 per cent of Jamaica's bauxite was being exported and converted into alumina abroad. This is not a favourable situation from Jamaica's point of view since the value added when bauxite is converted to alumina is considerable. Increasingly alumina made from Jamaica bauxite in the United States is fighting for markets previously based on supplies of alumina made from Jamaican bauxite in Jamaica. This is not the whole of the picture because the United States aluminium industrial groups are expanding their operations on a world-wide scale but whether in Europe, Africa, Australia, Asia or South America their smelters are geared to plans which rely on supplies of alumina, coming from elsewhere than from the Commonwealth Caribbean. The United States companies are, in the context of this policy, increasingly putting investment in alumina plants abroad in territories other than the Commonwealth Caribbean. Therefore the time could come when, if competition became keen, they might elect to replace their bauxite operations in the Commonwealth Caribbean with alumina supplies from Australia or Guinea or Greece or Surinam. And even the United States domestic market itself is no longer safe from invasion. Late in 1962 the Nippon Light Metals of Japan reported that there were plans to increase their aluminium exports to the United States. Such aluminium would be based on alumina originating in Australia and elsewhere. Pechiney put forward proposals to purchase the common stock of a large aluminium sheet roller (Quaker State Metals) in the United States. Pechiney's supplies of alumina would come increasingly from Guinea. There were therefore growing signs indicating that Commonwealth Caribbean's bauxite was being replaced in the United States by alumina from elsewhere. Jamaica's purpose should have been to achieve a conversion in Jamaica of a higher proportion of her ore into alumina. This is another way of saying that Jamaica's purpose should have been to bring about the conversion in Jamaica of some of the bauxite which the United States companies are exporting from Jamaica for processing in plants not located in Jamaica.

It has been argued here that a factor influencing the United States companies in their decision not to locate any of their alumina processing plants in the Caribbean was supported by the subsidization policy of the United States Government.[1] The two companies which most benefited from this – certainly as far as alumina plants were concerned – were Reynolds and Kaiser. Some weight is added to the argument that the United States Government's influence was considerable by the circumstance that these two companies, despite massive expansion in capacity in the United States, could find no virtue in locating alumina processing in Jamaica in the 1950s. The third United States company, Alcoa, which did not receive such aid and which also depended on supplies of ore from the Caribbean proceeded in the 1950s to make plans for processing in Surinam.

1. In Chapter I an account has been given of the anti-trust proceedings brought by the United States Government against the Aluminum Co of America. In 1945 the Court's ruling was handed down that Alcoa was a monopoly and the decision was taken to dispose of the Government-owned aluminium and alumina facilities to encourage competition. The Second World War had induced a substantial expansion of aluminium production and some 60 per cent of this new capacity was the property of the United States Government. The allocation of the alumina plants at very attractive figures to Reynolds and Kaiser made it certain that these new companies would have excess alumina capacity at home for some time ahead. One cannot criticize what the United States Government does in its internal policy and for the regulation of its own economy. The suggestion here is that this action by the United States Government had far-reaching effects on the policy of the United States industrial groups outside of the economy of the United States and discouraged them from alumina processing in the Caribbean. The argument concludes that the Caribbean Governments should ask the United States Government to view with sympathy any efforts on their part to redress this harm done to their economy.

The fourth United States company, Harvey, with mining interests in the Caribbean and British Guiana, also has plans for processing in the Caribbean (the American Virgin Islands). There is no suggestion here that there was malice aforethought in the policy of the United States Government but the fact remains that the effect of that policy was to make it most unlikely that either Reynolds or Kaiser would process outside of the United States alumina derived from bauxite from the Caribbean. Both of these companies' United States smelters depended preponderantly on the Commonwealth Caribbean for their ore supplies. These ore supplies in the circumstances, would be taken to the alumina stage in the Caribbean only if bargaining and negotiation compelled it. To have denied the Commonwealth Caribbean this manufacture made little difference to the United States economy but a great deal to that of the territories which have so few natural resources to form a base for industrial activity. It would not be unreasonable to have asked that the United States Government use its influence to encourage these particular investors to remember that, in the under-developed countries, especially in the long run, private interests may best be served by promoting the public good. Since a non-recognition of this principle may have flowed directly from decisions taken not only by the private companies but by the United States Government itself, the submission could hope for sympathetic attention. Much would depend on enlisting this sympathy because, whatever may have been the causes, one has to deal with their effects today. The United States industrial groups have their organization in existence. It would not be easy to persuade them that a modification of that organization might be justifiable on the grounds of a more viable structure in their enterprises in the Caribbean and especially in Jamaica. Even if one were to succeed in this persuasion of changes in the organizational structure, there would be the question of financing the new investment involved. The following are some of the considerations that would arise in, say, the case of Jamaica, which being the largest producer, is used for a case study.

Timing: In the 1960s the United States companies could be expected to show strong resistance to the proposal that they convert some or most of their Jamaica mined bauxite into alumina in Jamaica. If such a suggestion had been put forward in the 1940s and had it suited their over-all policy, it would have been reasonable to ask for it then to be done. Such a proposal having in fact been put forward in the early days of planning and having then presumably been carefully considered by the companies, been found irreconcilable with their organizational structure, could hardly be raised again in the 1960s (when each of the firms in question had idle capacity in the United States) with any hope of being taken seriously. This was a telling argument. There was the likelihood that the possibility of alumina manufacture in Jamaica was raised with the United States companies in the 1940s and 1950s but one must not lose sight of the circumstance that around the negotiating table there were some of the most powerful industrial groups in the world who held the advantage both in experience and expertise. In this context it would have required much sophistication and persistence to put forward the proposal effectively enough for it to be brought to a favourable conclusion. One wonders if the climate of opinion in Jamaica at that time was right to engender the required degree of persistence. Thus when in 1944 there appeared in the Jamaica press a statement outlining plans for the mining of bauxite in the island, the prospect was received by the general public with notable lack of interest. The chief newspaper thought this lukewarm reception serious enough to deserve editorial attention. The Report in 1945 of the powerful Economic Policy Committee dismissed the bauxite enterprise with brief reference and made no mention of the possible stimulating effect on the economy and of the possibility of processing ore in the Island. The Government Minister introducing new mining legislation in 1947 complained about the lack of interest that members of the House of Representatives had shown in the whole subject. The opposition retorted by charging the Government with dilatoriness since the Defence Regulations affecting mining policy were repealed in 1944 and were replaced with nothing on the books until 1947. A search of the Press and of *Hansard* in the intervening years has shown that the subject of alumina production by the United States companies has received little comment in the Caribbean either by the public or by the legislature.

It could therefore be that in the early years the robust support of the local community for negotiation on the subject of United States processing bauxite into alumina locally was absent. Scepticism prevailed then more than now about the desirability or even feasibility of such successful manufacturing in under-developed territories like the Caribbean. The United States companies would be strongly influenced by traditional policy; by caution, on political grounds, against locating plants abroad which could be built at home; by external economies whose claims would be pressed especially by the domestic chemical industrial groups or chemical branches of the aluminium group itself. In the absence of sufficient importunity the decision makers of the firms could forget that the Caribbean activity was a joint enterprise in which the United States companies were contributing the management and some of the capital (investment funds) while the Caribbean was supplying labour and some of the capital (land). In this relationship it was equitable that the broader question about the fair and reasonable benefits to the Caribbean economy should also be asked.

Such a question was not only advisable but expected in the 1960s, and in order to see things in perspective one might look at the world's main producers of bauxite. In 1960 they were Jamaica, U.S.S.R., Surinam, British Guiana, France, United States, Guinea, in that order of importance. One is impressed by the fact that there is probably no other country owning major deposits of bauxite where the American firms could adopt the policy of non-processing which they now pursued in the Commonwealth Caribbean. Of the seven countries mentioned above, the U.S.S.R., the United States and France have conditions which are well known and which one might reasonably claim are not strictly comparable. The other two not in the Commonwealth Caribbean are Surinam and Guinea. Reference is made earlier to Alcoa's decision in the 1950s to finance, not in part but in whole, the hydro-electric works to operate a smelter and later an alumina plant in Surinam. There has also been reference to developments in Guinea. Although Alcan had been engaged in mining bauxite in Guinea since the 1930s, the Government of Guinea decided that it was requisite that the company should take its operations a stage further to the processing of alumina. A date was fixed. Before the date arrived and because the Government considered that plans were not going forward with all practical speed the association with Alcan was discontinued and mining activities terminated. One may look further down the list and include for good measure territories with much lower output in 1960 than the Commonwealth Caribbean – places like Australia (with one one-hundredth of the Commonwealth Caribbean output), Brazil (with one-seventieth), Ghana (with one-fortieth), India (with one-twentieth). In each of these territories the measures to ensure reasonable contribution to the economy operate effectively. In Australia an Aluminium Production Commission operates under the Aluminium Industry Act which was set up to initiate and implement proposals to ensure the development of the ore along lines that would ensure appropriate returns to Australia. Thus it was considered desirable to build an alumina refinery at a cost of £10 million at Kwinana to process West Australian bauxite. The decision to bring this about was taken and an agreement signed by the State Government and a subsidiary of the Western Mining Corporation in association with Alcoa. The Government participated actively in this because it was considered important from the point of view of the country's overall economic development. As far as Latin America is concerned, R. S. Reynolds Jr[1], President of Reynolds Metals Company, sums up the situation as follows: 'The Latin American industry is a notable co-operative effort between local industry and experienced European and North American companies.' Venezuela is reported to have discovered bauxite deposits and the whole territory was declared a reserved area for exploration and extraction in 1960. By 1961 the Government was negotiating with Reynolds for processing.[2] Ghana has now succeeded in making financial arrangements for the Volta project which will achieve local processing. In India, Reynolds was reported to have decided on participation in the industry and the project is in the public sector. Greece, long only an exporter of bauxite, has plans for processing well advanced.

One can show that the conditions in many of the territories mentioned above are in some ways different from those of the Commonwealth Caribbean but there are enough similarities to bear examination. For example, the differences between Surinam and British Guiana do not seem great enough to explain the policy of Alcoa in the one and Reynolds in the other.

Even if one accepts that differences exist they would have little relevance to the submission being made here – that, whatever the reasons are, the Governments of all the territories with comparable bauxite deposits are using their influence, and in most cases their participation, to ensure that as much processing as is feasible is done locally.

Another question which is likely to be raised is whether or not the United States companies can be expected to begin processing in the Caribbean at a time when they have excess capacity at home. The anomaly of the present situation is that, although there is

1. Reynolds, Jr, R. S. 'The aluminium industry in North and South America.' Paper delivered at International Light Metals Congress, Leoben, Austria, 1961.
2. *Light Metals* (London), January 1961, p. 3.

excess capacity at home, each of these companies is financing massive expansion abroad in order to take advantage of the growing markets in the trading blocs of the world. Kaiser is engaged in Australia. Reynolds is engaged in Greece. Alcoa is engaged in Surinam.

Another aspect of the same question was whether or not, even if additional facilities for alumina could be made available in Jamaica, the United States companies might not contend that they already had their supply lines drawn, their organizational structure in existence and that the change envisaged would cause dislocation of their affairs. One could not ignore this problem but hoped that the companies involved would tackle it in a spirit of understanding since the Caribbean was in the 1960s negotiating for conditions that should have been established before. The position of Jamaica in the 1960s was that it would in the long run be healthier for Jamaica's economy to bring about more domestic processing of alumina even if it curtailed current exports of bauxite.

As an historical footnote to this general question of the extent of the responsibility of a government for safeguarding for its territory adequate returns on an endowment such as ore, one wonders to what extent in this instance traditional predilections played a part. During the formative years of the development of the bauxite enterprises of the Caribbean there was a degree of identification with the metropolitan attitudes of the United Kingdom. Due partly to having limited sources of cheap power, Britain seems never to have developed the emotional attachment to aluminium which she did to textiles or to steel or to vegetable oils or to sugar. She has never evolved a hard core of lobbyists and business representatives dedicated to the promotion of aluminium's cause. This is not the case with West Germany, France or America. France and America both enjoy many features which make aluminium production a natural choice and have pioneered in the technology to such an extent that a strong aluminium tradition has now grown up in both countries. This emotional attachment developed in West Germany although, like Britain, she does not at first sight have many special advantages for aluminium production. Like Britain she has no ores (or practically none), has only limited hydro-power and is a heavy consumer. Unlike Britain, but like the United States, she came to attribute a glamorous and important part to the national production of the metal during a war effort twice in the same generation. This difference in attitude is reflected in the relatively unperturbed atmosphere in which the American interests came to dominate both the reduction and fabrication of the aluminium industry in Britain. In West Germany fabrication is largely in the hands of small firms and there have been signs of North American interests buying up some of the fabricators. The German industry reacted vigorously. The State-owned and largest aluminium company, Vereinigte Aluminium Werke, was reported to have formed a holding company for the purpose of taking over domestic fabricators that came, or were likely to come, on the market. One wonders to what extent this lack of an aluminium tradition found its way into Britain's Colonial Office policy. The development of bauxite resources is not one of the bright pages in the history of the British Colonies. As the President of Pechiney has pointed out, the first project which received attention in Africa was the then Gold Coast project, but French enterprises in alumina in Guinea and in aluminium in the Cameroun got off the ground first. British Guiana's achievement is a poor second to Surinam's. That so little has been done with so much, in the case of Jamaica, is the most notable of all.

Financing: A second major consideration in establishing alumina plants in Jamaica would be financing. One possibility is to invite each of the companies operating in the island to erect and finance an alumina plant. Since the Canadian company, Alcan, has already done this it would mean that Reynolds, Kaiser and Alcoa would each be asked to finance an alumina plant for operation in Jamaica. We have argued that these companies are not likely to be easily persuaded.

A second possibility, and a variant of the first, is that the three United States companies be asked not to finance three plants but to combine and establish one plant to meet the needs of the three companies. This would have the attraction that the capital to be found by each of the three firms would be reduced. It is, however, improbable for various reasons, including the geographical distribution of the bauxite holdings of the three companies, that one plant would suffice.

A third possibility is that Alcan Jamaica be asked to expand its two alumina plants to make provision for processing bauxite from the United States companies. There could be several advantages to such an arrangement. It would permit the whole Jamaican bauxite enterprise to gain from Alcan's past policy and its experience in reconciling its own interests with those of the local economy. Alcan's two existing alumina plants are so located as to make the question of bauxite supply from some of the main deposits of the several companies worthy of exploration. If the transport problems made the two existing alumina sites inadequate a third unit, located so as to be complementary to the two plants in operation, would serve the economy better by rationalizing the alumina operations to the advantage of the mining enterprise as a whole. Yet another advantage would be that because alumina production profits from economies of scale there would be benefits from large plants. There are possible reservations and these may be formidable. Even if the arrangement for the expansion of the Alcan plants were feasible, the problem of financing would not be disposed of. It is possible that Alcan might be disposed to finance the expansion on the grounds that a large plant would be a more economical producer of alumina, not only for its allied customers, but for itself. It is improbable that Alcan would want to do so. It is even more improbable that the United States companies would want Alcan to do so. It is not easy to envisage the United States companies placing the control of an important proportion of their alumina processing under the control of another independent company or under the control of any organization in which they did not have a voice.

A fourth possibility would be to finance the new alumina production facilities by means of a consortium. This is becoming an increasingly popular method of financing in the aluminium industry. Thus when Aluminium Limited had under discussion the erection of an alumina plant at Boké, Guinea, the President of Pechiney drew attention to the possibilities of a consortium for the project.[1] The membership of the Jamaica consortium that suggests itself would be in two groups:

a. Participation by Government – the Government of Jamaica who, it is hoped, would be supported financially by the United States Government;
b. Participation by Companies – Reynolds, Kaiser, Alcoa and Alcan and, perhaps, Harvey.

a. *Participation by Government:* Reasons have already been given why it is hoped that the United States Government would give

1. Vitry de, Raoul. Fourth International Light Metals Congress, Leoben, Austria, 1961.

moral as well as financial support to encourage the United States companies to undertake processing in Jamaica. There is good precedent for participation by the Jamaica Government in a project to promote processing of its ore – the precedents of the Governments of Ghana, Guinea, Australia, Surinam. As an illustration, in Australia, the Aluminium Production Commission Ltd. took over an aluminium plant in Tasmania. The Government has a one-third share and Kaiser interests two-thirds. Nor have the governments of the older economies been any different. The chief Norwegian aluminium enterprise, A.S. Ardal og Sunndal Verk, was State-created. Reference has already been made to the subsidization by the United States Government of expansion in its industry – particularly in the cases of Reynolds and Kaiser. The United Kingdom regarded the Canadian output as a part of its domestic structure and provided financial assistance for the expansion of Aluminium Ltd. The case of West Germany has particular relevance for Jamaica. The largest aluminium firm in West Germany, Vereinigte Aluminium Werke, has derived its finances chiefly from government sources. Now that it has become firmly established and a successful business undertaking, the State is reported to have taken the decision to sell some of its shares to the German public. One of the handicaps of the Caribbean enterprise is that local interests have little part and less say in its affairs. Were the contrary true, it is probable that the policy towards processing by the bauxite mining firms would have been different. Recognition of this may explain the policy in Japan. Nippon Light Metals is the largest producer of aluminium in Japan. Aluminium Limited owns 50 per cent of the shares, the others being owned publicly in Japan. When recently Aluminium Limited put another $4.4 million in equity capital, one condition was that an equal amount be subscribed by other shareholders so that equity remained at 50 per cent in Japan.

b. Participation by Companies: The participation of the second group, the aluminium companies, is the second consideration in relation to the composition of the consortium. Since most of the known bauxite deposits which are not available for processing by the existing alumina plants are in the hands of Reynolds, Kaiser and Alcoa, the participation of these companies is essential if the plan is to work. One source of opposition to collaboration is that these companies have for some time been in existence independently and are not likely to be enthusiastic about surrendering their independence of action. This opposition could hardly be sustained since the consortium is now being widely employed by these same and other aluminium companies elsewhere. It is the pattern of development in Africa and the French have led notably in its use. The Associate of the Six which is the chief supplier of alumina to the Common Market is Guinea. Alumina processing has been undertaken there by a consortium,[1] Compagnie Internationale pour la Production de l'Alumine, Fria, of which British Aluminium, owned in part by Reynolds, is a member. Reynolds is associated with Aluminium Limited in the Tyssedal reduction plant of DNN in Norway; with Hungary and Yugoslavia in an Indian project, the Bharat Aluminium Co. In the Ghana consortium, Kaiser is a senior member.

The United States companies in Jamaica could argue that they became involved in bauxite operation on the understanding that they would have freedom of action in regard to policy and that they had control of the use and destination of bauxite derived from deposits on lands which they controlled. Presumably these companies would not be averse to some modification of this policy being introduced with the object of benefiting the economy of the territory in which the bauxite was found. Greece provides a precedent for a modification of relationships. The decision was taken by Pechiney, Reynolds and Greek interests to establish in Greece an aluminium company, Aluminium de Grêce. Greece has an established export trade in bauxite and it was not easy for the new project to be assured of adequate supplies of bauxite. The remedy for this was found when an agreement, by which Hellas Bauxite would supply Aluminium de Grêce with some supplies of bauxite, was made. In addition it was agreed that the bauxite company would 'set aside a part of its concessions for exploitation by the aluminium company'. A corresponding type of arrangement was being negotiated with another company which controlled bauxite deposits, Parnassus Bauxites.[2]

1. *Light Metals* (London), May 1962, p. 115.
2. Having these events in mind one wonders whether there is not a moral in regard to the incident of Harvey's exploration in Jamaica. Harvey, a United States company, with its plant on the Pacific Coast, had depended on supplies of alumina from Japan. In 1958 its representatives carried out investigations in Jamaica and afterwards elected not to make investments there. It is understood that one reason was that they did not find it possible to acquire large enough blocks of bauxite-bearing lands. Harvey, one of the smaller companies, was said to have dynamic leadership and was expanding. In 1962 the company announced that it had effected French associations and was to explore mining

There might be opposition by the United States companies on the grounds that they should not be saddled with the concerns of developing Jamaica. Such opposition would have little justification if the modification not only benefited the Island's economy but, by reducing the cost of alumina to the United States aluminium industry, also made the firms' activities more competitive. Reduction of costs of production of United States aluminium is becoming increasingly urgent since, as the President of Reynolds pointed out, imports from abroad (including Europe and Japan) were being delivered at prices below those on the United States domestic market.

A consideration in favour of a consortium, in which the different companies are involved, is that it will contribute to the strategic location of the new plant. Alumina processing requires heavy capital investment. It would lead to orderly exploration of the Island's deposits if the new unit could be so placed as to service bauxite deposits other than those which are in the vicinity of the two existing plants.[1] Another consideration in favour of a consortium from the companies' point of view would be that the investment being spread, no company would presumably be expected to shoulder an investment large enough to be an insurmountable problem.

The Interaction of Developments in America, Europe and the Commonwealth Caribbean

In Part I, the discussion deals with the situation which in the earlier period appeared relatively orderly and predictable but which was later associated with a series of developments which modified relationships within the industry in the Western world. In the earlier period the Caribbean enterprise seemed inextricably inter-

deposits in French Guiana. The Company has also decided to erect an alumina plant of 100,000 tons capacity in one of the United States Virgin Islands, St Croix. If it was a question of Jamaica's economy losing this opportunity of having a United States company start alumina processing in the Island one wonders whether Reynolds, if invited, would not have been sympathetic to the idea of letting Harvey have some of its bauxite for conversion into alumina in Jamaica. This would after all be collaboration in much the same way that other bauxite companies were induced to collaborate to make a success of the Reynolds venture in Greece.

1. This rationalization of processing facilities is a measure which, for example, the sugar interests in the Caribbean have given thought to implementing in order to improve their competitive position.

woven with the North American smelting and marketing organizations on the supply side and with domestic demand and this outlook gave cause for concern to no one, certainly not to the Caribbean. In the later period the outlook and marketing policy of the North American producers underwent a change which was distinctly unfavourable to the Caribbean enterprise. Still further change, both present and future, promised to be forthcoming from the birth of the two trading communities in Europe, the European Free Trade Association and the European Economic Community. Part II deals with some of the implications of the EFTA and the EEC.

The European Free Trade Association

Although the EEC came into being before the EFTA, it is in the latter that Britain, as a member, participates. In the light of this, there may be some advantage in considering some of the implications of the EFTA before examining those of the EEC. One can understand EFTA's relationships only if one understands its origins. Britain had emerged from the Second World War with a higher claim to leadership than that of any other country of Western Europe. She alone had successfully defied Hitler. She had not been occupied. These circumstances, as well as her war-time offer to France of full political union, made her the ideological centre for a joining of the free forces of Western Europe. In 1948 the Hague Congress, having Churchill as Honorary President, recommended that the nations of Europe should 'create an economic and political union'. The European movement received an impetus but, to the dismay of its advocates, the British Government proved anything but enthusiastic about identifying itself with such proposals, far less taking the lead in implementing them. The blame was at first attributed to the Labour Party which was then in power in Britain, but Churchill's Government, when returned, made it clear that they would hasten, at least as slowly, towards their involvement in the unification of Western Europe. Those in favour of union clearly had to settle for something less ambitious. The European Coal and Steel Community came into being and for the first time the Six – France, West Germany, Italy and the Benelux countries – counselled together as a unit, Britain having declined to participate. This led to the creation of a Common Market in coal and steel in 1953.

The direction of the movement had now changed and union was

on its way, without Britain. Plans were under discussion for another and more ambitious community, the European Economic Community. Britain had cut herself off from this and it became increasingly clear that the developments could mean for Britain a diminution of effectiveness in European politics and some diversion of trade. It was to meet this new situation that Britain suggested that some form of relationship with the projected EEC and certain other countries be established. The OEEC set up a committee to examine these proposals and the findings were that a Free Trade Area was feasible technically. The chief difference from the EEC proposals was that the Free Trade Area would have very limited features of economic union, would not have a common external tariff and would exclude agricultural products from its list of subjects. The idea of a Free Trade Area was rejected by the Six. After these negotiations failed Britain was faced with one of several choices: to implement the idea of the Free Trade Area; to apply for membership of EEC; to take no positive action but to let future developments dictate policy; to strengthen the trading bonds in the Commonwealth. She decided on the first of these and took the initiative in forming the European Free Trade Association – the EFTA. The chief features of the Stockholm Convention, which was signed in late 1959, was that there would be a free trade area in industrial products by 1970 with scheduled reductions in tariffs between the members. Members would be able to withdraw on twelve months' notice. There was no common external tariff and, in consequence, comprehensive rules of origin to control possible deflection of trade were needed. The members of the Association were 'the States which ratify this convention and such other States as may accede to it'. This meant that Britain was a member but not the Commonwealth Caribbean.

Of the seven countries in EFTA, five were producers of aluminium: Sweden, with a small output; Austria and Switzerland, both closely integrated into German and French operations; Britain and, most important of all, Norway. It was the demand and supply in the last two which would dominate the influence on developments in the industry within the Association. If the developments in the EEC were taken as a precedent, one would have been justified in anticipating planning and stimulation for increased EFTA supplies of alumina as well as of aluminium. In the EFTA the really big market for aluminium was Britain and the big producer, present and potential, was Norway. Neither country had an external tariff on aluminium and neither would be called on by the Stockholm Convention to change this policy. There was therefore no indication that the EFTA arrangements should affect the aluminium supply policy within the Area. And this was not only because of the spirit and the letter of the Convention since, even if there was provision for interfering with external tariffs, aluminium would have been likely to prove a special case.

The EFTA came into being in 1960 when the events which are described in Part I of this study had taken place. The United States industrial groups had already come to play a major role in the management and policy of the United Kingdom industry, not only in fabrication but also in the supplies of primary aluminium. In these circumstances the United Kingdom industry was unlikely to speak with a united voice for the introduction of an external tariff in the United Kingdom market which would, in effect, discriminate on the most important West European market against United States aluminium in favour of products from Canada (on a Commonwealth basis) or from Norway (on an EFTA basis). Admittedly Canada was unlikely to take a prominent part in supporting the claim for the introduction in EFTA of an external tariff on aluminium (even if the spirit of the Stockholm Convention had condoned it). Canada was aware that her other chief market, the United States, had for some time been agitating for a higher external tariff against Canadian and other aluminium from abroad. Canada might well in such circumstances have decided to seek no interference with the United Kingdom tariff structure since a change would probably give added strength to those lobbying in Washington to raise the United States external tariff. Another factor, which would have given Canada reason to pause, was that it was widely believed that EFTA was not a permanent organization and was but a step to a united Europe. Even had Canada been able to secure preferential treatment for some of her aluminium within EFTA (because of her Commonwealth association and because EFTA did not call for a common external tariff) it was clear that she would not get such treatment if Britain entered the EEC. The real fight would have come if Britain had been admitted into the Community. The Six, led by France, could have been expected to fight for the maintenance of a high external tariff against, and especially against, all North American aluminium. Canada would have had to judge carefully whether it would be wise so to act in the EFTA as to give the French ammunition if or when the battle was joined in the EEC.

As far as Norway is concerned let us assume that the spirit of the Stockholm Convention encouraged preferential treatment for aluminium of fellow members.[1] If EFTA survived, Norway was the producer most likely to benefit from such preferential treatment in EFTA of EFTA produced aluminium and one might assume at first sight that she, having regard to her planned expansion, would have wished to press for as much protection as she could achieve. But she did not do this. The question as to why she did not is worth pursuing because there are implications for corresponding questions which would arise if Norway and Britain were admitted to the EEC. It is improbable that, even had protection for aluminium within the EFTA been attainable, the support of Norway's industry for seeking it would have been unanimous. There are four aluminium producing firms in Norway. Of the four, one (Mosal), was associated with AIAG, the Swiss Company, which having such international and diversified aluminium interests might reasonably have reservations about any attempts to tamper with the free trade policy of the United Kingdom aluminium market. A second company (Ardal) associated with Alcoa and a third (DNN) associated with Reynolds through British Aluminium might also have been less than enthusiastic about restrictions on entry into the EFTA (i.e. chiefly the United Kingdom) market.

While Britain was the chief market for aluminium, Norway was the chief market for alumina. Britain's demand for alumina for aluminium production was about 60,000 tons of alumina in 1960 and was expected to be about the same in 1965. Norway's demand, about 360,000 tons in 1960, would be about 600,000 tons in 1965. Britain's production of alumina exceeded her requirements while Norway's was nominal. Therefore in the same way that Britain dominated the demand for aluminium in EFTA, Norway dominated the demand for alumina. The chief supplier of alumina[2] for Norway was Jamaica and it would have been provident for her to seek not only to strengthen her hold on the market but to increase her share of it. In 1960 the imports of alumina into Norway were somewhat

1. The principle was of course taken much further in the common external tariff in the EEC, and Britain, if admitted, was one day likely to have to give preferential treatment to EEC produced aluminium.
2. There was unlikely to be any question of preferential treatment for bauxite since it is not the tradition either in Western Europe or America to impose a tariff on the ore. Switzerland and Portugal provide the exceptions to this rule and do impose a tariff on bauxite but this was unlikely to be regarded as a precedent to be followed by the EEC or any of the other countries of EFTA.

more than 300,000 tons and the demand in five years' time was expected to be twice that figure. Jamaica had provided 70 per cent of those imports but, as far as the records show, there were no plans so to increase her alumina capacity as to ensure that she could retain or increase her proportion of the Norwegian expanded market if Norway did decide to look to her.

The Stockholm Convention made provision only for those countries which had ratified the Convention (Article 1) and specifically envisaged the purpose to be, in the first instance, co-operation in Western Europe. It provided for (Article 43) the possible application by member states for reciprocal rights and obligations in relation to those territories for whose international relations such states were responsible. In 1959–60 the only territory capable of supplying alumina to EFTA, which would qualify under this provision, was Jamaica. This special relationship, if requested, could have had a powerful sponsor in the person of Britain. Britain was assured special consideration not only because of her unique position in the aluminium market but because she was larger than all the other members put together in population, wealth and trade – three-fifths of the population, two-thirds of gross production of all goods and services, and over half of the external trade. Had the Commonwealth Caribbean sought it and had the United Kingdom backed it, the territory was in a position to stake a strong claim for special treatment for alumina in the EFTA and this would have meant particularly, Norway.[1] Britain should have been sympathetic because she herself had recognized the principle. She imposed no duty on Commonwealth alumina as against 7 per cent on alumina from EFTA sources and 10 per cent on other alumina. The Stockholm Convention did not call for a common external tariff which meant that this relationship might have been sought in the Norwegian market without any necessary approval or commitment of the other member states. This should have made it easier to accede to the Caribbean's request. The Commonwealth Caribbean, holding the unique position that it did, could reasonably have hoped with Britain's support to get preference on the Norwegian market over alumina from, say, France or Guinea.

1. In addition Britain had been generous to the Scandinavian countries. Article 26 of the Convention specifically excluded fish and marine products, but Britain making a concession to Norway included these among the industrial products and so made tariff reduction a technical requirement of the Convention. As a concession to Denmark, she abolished the tariff on bacon.

The prize to be won in the EFTA by the Commonwealth Caribbean was so valuable and evidence of plans for winning it so absent that it should be useful to examine some of the influences which were predetermining the results. The most important of these influences were:

The Long and Short Term: The widely expressed view that EFTA was, and was intended to be, ephemeral might have discouraged too active agitation (with the consequent investment in time and thought) on the grounds that the benefits could accrue on a long-term not a short-term basis. Although the Convention was ratified only in early 1960, by July of the same year Mr Selwyn Lloyd, Chancellor of the Exchequer, was pointing out that free trade solutions had no chance of success.[1] Benoit observes that certainly some of the signatories viewed EFTA 'primarily as a temporary bargaining tool to pressure the EEC into renewed negotiations'[2]; de la Mahotiere[3] considered that EFTA '. . . was never an end in itself (but) . . . was intended . . . to force the Six into an association with the Seven . . .' There were, however, others who visualized EFTA not as temporary but as expanding. Thus Meyer[4] envisaged that the principles of Stockholm could be further extended so as to include a much wider grouping of people, that the principles could and should eventually be applied to nationals of other countries who wished it. Even if there was the conviction that EFTA would give place, it was probable that it would give place to a new grouping and that new grouping would be the EEC. The possibility that EFTA might be a transitional relationship would therefore have been all the stronger reason for the Commonwealth Caribbean to endeavour to strengthen its trade ties with Britain's fellow EFTA member, Norway, and so improve its tactical position in an enlarged market. In the EEC negotiations that might come later it was only realistic to recognize that Britain wielded a degree of power in EFTA which it could not hope to have in the EEC, and that the Commonwealth Caribbean enjoyed a freedom from competition in EFTA which Greece, Guinea and Surinam, in addition to France and West Germany, would challenge in the EEC. On the other hand if EFTA was going to be a permanent organization spreading its influence and operations, there would

1. Kitzinger, U. W. *The Challenge of the Common Market*. Oxford.
2. Benoit, Emile. *Europe at Sixes and Sevens*. New York.
3. Mahotiere de la, Stuart. *The Common Market*. London.
4. Meyer, F. V. *The Seven*. London.

have been also good reason for the Commonwealth Caribbean to have sought assiduously for favourable trade conditions for supplies of alumina for Norway.

Another aspect of the long and short term was that in 1959–60 when the EFTA negotiations were taking place the Commonwealth Caribbean qualified under Article 43 of the Stockholm Convention as territories for whose international relations a member state was responsible. It could therefore be argued that this qualification would survive only in the short term because the territories were already planning for independence. In the circumstances those territories would have been justified in regarding as all the more urgent the need to improve, during dependence, trade relationships which would give a stronger economic basis to independence. In all this, time was of the essence and the benefits could come only from assiduous negotiation, not from delay.

Policy: While in different countries little is put in writing, the policy in the Commonwealth Caribbean is very different from that of, for example, Australia in regard to the use of wasting assets. It may be relevant to refer to the policy in Australia guiding the development of its bauxite deposits. In the late 1940s when the known bauxite deposits in Australia were far less than those in Jamaica, the Federal and Tasmanian Government set up the Australian Aluminium Production Commission. Later, the Federal Government sold out to private interests (Consolidated Zinc which has since become associated with Kaiser) but the Tasmanian Government retained its one-third interest. This new consortium is now engaged in massive developments, including a large port in the Cape York Peninsula. While these works are in progress, and especially as there is heavy capital expenditure for some time without much income, permission has been given for the export of bauxite to Japan. The amount, however, is not unlimited and is restricted to 600,000 tons in the first instance. Further exports of bauxite, if approved, will have to be approved at Government level. The six states have somewhat differing policies in regard to the use of ore deposits (including bauxite) but the guiding principle is:

a. to have sufficient Government guidance in order that the deposits are exploited in a manner to ensure that the contribution to the economic development of the state and also the country is as great as possible;

G

b. to discourage the export of raw materials in unrestricted quantity and to try to ensure that, whenever feasible, processing takes place in Australia rather than abroad.

The effect of this policy is that even when surveys later indicated that deposits in Australia might be many times as large as those in Jamaica, permission to export bauxite from Australia had to be sought and, as the case of Japan illustrates, the scale of exports was kept under review. An effect of this policy is seen in what Alcoa has done in Australia. The company has decided to build an aluminium plant at Geelong with a capacity of 20,000 tons which would call for about 40,000 tons of alumina a year. It has plans for an alumina plant at Kwinana with capacity of 210,000 tons and in the light of this excess capacity entered into an arrangement to supply Japan (the Mitsubishi Company) with alumina. In these circumstances Alcoa found it in her interests to seek for outlets for some of this alumina and to negotiate a contract with Japan for alumina although the Japanese interests, with alumina capacity some 50 per cent in excess of their aluminium needs, would presumably be keener on importing Australia's bauxite.[1] Such bauxite if imported would have been converted into alumina in Japan and so integrated into the home complex of chemical and related industries and if Japan's interests were primarily to be considered this is the course which certainly would have been followed.

Another aspect of policy which influences the course of development is that the Australian Government does not award a mining permit until it is satisfied that the plans for the future are appropriate. The procedure adopted is that the Government may give a prospecting permit to Company A to carry out surveys and to prospect for ore. The Government gives the company about five years to decide what will be done to develop the deposits, and only then is a mining lease granted. One advantage from the point of view of the prospector is that there is no payment required for a lease during this period. The advantage from the point of view of the Government is that its hands are not tied and if the Company does not propose adequate development plans the Government is able to explore alternatives with competitors. This element of

1. Japan's aluminium capacity in 1960 was about 142 thousand tons with an alumina requirement therefore of 280 thousand tons. Her alumina capacity was 430 thousand tons.

competition is regarded as one of the most important measures encouraging mining developments in the country.

The policy in regard to the development of ores in many countries today tends to approximate that in Australia. A closer examination of the influences on the course of development not only in Australia but in Surinam, Greece, Guinea, might well point a moral for the Commonwealth Caribbean.

Supplies of Alumina: The arguments above are that a major challenge of EFTA was the demand of Norway for alumina. The Commonwealth Caribbean was in a unique position, both from the spirit of the Stockholm Convention and from traditional supply connections, to be asked to provide substantial increases of alumina for the expansion of aluminium production which Norway's hydro-electric resources were making feasible. It was not a question of whether there would be a demand for alumina, because Norway, already the largest importer of alumina in Western Europe, expected to quadruple its demand within a decade. The question was whether such a demand, if passed to the Caribbean, could be met.

The Canadian Company, Alcan, has three alumina plants in the Commonwealth Caribbean, and since alumina processing shows marked economies of scale the Company should be able to expand its alumina production substantially and rapidly. It would hardly be reasonable, however, to expect the Company to undertake the financing of this expansion with the risk and uncertainty that would be inherent. There was nothing monolithic about the Norwegian aluminium industry. There were different industrial groups with different geographical and trade allegiances. Alcan, if taking the decision to expand her Caribbean alumina capacity to meet the growing demand, would have to envisage the possibility that one or other of the aluminium units might at any time decide to make other arrangements for its alumina supplies. Alcan, while therefore sympathetic in principle, could not be expected to take the financial risk of expanding for so hypothetical a demand. Yet without such a supply seeking and probing for an outlet, the Commonwealth Caribbean could by default lose to competitors, who were less logically the suppliers of Norway but who had built up conditions which provided them with excess alumina capacity able and willing to meet the demand. This is an instance where supply will have to go ahead of demand.

The companies other than Alcan operating in the Commonwealth

Caribbean had thus far refrained from processing alumina there, and demand for increased supplies of alumina from the area would therefore give an advantage to the Canadian company which a disinterested party might view with detachment. The United States companies were not disinterested and were themselves supplying alumina or aluminium in competition with Alcan. There was therefore need for excess capacity in alumina in the Commonwealth Caribbean and to achieve this one or all of the following measures could be required:

a. the bringing into being of a consortium which would begin immediately to expand alumina capacity;

b. the involving of the bauxite companies in collaborative effort to provide bauxite supplies for the new alumina capacity, with cognizance of comparable measures adopted in Greece;

c. the modification of existing policy towards the exploitation of deposits in order to induce adequate emphasis on the claims for economic development of the ore-bearing territory. The policy should aim to be as effective as that in Australia which induced Alcoa to exploit its Australian controlled deposits with emphasis on processing. Alcoa's decision was aided by the Australian Government's authorization to export bauxite only in sharply limited quantities. Australia instituted these controls although her bauxite deposits were said to be as large as or larger than the Commonwealth Caribbean's.

Possible Preferential Treatment for the Caribbean: The Commonwealth Caribbean, while the logical choice for supplying a major part of Norway's expanded demand for alumina, might have felt that the chances of getting appropriate action within the framework of EFTA were so small that the cause was from the outset lost. EFTA was after all an international organization which, by the spirit and letter of the law, was intended to promote economic activity within the area of the Association (i.e. within Europe). While in the first round of negotiations for the purposes of the Convention, Greenland was accepted as 'in Europe', the rules were unlikely to be stretched to the Caribbean until the general principle of expansion was explored. The Caribbean might have had misgivings about its being allowed in practice the advantage which may have been implied in theory.

If by preferential treatment one has in mind tariff protection, then the resistance in the EFTA could be expected to be strong indeed and Britain herself might have major reservations. Not only was this question of external tariff adjustment omitted from the Stockholm Convention, but it was purposely omitted. There was wide international publicity given to this difference between the EEC and the EFTA and to the EFTA's emphasis on increased international trade, low tariffs and less discrimination against imports from third countries. The United Kingdom was unlikely lightly to use its influence to modify this policy because at the time of the formulation of EFTA policy the flight (or certainly change of direction) of foreign capital to EEC countries was a matter of major concern to Britain. Unless therefore the Commonwealth Caribbean producing alumina (with a population of a little over 2 million and a gross domestic product of about £300 million) had delusions of grandeur, it could hardly expect its views to carry much weight even against one of the large aluminium industrial groups. It certainly could not expect to bring about a fundamental change in policy of a European grouping to which it did not even belong.

The grounds for those fears could have been enough to have persuaded the Caribbean Commonwealth that efforts to get a preferential tariff for their alumina were doomed to failure. There were, however, means other than tariff of aiding the Caribbean territories in maintaining and expanding their participation in the EFTA expanding production of aluminium. One might even go further and say that tampering with the external tariff was likely to be one of the less effective measures. In the year in which EFTA had come into being, Jamaica's supplies of alumina expressed as a proportion of Norway's total imports, had increased sharply, from 54 per cent in 1959 to 70 per cent in 1960. This had occurred without any change in tariff. This change had occurred partly fortuitously because other and possibly competitive alumina facilities were not yet in production, and essentially because it happened to suit the policy of the aluminium companies in Norway. What had happened by chance, and in the short run, might not prove to be permanent. The aim of the Commonwealth Caribbean should have been to work towards an arrangement which should encourage the Norwegian companies by means other than external tariff to be sympathetic to maintaining the trade relationships in alumina with the Caribbean. With this approach Britain could have no contention and, with her support, Norway's approbation for a policy of working towards this end should have been assured. It could not have been unreasonable to ask Britain to try to get for Caribbean alumina in the United Kingdom–Norway complex the same kind of effective association which, under the hand of the French industry, alumina from Guinea was securing in the French aluminium industry. The benefits to Guinea alumina were only partly, and to a minor extent, derived from tariff arrangements.

The conclusion then is that the Commonwealth Caribbean should not, for tactical and other reasons, have sought in EFTA preferential treatment through tariffs. Rather the Caribbean territories had need of two requirements:

a. abroad, friends at court in EFTA to draw attention to the Commonwealth Caribbean's claim for special consideration so far as alumina was concerned and to advocate the establishment of agreements for favoured treatment which would emanate from the Board Room, not from the Legislative Chamber;

b. at home, a policy to ensure substantial expansion of alumina capacity (which expansion should have already been under way) to meet the demand that was being created in EFTA.

Of the two the second was at least as important as the other, perhaps more so.

The European Economic Community

Some General Implications: There has been above a discussion of the possibilities for negotiation about alumina in EFTA. It has been shown that EFTA, while having little impact on the aluminium industry as a whole, had potentially major implications for the Commonwealth Caribbean's enterprise. There is good cause to explore the question whether or not the Commonwealth Caribbean grasped the opportunity offered by EFTA as it should have done, both because of the importance of the question in its own right and because it is evident that if Britain and Norway were ever admitted into the Common Market the problems posed by the Community would present challenges having much in common with those which came from the EFTA. One difference is that as far as the Commonwealth Caribbean enterprises were concerned the penalties for failing (through sins of either omission or commission) to turn to its advantage the challenge of the EEC would be likely to be more severe than was the case with the EFTA. While the EEC and the EFTA had some similarities there were also fundamental divergencies which in large measure sprang from their separate and distinct origins. The difference in origin between the Association and the Community can in part explain why in the one the economic bonds were weak and in the other strong.

The Second World War had ended leaving Britain (with America and Russia) as one of the three world powers possessing armed strength, and neither Sweden, Switzerland nor Portugal had been overrun. These were four of the seven who formed EFTA. The countries who banded together to form the EEC had no such background, had each been overrun by war and were convinced that their future and survival lay in a Community which should be tightly integrated economically and eventually politically. While political integration was desirable in the long run, economic integration was tactically the first goal to aim for and they were convinced that the more effective was the economic integration, the greater was the likelihood of political integration. The group led by Britain supported the Commonwealth approach with loose ties.[1] The Six sought the Community approach, with a unified group strengthened by its larger size and made effective by close economic ties. The Community, setting out to strengthen itself economically, had succeeded for several theoretical reasons and Kreinen[2] and Benoit[3] have good discussions on this. The criteria put forward by Viner[4] and Meade[5] for determining on a welfare basis the effects of a customs union would indicate that the Community's success could be attributed partly to the following: its relatively large size in population and in production of goods and services, which confers advantages of specialization, both by region and by industry; its promotion of international trade, the averaging of the external tariff leading to a lowering of the weighted average of the area as a whole compared with an unmodified EFTA's external tariff; its stronger negotiating position in international trade both because of its buoyant economy and because a unit can bargain for greater concessions than unit members; and the wide spread of costs in many industries in the EEC countries tending to bring about, with

1. For a fuller discussion of this argument *see* Meyer, F. V., *op. cit.*
2. Kreinen, M. E. 'The "Outer Seven" and European Integration,' *American Economic Review*, June 1960, pp. 370–85.
3. Benoit, E., *op. cit.*, p. 83.
4. Viner, Jacob. *The Customs Union Issue.*
5. Meade, James E. *The Theory of Customs Unions.*

the equalization of protective tariffs, the elimination of the less efficient enterprises.

In the Community, France was wealthier, but with less trade, than West Germany; France and West Germany had more people but no more commerce than Benelux; Italy has as much population as but less economic development than either France or West Germany. Despite these equalizing relationships France in many ways played a dominating role in formulating EEC policy, which could be the more easily understood if one recognized what were some of the influences at work in France. A major factor in France's thinking is the farmer and the security of markets for his expanding production. Half of the agricultural land of the Common Market is in France. Agriculture has traditionally played a dominant part in the social framework of the country and has been able to secure for itself effective protection. With mechanization (the index of combined harvesters in French farming, if 100 in 1938, was over 230 in 1962), better husbandry (the index of fertilizer used in French farming, if 100 in 1938, was over 300 in 1962), higher labour productivity (the farming population in the nineteen-sixties was less than two-thirds that in the twenties), the agricultural output is expected to be in 1965 about 30 per cent higher than in 1959. She is in a good position to meet competition in the Common Market and, with her large surplus production, continues to strive militantly for adequate safeguards to ensure an outlet for her exports. This expansion in the agricultural sector, coupled with pride in efficient technology and need to ensure market outlets, has much in common with the attitude of the French aluminium industry which thus finds itself with the ideological support of the powerful farm bloc.

Another factor which determined one direction where French interests within EEC would lie and which has relevance to the present study was the relatively high French investment in aluminium and other developments in overseas territories. As Kitzinger[1] observes, few in the British sphere of influence recognize how much more the French have contributed to the much smaller number of people in the overseas territories than Britain did to the much larger number of people in her colonies and ex-colonies. In 1956–59, the contribution in public and private aid to under-developed countries expressed as a proportion of national income was for Britain and France respectively 1.3 and 2.7 per cent. In some industries including aluminium, this led to overseas expansion which

1. Kitzinger, U. W., *op. cit.*, p. 79.

involved close identification of economic activity with France itself. This was in the public sector and in the private sector it was the same thing. There was a Pechiney in France seeking and probing for a French self-sufficient production complex stretching from France to its overseas present and past spheres of influence – Guinea, Cameroun and French Guiana. There was no counterpart in Britain, West Germany or Norway.

It has thus come about that there were powerful forces led by France which advocated an inward looking community with high external tariffs, while West Germany and the Netherlands, which depended more on international trade, could be more easily placated on this point. These were some of the general and background features of the Common Market which would contribute to an influence on the aluminium industry that would be more complex and far-reaching than in the case of EFTA.

Some Implications for Aluminium: For almost the whole of the Community's history the aluminium industry, external to the Six, had been in trouble. This strengthened the position of those members who advocated precautionary measures to safeguard the interests of the Community's aluminium producers, which meant pre-eminently France. Western Europe had looked out on a world in which the sellers' market in aluminium, at the beginning of the decade, had given place at the end to excess capacity, severe competition, price wars and lobbying for protective legislation. But within the Common Market the demand for aluminium was still in excess of domestic supplies, a total capacity of the Six of about 620 thousand tons balanced by a demand of 680 thousand tons. And demand was buoyant. There was every indication that these Western European countries with their relatively low level of aluminium consumption would maintain their trend of increasing consumption at the rate of 7.2 per cent per annum, so doubling the existing demand in another ten years. Supplies, however, were also increasing. France's production, a little slow to get under way after the dislocations of the 1940s, had more than doubled between 1950 and 1955 and had continued to increase at a rate even faster than that of the United States. In addition the French had majority interests in financing aluminium production in the Cameroun and had other plans on paper which could make West Africa a major associate of the French complex. The other major producer, West Germany, was increasing output substantially and Italy, on a proportional basis, even more so. Both Greece, who had become a member, and Holland, who had discovered natural gas, had plans for reduction plants. The aluminium picture would change if Britain entered the Common Market because her requirements in excess of her 1960 capacity were about five times those of the whole Community. But if Britain were admitted so also would be Norway, and if this occurred projections indicated that a Community if enlarged by Britain and Norway would be self-sufficient in aluminium smelting capacity before 1970.

The Community's aluminium producers led by the French had firm views on what the problem was and how it should be met. Their argument went somewhat as follows. The chief danger was that the North American producers who, through errors of judgment, had found themselves with excess capacity, would be tempted to use, if they could, Western Europe as an outlet for the aluminium which they could not market elsewhere. France led in the charge that an inevitable threat was that if Britain were admitted North American producers would 'colonize' the Western European industry in the same way that they had come to control some 85 per cent of Britain's aluminium industry. In this context they pointed out that the duty on aluminium had ranged from 28 per cent in Italy through 20 per cent in France, to nil in the Benelux countries and the arithmetic mean of these duties, called for by the Treaty of Rome, would be 14.5 per cent. This was reduced by negotiation within the Community to 10 per cent and later through discussions with GATT to 9 per cent. Further reduction in the opinion of the French would be unreasonable. They pointed out that the harshness of the external tariff had been moderated but the gesture, instead of being regarded as a contribution towards good relations, was being used by Britain and the North American producers as an argument for further erosion of protection on the grounds that a moderate duty would be inadequate ultimately to prevent dumping. On the other hand interests within the Six expressed the awareness that too high a rate might urge the American industrial groups to establish in Western Europe plants under their financial control. Since plants so established would probably have to operate at higher costs than would under other circumstances be regarded as competitive, the purpose behind any such move by the North American producers would be to annex markets rather than to encourage healthy growth. With the French lead the European industry was efficient and competitive but in the long run could survive only under conditions of normal competition. If the tariff were any lower than the 9 per cent it could be ineffective since it would bear on only a small proportion of the American output. Experience had shown that a reasonable protective tariff did not lead automatically to high prices and that, on the contrary, higher prices were likely ultimately to result if the domestic producers allowed themselves to be supplanted, or manoeuvred out of production, by foreign interests.[1]

This was not at all Britain's position and her arguments ran on quite different lines. She protested that France and other members of the Community by-passed or ignored her special claims, that she did not possess a natural advantage in producing aluminium and that the British Government had financed expansion of Aluminium Limited in Canada in much the same way that the French Government helped finance the Pechiney and Ugine enterprises in West Africa. This was an historical situation and it hardly seemed appropriate in the circumstances for the French to lead in the attack against this traditional line of supply. During the negotiations in 1962 which were associated with Britain's application for admission, interests within the Community had pointed an accusing finger at Aluminium Limited's decision to reduce the European selling price of aluminium in West Europe as an example of price discrimination, and as a sign of things to come. But here the analogy with the ramifications of the French industry was all the more marked and the other members of the Community had been drawing attention to the price discrimination of French aluminium in the Belgian market. The price of such aluminium in mid-1962 was £160 a ton and the lowest from any Western source. There was general conviction that there was some connection between that low price and the Belgians having interests in the Edea plant in the Cameroun in which the French were the majority shareholders.[2] Britain had also

1. This argument is developed at length in *Journal du Four Electrique et des Industries Electrochimiques*, No. 3, 1962, p. 73.
The President of Pechiney addressing shareholders in 1962 and referring to the Common Market said: 'In these circumstances there can be seen no valid reason for exposing our market to the direct or indirect results of certain external lack of harmonization such as the pressure caused by an enormous gap between production capacity and the corresponding national market . . . It is not a question of obtaining special increase on the sales price within the Common Market, but essentially of an elementary precaution against a possible threat by some competitors which would be tempted to follow a more or less concealed dumping policy.'
2. *Metal Bulletin* (London), July 20, 1962, p. 20.

argued that, since she was such a heavy importer, the external tariff would discriminate unduly against her; that the French industry was acknowledged to be efficient and should have no fears from North American competition; that there were effective measures evolved by GATT to control dumping.

However good these arguments were, it seemed unlikely that the Community's industry would be persuaded. The writer spent the summer of 1962 in Europe and gained the general impression that the position taken by the French (vigorously supported by the Italians who had high costs of production, and not resisted by the Germans) was that the tariff was already lower than it should be and that if Britain were ever admitted this admission should not be associated with any further reduction in the external tariff. If, as one suspected, there was unlikely to be a further reduction of the external tariff on aluminium, Britain if she were admitted would still have a second claim which she could urge to meet her problem, at any rate in the short run. The Germans (West), who were net importers of aluminium, were granted permission under Protocol 12 of the Treaty of Rome to import quotas from non-members at a 5 per cent rate instead of the normal 10 per cent (later reduced to 9 per cent). Still more analogous than West Germany was the case of Belgium which, like Britain, had its interest concentrated mainly in fabrication and which, like Britain, had its operations dominated by supplies imported from abroad. Belgium on the same principle received, as a Benelux member, import quotas at a rate of 1.5 per cent. Britain when or if admitted could justifiably expect that these, and especially the latter, would be regarded as precedents for alleviating her problem.

Some Implications for Alumina: The EEC's capacity in alumina is in excess of the aluminium equivalent (Table IV.3). The capacity in aluminium in 1960 was about half a million tons (an alumina equivalent of 1 million tons of alumina based on 2 tons of alumina to 1 of aluminium) and in alumina 1.3 million tons, the excess being an alumina capacity of about 0.3 million tons a year. The picture is the same in most other major geographical areas. In Africa there is an excess in capacity of alumina over the aluminium smelter requirements, the Guinea capacity being much greater than the Cameroun needs; in North America there is a deficit of alumina capacity, but this is due to Canada's demand since in the United States alumina capacity is well in excess of aluminium requirements.

In Asia–Australasia, the alumina capacity is also in excess of aluminium requirements.

In the Common Market France is the largest producer of alumina. When the Community came into being she was a major net exporter of alumina, her excess alumina going primarily to Cameroun, but this has stopped since Guinea's plant came into production. With France's smelter capacity increased to 300,000 tons a year the exports previously directed to Cameroun will continue to find an outlet in the French complex. The French have traditionally come to regard themselves as the suppliers of alumina for the Swiss smelting and, in 1961, their plants in France and Guinea provided some 80 per cent of the Swiss alumina imports. Spain has also established a growing dependence on French alumina, in 1960 importing about two and a half times as much alumina from France as in the previous year, and in both 1960 and 1961 being the major destination for French alumina. A notable aspect of the recent developments is that France, while previously a major exporter (nearly 200,000 tons exports of alumina in 1959) by 1961 was importing approximately as much alumina (mainly from Guinea) as she exported. It was clear that, in French planning, Guinea production was an integral part.

The other main producer of the Six was West Germany with an alumina capacity in excess of its aluminium needs, even greater than that of France. Nevertheless, with the expansion in smelting capacity and her technological improvements in productivity of the existing reduction plants, West Germany may well be expected to increase her alumina capacity. Germany has been the traditional supplier of Austria's needs. Austria with no alumina plant in 1961 took about 94 per cent of West Germany's alumina exports.

Italy, like West Germany and France, had excess alumina capacity and exported mainly to Austria and Switzerland; but the current plans for expansion of reduction plants should eliminate the excess. The Italians were also implementing alumina expansion.

The overall picture (Table IV.3) was therefore that the EEC was not only self-contained in regard to its needs for alumina but was, and had traditionally been, a net exporter. The picture could be a very different one if the EEC was enlarged to admit the EFTA group. The Six offer little encouragement to those who, outside the existing EEC aluminium complex, might wish to expand alumina production, but the EEC, enlarged by the EFTA countries, might give an unprecedented challenge to some producers, including those in the Caribbean. The Caribbean was, however, likely to find that in the EEC the competition for the new opportunities was much fiercer than in the peace and quiet of EFTA.

The tariffs on alumina in the Community ranged from 20 per cent in Italy to nil in the Benelux countries and the common external tariff, to which the Six were working, was 11 per cent. There had been no agitation (in any of the literature seen) for any modification of the external tariff, as there was in the case of aluminium and it seemed likely that the figure of 11 per cent would stand. The protection, a higher rate than for aluminium, was likely to have an influence on the location of alumina plants,[1] an influence all the greater if the EEC were ever enlarged to include the EFTA countries. There were indications that the vertically integrated companies in competing countries recognized this and that there were plans for not only expansion of but addition to existing capacity. Thus the Swiss Group (AIAG) were said to be planning an alumina plant to be located in Holland and with adequate capacity for exports to be sent to Norway where the company had interests in one of the four aluminium companies. Some have attributed Alcoa's decision to undertake her developments in Surinam to far-sighted policy by that company to take advantage of Surinam's relation with the Community and of the projected increase in demand of Western Europe. The Commonwealth Caribbean was potentially an important participator in this expanding alumina trade if Britain ever entered the Community. In the event of Britain's entry, a question which the Commonwealth Caribbean would have to examine would be whether or not it would be expedient and in its interests to enter into an Associate relationship with the Community.

EEC Associate Status, its Background and Implications

Part Four of the Treaty of Rome (Articles 131–6) prescribes a form of association with the Community of 'non-European countries and territories which have special relations' with the Six. Association

1. In addition to the value of the tariff there is the added element of irrational behaviour. Producers of aluminium are no exception to the general body of manufacturers who do not like to pay taxes and who prefer to operate on the right side of a tariff wall. In various countries the offer of tax exemptions which in economic terms may not mean much can nevertheless be a potent factor in influencing location of a plant.

involves: (1) as far as exports are concerned, enforcement of the tariff reductions and elimination of quantitative restrictions which the member countries apply among themselves; (2) as far as imports are concerned, extension to others in the Community of the same tariff and other trade regulations which apply to the European State with which the Associate Territory has special relations; because of this favoured status the Associate Territory does not have to go further and remove completely its tariff on goods originating in the Community (which it would have to do were it a full member); (3) aid in investment required for development; (4) freedom of movement of workers to Member States only if a later convention, requiring unanimous agreement of Member States, so provides; (5) the implementing Convention (determining the particulars and procedure relating to associate status) being brought up for review in five years.

The countries originally named as qualifying for associate status were Netherlands New Guinea and those in special relation with France, Belgium and Italy. Algeria and the Overseas Departments being formally a part of France were thereby a part of the Community except that the conditions governing the movement of Algerian labour were those which applied to associate status, not to membership. To compensate, Algeria and the Overseas Departments although having membership status were allowed to participate in the Development Fund.

The chief territories for which alumina developments and some form of association with the Community might have implications were: Guinea, Ghana, Surinam and the Commonwealth Caribbean. Guinea was the third territory named in Annex IV of the Treaty as being granted associate status. Since then her special relationship with France has been denied, and she, while not formally denouncing, has avoided all positive steps which could be taken as a mark of her accepting association. She none the less continues, formally, to have associate status; her alumina continues to go into France free of duty and is also admitted into Germany on the same basis. In this context, therefore, Guinea, while probably not technically qualifying, and while appearing not to wish to do so, none the less enjoys the benefits. She will presumably indicate when the new Convention comes up for consideration what she will wish her position to be.

Ghana was not one of the territories included in Annex IV among the territories enjoying associate status, since the European State with which she had a special relation, Britain, was not one of the Six. She has since indicated that she is not interested in associate status and without a change in policy will not be offered the trading rights and privileges which the relationship entails. Since Ghana has large deposits of bauxite and now has under way the Volta project from which will come both alumina and aluminium, this has implications for supplies to the Common Market.

As far as Surinam was concerned, the Netherlands due to constitutional relationships were unable, in signing the Treaty, to secure Associate Overseas status for Surinam. This problem was met by a Protocol[1] of the Treaty which enabled Surinam's products, in effect, entry as from January 1, 1958, into the Common Market on terms equivalent to those enjoyed by the Associate Overseas Territories. Surinam has since then explored a normal association and relationship and been granted AOT (Associate Overseas Territory) status which means that her alumina and aluminium products are assured the protection of the Common Market.[2] The conviction that this relationship would come into being was one of the factors (suggested above) which probably persuaded Alcoa to undertake in Surinam development which went further than exporting the raw

1. Under the Protocol (entitled: Protocol relating to goods originating in and coming from certain countries and enjoying special treatment on importation into one of the Member States) it was agreed that Morocco, Tunisia, Libya, Surinam and Netherlands Antilles would continue to receive the special customs treatment from the respective Member States with which they had a special relation when the Treaty came into force. (Morocco being the first territory listed, the Morocco Protocol has become the accepted name.) The agreement was intended to cover only trade between the territory and its respective Member State and was therefore bilateral in nature. Goods imported under this Protocol were not intended to enjoy the benefits of the Common Market if directly re-exported to another Member of the Community. In principle therefore goods imported under this Protocol if re-exported should have been subject to the export levy but in practice this has not been done on the grounds that amount of trade involved did not justify the administrative machinery that it would call for.

2. The Netherlands Antilles also sought AOT status but ran into difficulties. Only a small proportion of their exports go to the Benelux countries; while the same is true of Surinam, the Netherlands Antilles export is chiefly refined petroleum to the United States. The chief export of Surinam is bauxite whose products are and are likely to continue to be complementary to rather than competitive with the Community's economy. There was in consequence the suspicion that the output of the refineries of Aruba and Curaçao might be diverted to Western Europe and be a competitor, especially with France's planned African expansion of oil production. While therefore Surinam was granted full AOT status, the Netherlands Antilles were granted such status with the important reservation that special provisional arrangements would apply in the case of oil.

ore – a most unusual step for a United States aluminium industrial group in the Caribbean.

The Commonwealth Caribbean do not participate in any special relationship with the Community, either in whole or in part, as both Guinea and Surinam do. The Commonwealth Caribbean territories have been offered AOT status and have, at the time of this writing, not indicated whether or not they would accept. It may be worthwhile to examine some of the considerations which the Commonwealth Caribbean must weigh in coming to a decision as to whether or not from the point of view of bauxite and bauxite products, to accept AOT status.

Bauxite and Bauxite Products: The three products involved would be bauxite, alumina and aluminium. The Commonwealth Caribbean, producing no aluminium and with no known plans to do so, would have little reason to seek AOT status on behalf of aluminium. A probable consideration is of course that if AOT status was a factor in aiding aluminium production in Surinam, such a status for British Guiana might induce one of the aluminium companies to look more searchingly at that country's hydro-electric potential with a view to aluminium smelting. Bauxite, admitted with a nil tariff into the Common Market, did not provide any justification for accepting AOT status.

The considerations in regard to alumina were different in 1961. Norway took 197,000 tons of Jamaica alumina and Sweden nearly 30,000. These together made up 32 per cent of Jamaica's total exports (703,000 tons). In 1962, Norway took nearly 208,000 tons and Sweden over 19,000 – the same total of 227,000 tons as in 1961. This was 36 per cent of total exports (627,500 tons). If this market were lost, alumina plants in Jamaica would presumably have to cut out a shift, and the loss in wages alone would exceed £400,000 annually. And already stockpiling must be taking place since production in 1962 was nearly 37,000 tons more than exports and the 100 tons of local sales. Even, therefore, in the interest of present alumina output, Jamaica had reason to look with favour on AOT status. In addition there was an expanding demand for alumina in the Community, but unless there was a major expansion of the alumina capacity in the Commonwealth Caribbean, the expanding EEC demand was only of academic interest and would not provide additional reason for association with the Community. Expansion in alumina capacity if brought into being – and one has heard of no plans to that end – would be a powerful influence in favour of AOT status. As there may be a chance that massive alumina expansion might be undertaken in Jamaica the question of association would assume increasing importance and would therefore deserve examination.

Preferential Treatment: The Caribbean is further from Western Europe than other major sources of supply, e.g. Greece, Yugoslavia and the Soviet allied Bloc countries. The level of the External Tariff could therefore be an influence and was one of the items still to be negotiated at the time of writing. Britain imposed a 10 per cent duty and was unlikely to quibble at the EEC's 11 per cent. It was true that such a duty levied in Britain was of little significance to the United States producers since Britain's aluminium industry had its requirements more than met by domestic alumina capacity but such a duty in operation in Norway and elsewhere in an enlarged EEC was another matter. Alcoa with its alumina facilities being established in Surinam was unlikely to feel it incumbent to try to get the tariff reduced but the other United States companies (e.g. Reynolds with its interests in the Norwegian aluminium company, DNN) might regard this tariff on alumina as discriminating against their alumina made in the United States in favour of, for example, Aluminium Limited's alumina made in Jamaica. From these other United States companies might come pressure for the reduction of the alumina tariff in the EEC.

If one assumes that the present tariff policy is maintained and if time and circumstance made associate status acceptable, the Commonwealth Caribbean's alumina would be able to explore any of several methods of preferential treatment:

a. First, there was the possibility of the encouragement of expansion of alumina capacity within the protection of the Common External Tariff.

b. Secondly, there should be the possibility of entering into a contract to sell some of its alumina to smelters within the Common Market and to be paid for it in aluminium. Some North American alumina is sold to Norway and paid for in Norwegian aluminium.

c. Another related type of precedent would be the quota granted West Germany for the import of aluminium in relation to West German alumina which is converted abroad into aluminium. The aluminium for which the quota is granted is the equivalent of alumina which is produced in a non-integrated alumina plant in Ludwigshafen in West Germany. The alumina plant not being tied to a smelter sends some of its output abroad for reduction. West Germany is then allowed the transfer of the equivalent amount of aluminium into the Common Market without the payment of duty.

d. Another possibility, which might be explored, was to seek the benefit of the tariff of 11 per cent on alumina even if that alumina were converted into aluminium outside the Common Market. This provision would be particularly justifiable for a territory which had bauxite deposits but no potential for aluminium production and an example of this was Jamaica. The aim of the member states was to promote economic activity in the Community, the term being used in its wider sense. There was good economic reason to process bauxite into alumina in Jamaica, but it was not feasible to go to the final stage, aluminium. In the circumstances it would be within the spirit of the Rome Treaty to seek special consideration within the Common Market for alumina processed in the Caribbean as against alumina processed in territories having no special relationship with the Community. One way to effect this would be to devise some means of passing on to AOT alumina the benefit of the External Common Tariff on alumina produced within the area. It was this principle which lay behind the grant of special concessions for aluminium coming into the Common Market from a third country and which is referred to at *c* above. Because of the special case – the special case being that the West German company which produced the alumina in question was not vertically integrated and had no smelting capacity of its own – alumina, produced under conditions related to those in the Caribbean, received special consideration.

The Politics of Nationalism: The discussion here relates primarily to the considerations, as far as bauxite products are concerned, for or against AOT status for the Commonwealth Caribbean if the opportunity arose to secure such status and the subject of nationalism is included not with any wish to widen the argument but simply because it is so pervasive in its influence that it cannot be ignored. This influence is all the greater in countries just receiving their independence and with internal pressures not only to be nationalistic but to appear nationalistic.

With the background of the Korean War and the dollar crises the Strasbourg Plan in the early 1950s made proposals to rationalize the resources of the so-called overseas under-developed territories and to associate them not only with the economies of their respective metropolitan powers, but with the pooled activity of Western Europe. In addition it called for Europe's getting together to aid these territories with technical assistance both in skilled personnel and capital for investment. The plan was rejected, and even up to the stage of the Spaak Report (which became the basis of the Rome Treaty) the overseas territories were omitted from the proposals. It was only after the French made the inclusion of the overseas territories a condition of their participation that the idea was revived and AOT status in the Rome Treaty became the solution. Most of the overseas territories listed in Annex IV as having AOT status have since the Treaty was signed become independent politically and all with the exception of Guinea have asked to remain associated with the Community. In addition Greece, which is of particular relevance to the bauxite and bauxite products argument, became an associate member in 1962.

On the other hand, certain of the African territories (e.g. Nigeria, Ghana) have indicated that they are unlikely to accept what they regard as the inferior status of 'association'. Article 131 states that the object was 'to establish close economic relations . . . to lead them . . .' Such sentiments, admirable in intent in the 1950s could in the 1960s be resented by newly independent territories zealously protesting their non-alignment. It was in this context that Nigeria refused associate status and the Commonwealth Caribbean were deliberating their decision.

A new Convention defining the relationship of AOT status was to come into being in early 1963 and there was indication that the member states were responsive. In 1961 some of the African States had met with the European Parliamentary Assembly and certain resolutions there adopted had influenced the nature of the new relationships. Some of the more important recommendations of the meeting in 1961 with the Assembly were: (a) that there should be equality between the African and European partners; (b) that there should be, between the partners, conferences held alternately in Europe and in Africa; (c) that the Development Fund should be increased and renamed the Common Development Fund to which all partners would contribute, some greater, some less and that all contributors should have a say in the allocation of the Fund; (d) that there should be association with the European Coal and Steel Community and the European Atomic Energy Community; (e) that protective measures should be retained and that any modifications in tariffs or commodities in which the territories were interested should be made only after consultation with the territories involved. It therefore looked likely that the new Convention might provide a means of removing some of the political opposition to Associate relationship.

Those who, on grounds of nationalism, were against AOT status might propose even if the opportunity arose for Associate Status the Commonwealth Caribbean need not accept it since it might be possible for the Commonwealth Caribbean to eat their cake and have it too. The argument would be that these territories, even if Britain were admitted, could on the one hand avoid any possibility of a compromising relationship by refraining from becoming formally associated while, on the other, enjoying the rights and privileges of the Common Market. At any rate, as far as alumina was concerned, Guinea had done precisely that. Even more remarkable was the case of Tunisia which enjoyed special trade relationships with France when the Rome Treaty was signed. By the Morocco Protocol nearly 90 per cent of Tunisia's trade with France continued to be given preferential treatment. The Commonwealth Caribbean might, however, be rash to conclude that such privileges would automatically be theirs. France has been a powerful member of the Six and has with dedicated purposefulness safeguarded the interests of territories associated with her. Britain might have been a correspondingly effective advocate in the EFTA had she been equally determined. In the EEC she, when or if admitted, was unlikely to be either as ardent or as potent as France when it came to the affairs of the ex-colonies.

The Development Fund: The Fund established at $581 million was to be increased to $780 million in the Convention due to come into force in January 1963. The Fund was not large in relation to the territories to be covered but participation did not preclude aid from other sources. The Fund was an argument in favour of association.

Movement of Labour: Britain applying for admission to the Community in 1961 was said to have been asked with some apprehension by the Six whether admission would mean that Britain's immigrants – especially her coloured ones – coming across the oceans would also expect to come across the Channel. The attitude of the Community was reflected by its policy in restraining movement of labour from Algeria. Labour from the Commonwealth Caribbean was unlikely to be granted freedom of movement. Freedom of movement of labour therefore did not provide an argument for accepting AOT status.

Summary of Considerations relating to Alumina and Western Europe

The growing demand for alumina in Western Europe provided a major challenge for the Commonwealth Caribbean. The opportunity was likely to be missed if there was not early expansion of alumina capacity in the Caribbean. There was need for speed because other interests, seeing the opportunity, were already embarking on plans to grasp it and even if the enlarged EEC aluminium expansion decided to look to the Commonwealth Caribbean for alumina the Caribbean had not the capacity to meet it. The Swiss aluminium interests were putting up a plant in Holland large enough to have an excess for diversion to Norway. Yugoslavia, the second largest producer of bauxite in Western Europe, was said to be seeking some form of relationship with the Community and already a trade mission from Norway was exploring the erection in Yugoslavia of an alumina plant to help meet the needs of the smelters in Norway. Greece had secured associate status and firms including Reynolds were associated with the erection of a fully integrated plant with excess alumina capacity. These were in addition to the plans at home, and in West Africa, of the major alumina producers of the Six. United States alumina was also making its appearance on the European market, and imports from the United States while not large, were considerably higher than in 1959. Another significant development was the appearance of Australian alumina on the Norwegian market. The Australian industry, developed largely by the United States companies, particularly Kaiser, Alcoa and Reynolds, had vast potential demand in the Far East but was already probing the possibility of alumina shipments to the West as well.[1]

While more Commonwealth Caribbean capacity in alumina was desirable, equally so was the need for sufficient representation in Western Europe of the Commonwealth Caribbean interests by

1. An indication that alumina can remain competitive even when the transport distances are great was the reputed feasible shipments by Alcoa to the Mitsubishi smelters in Japan. *Metal Bulletin* (London), August 10, 1962, p. 22.

industrial groups whose aluminium policy could be reconciled with reasonable alumina development of the Commonwealth Caribbean. Since the aluminium industry is tightly integrated vertically the spokesman for alumina tends to be the producer of aluminium. He admittedly produces alumina but this he produces primarily according to his aluminium need. In the same way that in the EFTA the forces at work dictating the trends in aluminium policy were shown to be in more than one particular different from those dictating the trends in alumina policy, so the interests of those territories predominantly concerned with the location of alumina manufacture could diverge from the interests of those companies predominantly concerned with aluminium. Thus Guinea's case for growing participation in the alumina market of the EEC was likely to be promoted because these interests coincided with those of Pechiney, Reynolds and others who had been persuaded to process alumina in Guinea. Similarly Surinam's alumina interests were likely to be pushed by Alcoa. In neither country were there any major aluminium industrial groups whose business interests conflicted with those of the economy of the ore-bearing territory. In the Commonwealth Caribbean, Alcan was a producer of alumina and therefore had, both in the Caribbean and abroad, interests which identified themselves closely with the interests of the Caribbean economies. In the case of those industrial groups which mined ore in the Caribbean and did not process alumina, their interests would not necessarily be closely identified with the Caribbean's if the Caribbean's interests called for processing at home rather than abroad. Not only were the interests of these latter industrial groups not necessarily closely identified, but it has been shown that in the case of the European Free Trade Association there could be and probably was conflict of interests. Thus it was improbable that Reynolds could be expected to support without reservation greater participation by the Commonwealth Caribbean in the alumina market of Western Europe in a context which meant that the choice was between Alcan's alumina from Jamaica and alumina from the Reynolds alumina investments in Guinea or in Greece. Nor in the same context could Alcoa be expected to explore with zeal opportunities for Alcan's alumina from Jamaica to replace in competition Alcoa's alumina from Surinam. Provided the structure of the industry remained as at present, the policy of the industrial groups not making alumina in the Caribbean could be a positive and inhibiting force against the Commonwealth Caribbean's expanded alumina participation in Western Europe.

Technology and Innovation

Reference has been made to some of the active research which is being undertaken in different countries and by different industrial groups to improve the efficiency in the production of aluminium. Some of these methods are well enough advanced to be considered worthy of the investment of formidable sums in pilot plants. Some are radical and may one day result in the extraction of the metal from lower grade clays than bauxite (and this is reported to be taking place on a commercial scale in Russia) or may eliminate the need for alumina plants. At the same time the traditional techniques themselves continue to make technical advances and, on present indications, are maintaining their dominance. Proof of this is the large investment being put by North American, European, Australasian and Japanese producers into new plants based on the traditional methods of production.

The new technological developments in production would have to be taken into account if investment were being sought for new alumina capacity in the Caribbean. One would certainly have to weigh seriously the proposition that in the not distant future the present technique of alumina production may be not only partially supplanted but eliminated. Since, however, so many aluminium companies including those most actively involved in the Caribbean are continuing to put traditional plants in many countries one could hardly expect this reason to be pressed unduly.

A possible technological development of special concern especially to Jamaica is the domestic production, by electrolysis, of caustic soda which is one of the main ingredients in the chemical conversion of bauxite into alumina. There are many doubtful factors which could discourage the setting up of a chlor-alkali plant. The investment is heavy. The labour employed is small. Caustic soda is in over-supply and the price for which it can be produced in, say, Jamaica can, and almost certainly would, be bettered by any of several chemical companies in North America or Europe. Jamaica has no cheap sources of power in quantity – neither hydro sources, coal nor gas – and has little tradition for this type of industry.

There are also several factors in favour. Caustic soda is in world over-supply but the Caribbean has a demand large enough to keep a relatively large unit fully occupied. Jamaica alone on the basis of imports, would provide the demand for a 150–200 ton a day caustic soda plant and anything over 50 tons a day can be economic. In

the production of caustic soda another chemical, chlorine, is produced in almost equal quantity. Chlorine, unlike caustic soda, is in
short supply but would have at first almost certainly to be exported.
There would therefore be expected to follow a bold programme
for developing chemical industry based on chlorine and the products
derived therefrom. Chlorine is used in the production of plastics
(e.g. PVC which is in heavy demand for shoes, bottles, hosing). The
variety of uses for chlorine would be increased by the establishment
in Jamaica and the existence in Trinidad of oil refineries. Thus
chlorine and ethylene (which is a by-product of the oil refinery)
will produce trichloroethylene and perchloroethylene and these
are important as solvents. Chlorine and methane, also from the
refinery, produce methyl chloride, methylene chloride and carbon
tetrachloride.

Because a chemical industry so proliferates, the basic demand
for large supplies of caustic soda might well provide the nucleus
for important economic growth. The consortium which, it is
suggested, should provide the alumina capacity should, like the
Kaiser alumina plant in Louisiana, combine caustic soda operations
with an alumina installation. A chemical industry, if established,
might in its own right and with its proliferations prove a major
ingredient in Jamaica's economic development. It would as an
ancillary contribute to the direct value added in the processing of
bauxite to alumina in the Island.

Appendices

Bibliography

Glossary

Index

Appendix A. Background to Developments in Aluminium in Europe and Africa

Developments in Europe

In Europe, as in America, the aluminium industry is closely integrated vertically so that the story of alumina must in large measure involve the industry as a whole. In the early period of the industry, before the First World War, the existence of patents helped set the pattern of a small number of dominant enterprises. The three Continental enterprises – one in Switzerland, partly owned by German interests, and two in France – were diversified chemical manufacturers of chemical and electro-chemical products rather than sole producers of aluminium. It was only the company in the United Kingdom – British Aluminium Limited – that was a vertically integrated enterprise established for the production of aluminium alone. Of these countries France alone had within its borders all the ingredients for production: bauxite deposits, hydro-power and, significantly, leadership in the arts and sciences which concern the electro-chemical and electro-metallurgical industries.

After the disruption of the First World War the European companies found themselves with an expanded demand for the metal. This, associated with growing economic nationalism, encouraged countries to develop their domestic resources such as hydro-power. In Germany, for example, a fully State-owned enterprise (VAW) was protected from external competition by import restrictions and internally by a control of expansion through licensing. VAW pushed its vertical integration by acquiring bauxite deposits in Hungary and elsewhere in Europe. In France the Pechiney empire emerged from the combine of the two major companies. Ugine was independent of Pechiney, but they both accepted the common regulatory powers of L'Aluminium Française. The Swiss also moved towards vertical integration and acquired bauxite rights abroad (e.g. in Hungary). British Aluminium[1] sought

1. British Aluminium owned bauxite deposits in Ireland and France, alumina and reduction plants based on Scottish hydro-electric power, with fabricating plants in Scotland and England.

to consolidate its integration by exploring bauxite deposits in the overseas territories and the Government guaranteed the programme for power expansion to meet the reduction needs of the industry.

The 1930s, beginning with a depression and ending with a much increased demand for war purposes, saw the industry in Europe consolidate its position by organized co-operation. Alliance Aluminium[1] controlling some 60 per cent of the world's production, played an important part in the handling of excess stocks and established a cartel stock-pool to hold the output of members which found no market. In 1932, during the first Five Year Plan, Russia produced its first lot of metal.

During the Second World War, bombings and sabotage did much to harass the industry and despite the efforts of the German High Command, production in important areas like France and Norway declined. The United Kingdom expanded its production, but made the decision to look to Canada for the major part of its supplies, and to this end the United Kingdom Government made loans to Alcan aggregating some $78 million.

It is not easy to get figures on production and capacity of alumina over time for the different countries since – for reasons which one does not at first sight see – many producers do not readily release figures on either output or capacity. Nevertheless data on alumina production have been collected and are presented in Appendix B.

Developments in Africa

In the field of the aluminium industry French public and private capital and French initiative took the lead. There was increasing conviction in France that, with the shortage of investment capital and the foreseeable limits to expansion at home, the main hope

1. This was the most powerful and most effective of the aluminium cartels, the cartel playing an important part in the development of the industry. Alliance Aluminium Compagnie, registered in Switzerland, had its shares allocated on the following basis:

French	Aluminium Française	21 per cent
Swiss	Aluminium Industrie A/G	15 per cent
British	British Aluminium Co.	15 per cent
German	German Group	20 per cent
Canadian	Aluminium Limited	29 per cent

(For more detailed discussion see *Materials Survey – Aluminium*, United States Department of Commerce.)

for substantial development lay overseas. In France there had been established in 1946 the Investment Fund for the Social and Economic Development of French overseas territories (FIDES) and the Central Bank of Overseas France. The plan was that the financing of development in the overseas territories should be encouraged by the participation of these two organizations together with the contribution from the territory. The flow of funds from private sources had been feeble, especially in the early stages but the Central Bank helped to channel this flow, adding to it from its own funds, and in certain instances guaranteeing the financing of some of the important basic services.[1] The French metropolitan industrial groups, supported by their Government, had developed an aggressiveness in expanding the aluminium-alumina-bauxite industry in Africa that no one else displayed. Admittedly there was inducement. One engineering estimate claimed that the territory in Africa between 10° N and 10° S possessed about 40 per cent of the world's hydro-power resources.

Guinea

In the area near Fria on the Konkuré there was not only a large potential of hydro-electric development but deposits of good quality ore. In the 1930s Bauxites du Midi, a subsidiary of Aluminium Limited, having prospected for bauxite in the Boké region, also secured mining rights in the Los archipelago. At the same time the French aluminium companies secured similar rights for large deposits in the Fria region. By the early 1950s plans were discussed to erect alumina plants at both Boké and Fria. In 1956 the Compagnie Internationale pour la Production de l'Alumine, Fria, came into being.[2] In 1958 they agreed to establish an alumina plant which would have a capacity of some 500,000 tons and which would begin production in 1960 or 1961. Those responsible for planning claimed that the development of the hydro-electric resources in Guinea was

1. Henin, L. L'Industrie de l'Aluminium en Afrique Nord. Academie royale des Sciences Coloniales, Brussels.
2. The shareholders were in 1956:

Company:	% of shares owned:
Olin Mathieson (United States)	53.5
British Aluminium Co. (British)	10.0
A.I.A.G. (Swiss)	10.0
Pechiney	21.2
Ugine	5.3

so costly in time and money that it was more expedient, at the outset, to develop the resources in Cameroun and to export the alumina for reduction there. The Guinea project was estimated, in 1958 terms, to cost over $500 million. For the longer range project (hydro-electric development for aluminium) the French Government had consented to put up most of the capital and various companies[1] had agreed to come together to form a consortium for aluminium production. The objective was to produce 150,000 tons of aluminium which would be exported to the countries of the participating companies. The power was to be provided, in the first instance, from a dam erected on the Konkuré. It was so highly desirable for an aluminium producer to have his ore near hydro-electric power that there must have been difficulties of many kinds which brought about the decision not to push forward with a vertically integrated industry including the aluminium stage in Guinea.

The alumina plant at Fria was the first to be erected in Africa and by 1960 was producing at the capacity output of 480,000 tons.

When the international market for the metal deteriorated in 1957–59 and when in 1958 the political relationships between Guinea and metropolitan France changed abruptly, there were indications that the French Government, one of the main participants, thought that there had been grounds for their circumspection. The emergence in Guinea of a newly formulated policy and vocal nationalism gave rise to claims for processing within the country. Bauxites du Midi, a subsidiary of Aluminium Limited and associated, as we have mentioned above, with Guinea since the 1930s, made an agreement in 1958 to set up an alumina plant by July 1964. In 1961 the Guinea Government requested Bauxites du Midi to cease mining operations in the country on the grounds that it was evident that the agreement as to the alumina plant was not being fulfilled. The Government went further and, according to a statement from Aluminium Limited, took over the Company's investment in Guinea as compensation. This investment amounted to some $23,000,000. Later the Government announced that they had arrived at agreements with Bulgaria and Czechoslovakia to sell bauxite as well as some alumina.

1. The French Government had agreed to put up $100 million and the companies involved with smelting were:

V.A.W. (West German)
Montecatini (Italian)
Aluminium Limited (Canadian)

Cameroun

In 1948 as part of the economic development plan of the Cameroun an electric energy company (ENELCAM) came into existence. Its purpose was to develop electrical energy and to distribute it to towns and local industries. ENELCAM established a hydro-electric centre at Edea. Later in 1954 the Aluminium Company of the Cameroun (ALUCAM) was created to carry out industrial plans. The capital in these two companies was subscribed from different sources.[1] As an inducement the aluminium producers were granted certain privileges relating to price of electricity and tax relief.

The aluminium plant produced its first ingots in 1957 and 47,000 tons in 1961. At the outset the reduction plant imported its alumina from France but the intention was to import requirements from the Fria plant in Guinea. The industry could point out that it was not really as odd as it might at first seem to export alumina from France to the Cameroun since France had been in the habit of exporting alumina for reduction to Norway, a roughly equal distance. The plant was technologically one of the most modern in the world. This coupled with the low cost of electricity (about 0.17 United States cents compared with 0.48 to 0.96 cents in metro-politan France) promised to make production competitive. Plans were already under discussion for the fabrication activities in the Edea area. The port facilities of Douala had to be increased because with shipments of the metal and imports of alumina the traffic increased substantially.

The Belgian syndicate Cobeal was in 1957 granted about 9 per cent of the ALUCAM shares. Out of this arrangement came the agreement that the Belgian syndicate would secure their needs of alumina from Pechiney-Ugine. The Belgians also secured an option to negotiate with ALUCAM for 11 per cent of the capacity of the Edea plant.

1. Basis on which capital subscribed in ENELCAM and ALUCAM. (Source: Henin, L., *op. cit.*)

ENELCAM	Percentage capital	ALUCAM	Percentage capital
	%		%
Territory of Cameroun	34	Pechiney	66
Electricité de France	20	Ugine	16
Central Bank through FIDES	14	Central Bank, France	10
Customers	32	Cameroun	8

The Congo

There was under discussion a long-term project to dam the Kouilou River. The project was likely to yield power resources even larger than Guinea's. Plans were in terms of an aluminium plant of 250,000 tons a year. The project was being considered in relation to development of the Inga site, and the thoughtfulness of the French companies in bringing the Cobeal into the Cameroun project established a basis for relationship in the future. The President of Pechiney was of opinion that the Inga development was the most promising of all the projects in Africa.[1]

One of the early projects planned in association with the developments was a plant for the electrolysis of salt and the production of chlorine and its by-products on the one hand, with caustic soda on the other.

Ghana

The Volta River project was the subject of studies and preparations which, in their degree of thoroughness, were exceptional outside the more industrialized countries of the world and probably compared favourably with many projects that have been investigated in those countries.[2] The cost of investigations alone up to 1955 when the commission issued the report was £1,300,000.

The early proposals put forward in 1952 were that the United Kingdom and Gold Coast Governments, the United Kingdom and Canadian aluminium producers would unite to produce aluminium on a large scale in Ghana (then the Gold Coast). One advantage claimed for the scheme, from the point of view of the investor, was that on the one hand it would guarantee to the United Kingdom additional sterling area aluminium and on the other that it would aid materially in the development of the Gold Coast (Ghana). In 1951 the United Kingdom relied on the dollar area for some four-fifths of its virgin aluminium. Everyone seemed convinced that the Volta River provided a most promising site for the expansion of aluminium production. Although the potentialities of the Volta for hydro-electric resources had been long recognized, the order of investment required was a major discouragement unless economic use could be found for marketing this power. The heavy needs of

1. Vitry de, Raoul, *op. cit.*
2. Preparatory Commission. *Report on the Volta River Project*, para. 56 and Appendix II. H.M.S.O., London, 1956.

H

power for the electrolytic process in aluminium production seemed to offer in the Volta region, as it had offered in the South East and North West United States, in the East and West of Canada, in the Highlands of Scotland, justification for the type of massive investment which aluminium production had in the first instance called forth and later justified by the ancillary activities which had followed. The dream of the possibilities of the Volta Scheme was not new. Since the early 1920s the Gold Coast Government had discussed a possible project, and serious exploration in 1938 was interrupted by the war. As soon as the war ended in 1945 negotiations began again and the West African Aluminium Company came into being. Between 1947 and 1949 Aluminium Limited acquired both extensive concessions in the territory's bauxite deposits and an interest in the West African Aluminium Co. In 1951–52 discussions took place both in London and Accra between the (Ghana) Gold Coast Government and private agencies.[1] The approach to the scheme was that there would be a partnership. To explore and examine those problems still further the parties concerned agreed that the Gold Coast should in 1953 appoint a Preparatory Commission and that the scheme should not be embarked upon 'without every practical assurance that it can be carried through to a successful conclusion'.[2] A few months later the Gold Coast Government set up a National Committee for the project. It consisted of persons of different political parties and had as one of its objects that of raising the project above party and ensuring its acceptance as a subject of national concern.

The conclusions, after the exhaustive investigations, was that the project was technically sound and should be able to produce aluminium competitively since at the final stage power could be produced at 0.199 cents per unit. As late as 1958 no decision had been taken about bringing the project into being but the Ghana Government persisted with its efforts to have the scheme financed. Aluminium Limited, which held bauxite leases, announced that they had decided to withdraw. Later, Kaiser became involved in the operations. In 1960 the long drawn-out negotiations at last met with success and the World Bank, the United States and Britain

1. The scheme which they arrived at could be divided into three parts: (i) a power station at Ajena, about 70 miles from the mouth of the Volta River to have a continuous generating capacity of 564,000 kW; (ii) an aluminium smelter (near Kpong and 12 miles from Ajena) with an ultimate capacity of 210,000 tons; (iii) extensive public works including new port facilities.
2. White Paper (Cmd. 8702) Summary of proposals. H.M.S.O., London.

decided to subscribe half the estimated cost. In 1961 an agreement was signed between the Ghana Government and the Volta Aluminum company (Valco), a consortium made up of Kaiser, Alcoa, Reynolds and Olin Mathieson. An aluminium plant of 200,000 tons capacity is to be built by about 1969 and the alumina for this is to be imported for the first ten years.

Appendix B. Tables—The Industry's Framework

TABLE I.a   *Bauxite – World Deposits*

	Estimated Reserves '000,000 tons	Estimated Low-grade Resources '000,000 tons	Year Production Started
U.S.A.	50	350	
Brazil	30	173	1936
British Guiana	80	70	1917
Costa Rica		50	
Colombia	1		
Dominican Republic	40	40	1959
French Guiana		70	
Haiti	23	7	1956
Jamaica	550	450	1952
Panama		25	
Surinam	200	200	1922
Venezuela		10	
The Americas	**974**	**1,445**	
Austria	1	1	
France	70	190	
Greece	84		
Italy	11	13	
Spain	7		
Yugoslavia	128	172	1918
Western Europe	**301**	**376**	
Cameroun		50	
Congo Republic	100		
Ghana	229		1940
Republic of Guinea	600	2,400	
Mozambique	20		1936
Nyasaland		60	
Africa	**949**	**2,510**	
British Borneo	11		
India	58	192	1910
Indonesia	15	10	1932
Iran		15	
Malaya	10	6	1936
Pakistan		9	
Sarawak	5	5	1958
Turkey	10	36	
Asia	**109**	**273**	
Australia and Oceania	600 3	400 3	1927
Western World	**2,936**	**5,007**	
U.S.S.R.	100		
Hungary	250		1914–18
Roumania	20	20	1919
China	50	950	1951
Soviet allied Bloc	**420**	**970**	
World	**3,356**	**5,977**	

TABLE I.b   *Bauxite – World Production ('000 long tons)*

Producing Countries	1938	1950	1957	1958	1959	1960	1961
U.S.A.	311.0	1,334.5	1,416.0	1,311.0	1,700.0	1,998.0	1,228.0
Jamaica			4,595.0	5,722.0	5,125.6	5,744.8	6,663.0
British Guiana	376.4	1,583.4	2,201.9	1,585.9	1,674.4	2,477.5	2,374.0
Dominican Rep.					759.0	678.0	722.0
Haiti			263.0	280.0	255.0	268.0	263.0
Surinam	371.3	2,047.8	3,324.0	2,941.0	3,376.0	3,400.0	3,351.0
Brazil	12.7	18.3	62.5	68.8	95.5	119.0	140.0
The Americas	1,071.4	4,984.0	11,862.4	11,908.7	12,985.5	14,685.3	14,741.0
Austria		3.0	22.0	23.2	23.6	25.6	18.0
Greece	177.1	76.0	820.5	842.7	904.0	915.0	1,280.0
EFTA	177.1	79.0	842.5	865.9	927.6	940.6	1,298.0
France	671.2	795.1	1,662.9	1,800.6	1,729.0	2,006.0	2,148.0
West Germany	19.4	4.1	4.6	3.7	4.4	3.7	3.4
Italy	355.1	151.0	257.5	294.3	289.6	313.0	318.0
EEC	1,045.7	950.2	1,925.0	2,098.6	2,023.0	2,322.7	2,469.4
Spain		12.0	8.1	8.2	7.5	3.0	
Yugoslavia	390.1	202.8	874.2	721.0	802.0	1,009.0	1,213.0
	390.1	214.8	882.3	729.2	809.5	1,012.0	1,213.0
Western Europe	1,612.9	1,244.0	3,649.8	3,693.7	3,760.1	4,275.3	4,980.4
Ghana		115.0	185.4	207.1	147.8	224.5	193.0
Guinea		10.0	360.1	325.0	296.2	1,356.1	1,739.0
Mozambique		4.2	5.0	4.7	4.2	4.8	5.0
Africa		129.2	550.5	536.8	448.2	1,585.4	1,937.0
India	14.8	64.4	107.9	166.2	214.6	377.5	468.0
Indonesia	148.0	320.5	237.7	338.5	381.1	389.4	413.0
Malaya	55.1		325.6	262.4	381.8	452.0	403.0
Pakistan			3.3	2.0	2.1	1.0	1.0
Sarawak				136.3	206.9	284.8	253.0
Asia	217.9	384.9	674.5	905.4	1,186.5	1,504.7	1,538.0
Australia	1.8	3.5	7.7	6.9	15.0	70.9	18.0
Western World	2,904.0	6,745.6	16,744.9	17,051.5	18,395.3	22,121.6	23,214.4
U.S.S.R.	246.1	738.2	2,410.0	2,710.0	2,950.0	3,445.0	4,000.0
Hungary	532.2	563.4	893.1	1,032.5	941.6	1,169.8	1,337.0
Roumania	11.6	4.9	60.0	72.0	70.0	87.0	87.0
China				150.0	295.1	344.5	400.0
Soviet allied Bloc	789.9	1,306.5	3,363.1	3,964.5	4,256.7	5,046.3	5,824.0
World	3,693.9	8,052.1	20,108.0	21,016.0	22,652.0	27,167.9	29,038.4

TABLE I.c   *Bauxite – Exports* ('000 *long tons*)

Exporting Countries	1938	1950	1957	1958	1959	1960	1961
U.S.A.	90.4	72.0	61.0	11.9	17.4	29.3	150.7
Jamaica			3,641.4	4,799.0	4,196.8	4,147.6	4,975.0
British Guiana	376.4	1,583.4	2,021.2	1,364.3	1,514.7	2,094.9	1,606.3
Dominican Rep.					481.3	774.7	722.0
Haiti			373.0	370.6	338.2	395.0	
Surinam	371.3	2,013.1	3,324.7	2,820.0	3,338.0	3,577.0	3,360.0
Brazil			3.1	3.5	2.8	2.0	
The Americas	838.1	3,668.5	9,424.4	9,369.3	9,889.2	11,020.5	
Austria			6.8	8.5	6.5	5.6	
Greece	177.1	76.0	769.0	823.3	841.2	891.4	
EFTA	177.1	76.0	775.8	831.8	847.7	897.0	
France	287.6	257.7	329.2	303.8	271.3	312.1	
West Germany			0.1	0.2	0.7	0.4	
Italy	74.1						
EEC	361.7	257.7	329.3	304.0	272.0	312.5	
Yugoslavia	373.8	150.6	688.9	583.0	592.0	790.4	
Western Europe	912.6	484.3	1,794.0	1,718.8	1,711.7	1,999.9	
Ghana		115.0	185.4	207.1	147.8	224.5	169.1
Guinea			369.4	259.5	275.7	693.7	
Mozambique		3.7	4.5	2.9	6.1	4.4	
Africa		118.7	559.3	469.5	429.6	922.6	
India	3.3	0.3	8.5	20.6	23.2	88.0	
Indonesia			253.8	385.6	243.1	342.5	
Malaya		15.9	340.6	246.6	363.8	448.0	284.4
Sarawak				92.9	202.9	260.1	
Asia	3.3	16.2	602.9	745.7	833.0	1,138.6	
Australia						30.0	41.6
Western World	1,754.0	4,287.7	12,380.6	12,303.3	12,863.5	15,111.6	
Hungary	356.7		459.4	530.0	458.9	491.0	
Roumania				36.4	80.7	86.7	
Soviet allied Bloc	356.7		459.4	566.4	539.6	577.7	
World	2,110.7	4,287.7	12,840.0	12,869.7	13,403.1	15,689.3	

TABLE I.d   *Bauxite – Imports* ('000 *long tons*)

Importing Countries	1938	1950	1957	1958	1959	1960	1961
U.S.A.	455.7	2,516.3	7,165.4	7,944.5	8,257.7	8,862.7	9,206.0
Canada	328.9	1,662.2	2,118.0	1,776.0	1,692.0	2,263.0	
Mexico			2.2	3.7	3.5	5.9	
Argentina			12.6	26.6	16.0	29.5	
Colombia				1.8	3.0	4.6	
The Americas			9,298.2	9,752.6	9,972.2	11,165.7	
United Kingdom	249.6	198.5	354.5	350.8	327.2	378.8	395.0
Austria	1.1	5.0	5.5	6.1	0.1	10.4	
Norway	25.5	36.6	28.1	36.1	35.4	28.1	
Sweden		9.3	8.0	3.2	12.9	5.5	
Denmark			0.7	0.6	0.2	0.4	
EFTA	276.2	249.4	396.8	396.8	375.8	423.2	
France			23.2	38.6	44.3	59.7	
West Germany	1,165.9	210.8	1,236.6	1,055.2	897.6	1,322.1	
Italy	0.4	81.2	259.8	180.8	232.5	275.7	
Belgium			1.5	1.5	16.6	7.2	
Netherlands			5.9	7.9	7.7	3.5	
EEC			1,527.0	1,284.0	1,198.7	1,668.2	
Spain			18.6	17.6	9.0	23.3	
Western Europe			1,942.4	1,698.4	1,583.5	2,114.7	
Algeria			3.0	1.6	2.3	2.2	
Morocco						2.4	
Africa			3.0	1.6	2.3	4.6	
Japan	217.0	106.5	485.0	509.1	816.7	1,077.4	
Taiwan			41.3	40.6	32.1	24.0	
Hong Kong			0.2	0.3	0.4	0.4	
Asia			526.5	550.0	849.2	1,101.	
Australia			35.2	69.5		96	
Western World			11,805.3	12,072.1	12,474	..0	
U.S.S.R.			398.4	443.0	447.2	422.0	
Czechoslovakia			224.0	316.0	242.0	265.0	
East Germany			252.0	226.3	251.2	264.2	
Poland			21.0	18.0	23.0	34.0	
Soviet allied Bloc			895.4	1,003.3	963.4	985.2	
World			12,700.7	13,075.4	13,437.4	15,468.2	

TABLE I.e *Alumina – World Production ('000 long tons)*

Producing Countries	1938	1950	1957	1958	1959	1960	1961
U.S.A.	243.4	1,219.0	3,073.0	2,846.0	3,579.0	3,595.0	3,432.0
Canada	149.0	782.5	935.0	886.0	837.0	1,131.9	636.0
Jamaica			436.0	373.0	399.0	665.0	703.0
British Guiana							130.0
Brazil			21.0	16.0	28.5	29.5	
The Americas			4,465.0	4,121.0	4,843.5	5,421.4	
United Kingdom	10.0	14.0	120.0	120.0	120.0	120.0	
Norway	13.7	15.0	15.0	18.0	18.0	15.0	
Sweden			10.0	2.0	7.0	3.0	
EFTA			145.0	140.0	145.0	138.0	
France	111.9	197.8	443.0	515.0	558.0	586.0	
West Germany			415.0	370.0	406.0	430.0	
Italy	90.5	82.9	189.0	191.0	202.0	218.0	
EEC			1,047.0	1,076.0	1,166.0	1,234.0	
Yugoslavia			49.0	50.0	60.0	66.0	
Western Europe			1,241.0	1,266.0	1,371.0	1,438.0	
Africa, Guinea						182.0	393.7
India			17.0	19.5	24.1	25.7	
Japan	36.4	52.1	151.0	218.0	294.0	349.0	
Taiwan			20.0	20.0	20.0	20.0	
Asia			188.0	257.5	338.1	394.7	
Australia			20.1	22.5	26.9	29.8	
Western World			5,914.1	5,667.0	6,579.5	7,465.9	
U.S.S.R.			1,000.0	1,100.0	1,300.0	1,500.0	
East Germany			49.0	51.0	54.0	58.0	
Czechoslovakia			99.0	99.0	99.0	99.0	99.0
Hungary			152.0	167.0	189.0	215.0	
China			49.0	59.0	140.0	160.0	190.0
North Korea			15.0	15.0	15.0	15.0	15.0
Soviet allied Bloc			1,364.0	1,491.0	1,797.0	2,047.0	
World			7,278.1	7,158.0	8,376.5	9,512.9	

TABLE I.f   *Alumina – Exports* ('000 *long tons*)

Exporting Countries	1938	1950	1957	1958	1959	1960	1961
U.S.A.				11.9	28.2	29.3	150.6
Canada		67.8					17.0
Jamaica			436.0	373.1	399.2	665.4	703.5
British Guiana							130.4
The Americas							1,001.5
EFTA, U.K.	9.9	13.5	33.0	38.3	33.4	26.4	23.8
France	21.4	67.3	114.0	172.2	184.7	139.4	138.3
Germany			76.0	84.8	90.4	66.4	73.9
Italy	39.0	11.0	38.0	53.1	42.0	42.7	29.5
EEC			228.0	310.1	317.1	248.5	241.7
Yugoslavia				3.6	23.5	19.3	
Western Europe				352.0	374.0	294.2	
Africa, Guinea						168.7	370.0
Asia, Japan			6.0	50.5	94.5	77.9	
Western World							
Soviet allied Bloc, Hungary			88.0	85.4	112.2	119.6	

TABLE I.g   *Alumina – Imports* ('000 *long tons*)

Importing Countries	1938	1950	1957	1958	1959	1960	1961
U.S.A.			1.6	48.0	115.5	79.1	169.0
Canada				292.6	324.4	410.9	629.1
Brazil			0.2		2.8	0.1	
Colombia			0.1	0.1	0.5	0.7	
Mexico			5.2	3.5	4.1	6.3	
The Americas				344.2	447.3	497.1	
United Kingdom	0.1	0.1	0.3	0.3	6.0	7.0	4.6
Austria	11.0	26.0	10.5	99.0	131.0	115.3	155.1
Norway	43.0	80.0	191.0	194.0	310.3	328.4	302.5
Sweden		13.0	27.0	19.0	29.0	31.5	22.4
Switzerland	52.0	40.0	62.0	60.0	50.1	85.9	91.1
Denmark					0.2	0.3	0.1
Finland				0.2	0.1	1.6	7.8
Portugal						0.1	0.1
EFTA – Alumina	106.1	159.1	290.8	372.5	522.0	562.7	570.6
Hydrate					4.7	7.4	13.1
France			0.1	0.3	0.3	44.6	135.0
West Germany				0.4	0.1	0.4	27.7
Italy			0.1	0.2	0.8	0.4	0.7
Belgium-Luxemburg			0.3	0.5	9.6	9.6	9.1
Netherlands			5.0	6.0	9.0	7.3	7.6
EEC – Alumina			5.5	7.4	3.1	45.9	163.7
Hydrate					16.7	16.4	16.4
Spain – Alumina		4.9	31.0	41.0	36.3	62.1	79.2
Western Europe			327.3	420.9	582.8	694.5	843.0
Africa, Cameroun				70.8	80.1	73.6	
Asia, India			0.6	0.1	10.0	12.2	
Australia			0.1	0.1	0.1	0.1	
Western World				836.1	1,120.3	1,277.5	
U.S.S.R.			22.0	10.0			
Czechoslovakia			32.0	27.0	26.0		
East Germany			42.0	18.0	15.0	26.0	
Poland			49.0	40.0	41.0	53.0	
Roumania			1.0	1.0	2.0		
Soviet allied Bloc			146.0	96.0	84.0	79.0	

TABLE I.h   *Primary Aluminium – World Production ('000 long tons)*

Producing Countries	1938	1950	1957	1958	1959	1960	1961
U.S.A.	128.1	641.6	1,471.3	1,397.8	1,744.8	1,798.7	1,699.8
Canada	63.6	354.4	497.1	566.2	530.0	680.4	652.7
Brazil			8.8	11.7	17.8	17.9	17.9
The Americas	191.7	996.0	1,977.2	1,975.7	2,292.6	2,497.0	2,370.4
United Kingdom	23.0	29.5	29.4	26.4	24.5	28.9	32.3
Austria	4.4	17.7	55.5	56.0	64.5	66.9	66.6
Norway	28.6	46.3	94.1	119.5	143.7	162.2	169.2
Sweden	1.9	4.0	13.4	13.5	15.3	16.4	16.5
Switzerland	26.6	18.9	30.6	31.0	33.8	39.1	41.3
EFTA Countries	84.5	116.4	223.0	246.4	281.8	313.5	325.9
France	44.6	59.7	157.4	166.2	170.3	231.5	274.8
West Germany	158.6	27.4	151.4	134.6	148.8	166.3	169.8
Italy	25.4	36.5	65.2	63.0	73.8	82.3	82.0
EEC Countries	228.6	123.6	374.0	363.8	392.9	480.1	526.6
Spain	0.7	2.1	15.6	15.9	22.3	23.6	27.8
Yugoslavia	1.2	1.9	17.9	21.3	19.0	24.7	27.0
	1.9	4.0	33.5	37.2	41.3	48.3	54.8
Western Europe	315.0	244.0	630.5	647.4	716.0	841.9	907.3
Africa, Cameroun			7.5	31.4	41.7	43.3	46.8
India		3.6	7.8	8.2	17.1	18.0	18.1
Japan	14.2	24.4	66.9	83.3	98.6	131.1	151.3
Taiwan	4.6	1.7	8.1	8.5	7.4	8.1	8.9
Asia	18.8	29.7	82.8	100.0	123.1	157.2	178.3
Australia			10.6	10.9	11.4	11.7	13.2
Western World	525.5	1,269.7	2,708.6	2,765.4	3,184.8	3,551.1	3,516.0
U.S.S.R.	43.1	178.6	490.0	540.0	620.0	670.0	884.0
Czechoslovakia			16.4	26.0	25.6	39.0	49.1
East Germany	2.0	6.0	34.0	33.5	34.5	39.3	54.1
Hungary	1.5	16.4	25.6	38.9	45.0	48.8	50.3
Poland			20.0	22.1	22.4	25.6	46.9
Roumania			10.0	10.0	10.0	10.0	10.0
China			20.0	26.8	69.3	78.7	98.2
Soviet allied Bloc	46.6	201.0	616.0	697.3	826.8	911.4	1,192.6
World	572.1	1,470.7	3,324.6	3,462.7	4,011.6	4,462.5	4,708.6

TABLE I.i *Primary Aluminium – Exports* ('000 *long tons*)

Exporting Countries	1938	1950	1957	1958	1959	1960	1961
U.S.A.	4.3	0.6	26.0	47.1	108.3	254.5	115.1
Canada	57.8	299.8	427.4	432.5	451.2	493.0	424.9
The Americas	62.1	300.4	453.4	479.6	559.5	747.5	540.0
United Kingdom	1.5	5.4	6.9	2.1	3.7	3.9	5.4
Austria		13.4	22.5	31.7	37.7	21.4	27.9
Norway	28.1	39.7	71.1	108.1	130.0	136.0	144.0
Sweden	0.1		0.5	3.1	2.0	0.1	0.1
Switzerland	24.9	9.4	2.9	8.5	11.0	7.4	6.0
EFTA Countries	54.6	67.9	103.9	153.5	184.4	168.8	183.4
France	13.8	21.9	16.0	49.0	50.8	69.0	104.8
West Germany	3.6	33.8	7.1	4.3	1.8	2.7	3.8
Italy	0.5	3.4	1.1	9.1	9.7	1.2	0.1
EEC Countries	17.9	59.1	24.2	62.4	62.3	72.9	108.7
Spain					0.2	11.0	3.6
Yugoslavia			2.6	5.4			
Western Europe	72.5	127.0	130.7	221.3	246.9	252.7	295.7
Africa, Cameroun			6.8	21.9	38.6	41.4	42.2
Japan	0.9	24.6	0.2	4.4	0.2		
Taiwan			3.3	1.8	2.1		
Asia	0.9	24.6	3.5	6.2	2.3		
Australia			0.8			0.1	
Western World	135.5	452.0	595.2	729.0	847.3	1,041.7	877.9
U.S.S.R.			84.1	113.1	76.2	67.0	85.6
Hungary			1.9	17.1	8.3	9.7	
Soviet allied Bloc			86.0	130.2	84.5	76.7	

TABLE I.j   *Primary Aluminium – Imports* ('000 *long tons*)

Importing Countries	1938	1950	1957	1958	1959	1960	1961
U.S.A.	7.8	157.8	198.4	228.0	214.3	138.1	177.7
Canada	0.1	0.1	1.9	15.4	7.2	6.4	
Mexico			8.7	12.2	9.4	11.0	
Argentina			12.4	12.9	9.2	11.9	
Brazil	1.4	6.9	12.5	13.9	8.8	14.6	
Colombia			1.2	2.2	3.0	3.0	
The Americas	9.3	164.8	235.1	284.6	251.9	185.0	
United Kingdom	46.3	141.2	191.2	210.4	252.1	311.9	235.9
Austria	0.0	0.1	0.2	0.4	0.5	0.4	0.1
Norway	0.9	1.0	0.1	1.6	0.2	0.6	2.4
Sweden	4.6	8.2	15.8	20.6	21.2	27.7	23.6
Switzerland	3.8	2.7	10.0	6.9	15.7	16.1	10.3
Denmark			3.7	4.3	6.3	6.0	
Finland			2.6	4.7	7.2	4.0	
Greece			1.3	1.8	2.5	4.3	
Portugal			2.5	2.7	2.6	3.5	
EFTA Countries			227.4	253.4	308.3	374.5	
France	0.1	0.5	8.7	28.7	32.8	53.3	41.8
West Germany	14.3	5.0	40.0	66.6	88.6	178.2	136.5
Italy	0.3	13.7	17.0	5.4	16.0	33.6	25.3
Belgium		8.5	27.3	41.4	48.6	63.3	68.5
Netherlands		4.3	8.3	8.9	14.0	14.5	13.6
EEC Countries		32.0	101.3	151.0	200.0	342.9	285.7
Spain		1.6	5.1	10.9	6.4	1.7	3.9
Yugoslavia		0.2	1.6	0.0	5.8	15.5	
Western Europe			335.4	415.3	520.5	734.6	
Africa, Republic of South Africa				6.6	6.7	7.3	11.1
India	0.0	1.8	5.8	7.1	6.8	10.3	
Japan	28.0	1.2	9.0	0.4	14.6	22.6	31.9
Hong Kong			1.6	2.6	10.1	16.4	
Pakistan			9.4	1.6	12.4	4.3	
Asia			25.8	11.7	43.9	53.6	
Australia			10.4	10.2	15.3	23.4	25.0
Western World			613.3	728.5	838.9	1,007.7	
East Germany				26.0	28.0	35.0	
Hungary			11.0	2.0	3.0	0.5	
Poland			4.7	6.4	9.9	13.6	
China				38.0	13.0	18.0	
Soviet allied Bloc				72.4	53.9	67.1	

TABLE I.k *Primary Aluminium – Consumption* ('000 *long tons*)

	1950	1957	1958	1959	1960	1961
U.S.A.	810.0	1,586.1	1,616.7	1,917.2	1,563.4	1,768.0
Canada	58.2	69.6	91.0	79.1	102.1	100.7
Mexico	2.6	8.7	12.2	9.4	11.0	10.3
Brazil	6.7	21.3	25.6	26.6	34.5	34.4
Rest of America	12.3	14.8	14.8	13.8	16.2	26.6
The Americas	889.8	1,700.5	1,760.3	2,046.1	1,727.2	1,940.0
United Kingdom	180.9	213.3	232.5	288.9	353.8	279.6
Austria	5.9	32.2	30.9	33.9	36.4	37.4
Norway	9.4	16.3	17.7	16.2	18.2	18.2
Sweden	14.2	25.0	31.9	35.4	37.3	33.1
Switzerland	11.9	38.7	31.3	41.5	47.1	46.8
Denmark	2.9	3.6	4.5	6.0	5.6	5.7
Finland	0.6	2.4	4.1	6.3	2.9	5.0
Greece		1.3	1.7	3.1	4.1	4.9
Ireland		2.3	2.4	3.5	3.2	4.4
Portugal		0.6	0.6	0.6	0.9	2.0
EFTA Countries	225.8	335.7	357.6	435.4	509.5	437.1
France	54.3	150.8	140.8	165.2	209.4	199.0
West Germany	49.0	182.7	187.0	224.7	299.2	285.1
Italy	46.8	65.1	61.7	81.7	97.4	103.3
Belgium	5.3	27.0	40.5	47.7	62.5	67.9
Netherlands	4.1	7.9	6.9	12.3	13.8	11.8
EEC Countries	159.5	433.5	436.9	531.6	682.3	667.1
Spain	3.8	20.7	26.7	26.7	19.7	19.7
Yugoslavia	2.6	16.8	15.9	24.7	40.3	35.4
Western Europe	391.7	806.7	837.1	1,018.4	1,251.8	1,159.3
Africa	2.0	8.2	8.3	9.8	13.1	12.2
India	5.5	13.6	15.4	22.5	24.1	29.3
Japan	18.7	73.5	79.4	110.8	148.1	182.4
Rest of Asia	3.0	9.6	10.0	9.8	14.3	20.2
Asia	27.2	96.7	104.8	143.1	186.5	231.9
Australia	6.2	18.6	26.4	32.8	38.4	33.5
Western World	1,316.9	2,630.7	2,736.9	3,250.2	3,217.0	3,376.9
U.S.S.R.	211.6	438.0	457.7	543.9	622.0	718.5
Czechoslovakia	13.8	35.9	35.4	43.3	45.3	49.2
East Germany	2.0	53.1	59.1	64.0	73.8	78.7
Hungary	5.9	22.6	21.7	36.4	39.4	44.3
Poland	4.9	22.1	28.0	32.5	39.4	44.3
Rest of Soviet Europe	0.3	15.7	17.2	19.7	21.7	24.6
China	2.0	9.8	59.1	78.7	88.6	83.7
Soviet allied Bloc	240.5	597.2	678.2	818.5	930.2	1,043.3
World	1,557.4	3,227.9	3,415.1	4,068.7	4,147.2	4,420.2

TABLE II   *Alumina Plants – By Countries*

			IIa. The Americas	
				Capacity
Country Operating Company	Plant Location	Year of Start	1961 '000 tons	To be added '000 tons
U.S.A. Aluminum Co. of America **(Alcoa)**	Mobile, Alabama	1938	880	
	Point Comfort, Texas	1958	335	335
	Bauxite, Arkansas	1952	375	
			1,590	335
Reynolds Metals Co. **(Reynolds)**	Hurricane Creek, Arkansas	1943	716	
	Corpus Christi, Texas	1953	782	
			1,498	
Kaiser Aluminum & Chemical Corporation **(Kaiser)**	Baton Rouge, La.	1943	759	
	Gramercy, La.	1959	384	
			1,143	
Ormet Corporation **(Ormet)**	Burnside, La.	1958	322	
Harvey Aluminum (Inc.) **(Harvey)**	The Dallas, Oregon			100
	St Croix (Caribbean)			100
	U.S.A.		4,553	535
Canada Aluminum Co. of Canada Ltd. **(Alcan)**	Arvida, Quebec	1928	1,140	

TABLE II   *Alumina Plants – By Countries* (continued)

IIa. **The Americas** (continued)

Country Operating Company	Plant Location	Year of Start	Capacity 1961 '000 tons	Capacity To be added '000 tons
Jamaica				
Alcan Jamaica Ltd.	Kirkvine, Manchester	1953	480	
	Ewarton, St Catherine	1959	240	
Argentina				
Industrias Siderurgicas Grassi, S.A.	Nihuel, S. Mendoza			N.A.
Brazil				
Aluminio Minas Gerais, S.A.	Saramenha, Ouro Prêto		24	
Cia Brasileira de Aluminio, S.A.	Sorocaba, Sao Paulo		30	
(Reynolds)	Paulo Afonso			90
British Guiana				
Demerara Bauxite Co. Ltd. (Demba)	McKenzie, Demerara River	1961	220	
Surinam				
Surinam Aluminium Co. (Suralco)	Paranam,			116
The Americas – Total			6,687	741

IIb. **Western Europe**

United Kingdom	Plant Location	Year of Start	1961 '000 tons	To be added '000 tons
United Kingdom				
British Aluminium Co. Ltd.	Newport, Monmouthshire	1914	45	
(Baco)	Burntisland, Fife	1917	60	

TABLE II   *Alumina Plants – By Countries* (continued)

IIb. **Western Europe** (continued)

Country Operating Company	Plant Location	Year of Start	Capacity 1961 '000 tons	To be added '000 tons
Norway A/S Norsk Aluminium Co. (Naco)	Höyanger, Sögnefjord	1928	18	20
Sweden A/B Svenska Aluminium- Kompaniet (Sako)	Kubikenborg		8	
Greece Aluminium de Grêce, S.A.	Acheloos			100
EFTA Countries – Total			131	120
France Pechiney, Cie de Produits Chimique et Electro- Métallurgiques (Pechiney)	Salindres, Gard Gardanne	1887	98 316	98
			414	98
Société d'Electro-Chimie, d'Electro-Métallurgie et des Aciéries Electriques d'Ugine (Ugine)	La Barasse		98	40
Société Française pour l'Industrie de l'Aluminium	St Louis les Aygalades	1908	59	
	France		571	138

TABLE II   *Alumina Plants – By Countries* (continued)

IIb. Western Europe (continued)

Country / Operating Company	Plant Location	Year of Start	Capacity 1961 '000 tons	To be added '000 tons
West Germany				
Martinswerk GmbH	Martinswerk, Bergheim	1915	153	
Vereinigte Aluminium Werke, A.G.	Nabwerk, Schwandorf	1937	110	23
(VAW)	Lippewerk, Lünen	1939	131	20
Gebrüder Giulini, GmbH (Giulini)	Ludwigshafen		98	
	West Germany		492	43
Italy				
Industria Nazionale Alluminio (Montecatini)	Porto Marghera	1937	123	25
Società Allumino Veneto per Azioni (Sava)	Porto Marghera	1928	113	
	Italy		236	25
EEC Countries – Total			1,299	206
Spain				
Alquimia, S.A.	Barcelona, Tarragona			20
Empresa Nacional del Aluminio, S.A. (Endasa)	San Balandrán, Avilés			148
Yugoslavia (Government)	Lozovac, Dalmatie		8	
	Moste		8	
	Kidricewo, Slovenia		89	54
(Norwegian and Yugoslavian interests)	N.A.			197
Western Europe – Total			1,535	745

TABLE II   *Alumina Plants – By Countries* (continued)

IIc. **Africa, Asia, Australia**

Country Operating Company	Plant Location	Year of Start	Capacity 1961 '000 tons	To be added '000 tons
Guinea				
Cie Internationale pour la Production de l' Alumine **(Fria)**	Fria, Kimbo	1960	473	
(Harvey)	Boké			220
Cameroun				
N.A.	Nkongsamba			N.A.
Africa – Total			473	220
India				
Indian Aluminium Co. Ltd. **(Indalco)**	Muri, Bihar	1948	18	37
Aluminium Corporation of India Ltd.	Jaykaynagar, Bengal		5	
Bharat-Reynolds Aluminium Corporation **(Bralco)**	Dandeli, Shravathi, Mysore			60
Hindustan Aluminium Corporation Ltd. **(Hindalco)**	Pipri, Rihand Dam, U.P.			40
Madras Aluminium Co. Ltd.	Salem, Mettur, Madras			20
National Industrial Development Corporation **(Nidc)**	Korba, Madhya Pradesh			50

TABLE II *Alumina Plants – By Countries* (continued)

IIc. **Africa, Asia, Australia** (continued)

Country Operating Company	Plant Location	Year of Start	Capacity 1961 '000 tons	To be added '000 tons
Bombay Mineral Supply Co. Ltd.	Khambhalia, Shaurashtra			N.A.
Koyna Aluminium Co. Ltd.	Koyna, Maharashtra			40
India			23	247
Japan				
Showa Denko K. K.	Yokohama, Kanagawa	1933	102	
Sumitomo Kagaku Kogyo K.K.	Kikumoto, Ehime	1936	118	
Nippon Light Metals Co. Ltd. (NKK)	Shimizu, Schizuoka	1941	200	
Japan			420	
Taiwan				
Taiwan Aluminium Corporation	Kaosiung, Takao	1935	29	13
Indonesia				
(U.S.S.R. assistance)	East Sumatra			70
Asia – Total			472	330
Australia				
Comalco Aluminium (Bell Bay) Ltd.	Bell Bay, Tasmania	1955	35	
Comalco Pty. Ltd.	Weipa, Cape York Pen.			360
Alcoa of Australia Pty. Ltd.	Kwinana, Freemantle			220

TABLE II   *Alumina Plants – By Countries* (continued)

IIc. **Africa, Asia, Australia** (continued)

Country Operating Company	Plant Location	Year of Start	Capacity	
			1961 '000 tons	To be added '000 tons
Australia			35	580
Africa, Asia, Australia – Total			980	1,130
Western World – Total			9,202	2,616

IId. **Soviet allied Bloc**

Country Operating Company	Plant Location	Year of Start	1961 '000 tons	To be added '000 tons
U.S.S.R.				
Soviet Aluminium Trust	Volkhov, Leningrad	1932	79	
	Zaporozhye, Ukraine	1934	196	
	Boksitogorsk	1938	147	
	Kamensk-Uralskiy	1939	344	
	Krasno-tourinsk	1943	344	
	Pikaleva	1959	787	
	Achinsk			800
	Kirovabad			200
	Pavlodar, Kazakhstan			500
	Akhta, Transcaucasia			N.A.
	U.S.S.R.		1,897	1,500
Czechoslovakia				
Ziar Aluminium Works	Svaty Kriz		98	
East Germany				
Volkseigener Betrieb	Lauta		35	
Elektrochemisches Kombinat (VEB)	Greiz, Dölau		20	
Hungary				
Bonautaler Alaunnerde	Alamásfüzito		113	

TABLE II   *Alumina Plants – By Countries* (continued)

IId. Soviet allied Bloc (continued)

| | | | Capacity | |
Country Operating Company	Plant Location	Year of Start	1961 '000 tons	To be added '000 tons
Ungarrische Bauxit Gruben, A.G.	Ajka		59	
Bauxit Industrie, A.G.	Mosonmagyaróvár		35	
Poland Kombinat Centrozap (Polish State Body)	Gorink, Krakow			200
Roumania (Government plant)	Oredea			120
China (Government plants)	Fushun, Liaoning	1937	22	
	Changtien, Nanting		40	
	Antung, Yalu River			20
	Kweiyang, Kweichou			20
	Kunming, Yunnan		N.A.	
	Yangchuan, Shansi		N.A.	
	Sian, Shensi		N.A.	
	China		190[1]	40
North Korea[2] (Government plants)	Chinnamp'o		5	
	Taedasa-do (Yoshi)		10	
	Hungnam (Konan)		21	
	Wonsam		36	
	Chinnamp'o			100
Soviet allied Bloc – Total			2,519	1,960
World – Total			11,721	4,576

1. Estimated production figure.
2. All figures for North Korea are 1945 figures.

TABLE III   *Primary Aluminium Plants – By Countries*

IIIa. **The Americas**

Country Operating Company	Plant Location	Year of Start	Capacity 1961 '000 tons	To be added '000 tons
U.S.A.				
Aluminum Co. of	Massena, N.Y.	1903	106	29
America	Alcoa, Tennessee	1914	140	
(Alcoa)	Badin, N. Carolina	1916	42	
	Vancouver, Washington	1940	87	
	Point Comfort, Texas	1949	125	
	Rockdale, Texas	1952	134	
	Wenatchee, Washington	1952	97	
	Evansville, Indiana	1960	31	125
			762	154
Reynolds Metals Co.	Listerhill, Alabama	1940	170	
(Reynolds)	Longview, Washington	1941	54	
	Troutdale, Oregon	1942	82	
	Jones Mills, Arkansas	1942	97	
	Corpus Christi, Texas	1952	85	
	Arkadelphia, Arkansas	1954	49	
	Massena, N.Y.	1959	89	
			626	
Kaiser Aluminum &	Mead, Washington	1942	157	
Chemical	Tacoma, Washington	1942	37	
Corporation	Chalmette, La.	1951	221	
(Kaiser)	Ravenswood, W. Va.	1957	129	
			544	
Anaconda Aluminum Co. **(Anaconda)**	Colombia Falls, Mont.	1955	58	
Ormet Corporation **(Ormet)**	Hannibal, Ohio	1958	161	

TABLE III *Primary Aluminium Plants – By Countries* (continued)

IIIa. **The Americas** (continued)

Country Operating Company	Plant Location	Year of Start	Capacity 1961 '000 tons	To be added '000 tons
Harvey Aluminum (Inc.) (Harvey)	The Dallas, Oregon Pacific North West	1958	72	67
Cerro Corporation (Cerro)	Longview, Washington Wauna, Oregon			36 50
Consolidated Aluminum Corp. (Conalco)	Johnsonville, Tennessee			223
Howe Sound Co.	Portland, Oregon			64
	U.S.A.		2,223	594
Canada Aluminum Co. of Canada Ltd. (Alcan)	Shawinigan Falls, Quebec Arvida, Quebec Isle Maligne, Quebec Kitimat, B.C. Beauharnois, Quebec	1900 1926 1943 1954 1943	63 333 103 171 34	80
			704	80
Canadian British Aluminium Co. Ltd.	Baie Comeau, Quebec	1957	80	40
	Canada		784	120
Mexico Aluminio, S.A. de C.V.	Vera Cruz			20
Reynolds Aluminio, S.A.	Tabasco			20

TABLE III *Primary Aluminium Plants – By Countries* (continued)

IIIa. **The Americas** (continued)

Country Operating Company	Plant Location	Year of Start	Capacity 1961 '000 tons	To be added '000 tons
Dominican Republic (Government)	N.A.			N.A.
Argentina Kaiser Aluminio, S.A. (formerly **Fadasa**)	Neuquen, Patagonia			20
(Reynolds)	Comodora Rivadavia, Patagonia			23
Industrias Siderurgicas Grassi, S.A.	Nihuel, S. Mendoza			10
	Argentina			53
Brazil Aluminio Minas Gerais, S.A.	Saramenha, Ouro Prêto Hiha	1945	11	8 20
Cia Brasileira de Aluminio, S.A.	Sorocaba, Sao Paulo	1955	10	10
Cia Nacional de Aluminios	Poços de Caldas			20
N.A.	Cachoeira de Fumaca			10
Kaiser Mineria de Aluminio	Paulo Afonso			N.A.
(Polish interests)	N.A.			50
	Brazil		21	118

TABLE III *Primary Aluminium Plants – By Countries* (continued)

IIIa. The Americas (continued)

Country Operating Company	Plant Location	Year of Start	Capacity 1961 '000 tons	To be added '000 tons
Colombia				
Aluminio de Colombia-Reynolds Santo Domingo, S.A.	N.A.			N.A.
Peru				
Aluminio Reynolds del Peru, S.A.	Pisco			N.A.
Surinam				
Suriname Aluminium Co.	Brokopondo			50
Venezuela				
Aluminio del Caroni, S.A. **(Alcasa)**	Puerto Ordoz, Caroni River			25
The Americas – Total			3,028	1,000

IIIb. Western Europe

United Kingdom				
British Aluminium Co. Ltd.	Kinlochleven, Argyllshire	1909	10	
(Baco)	Lochaber, Inverness	1929	25	
Austria				
Salzburger Aluminium GmbH	Lend, Salzburg	1899	8	
Vereinigte Metallwerke, A.G.	Ranshofen-Berndorf	1941	66	

TABLE III *Primary Aluminium Plants – By Countries* (continued)

IIIb. **Western Europe** (continued)

Country Operating Company	Plant Location	Year of Start	Capacity	
			1961 '000 tons	To be added '000 tons
Norway				
Det Norske	Eydehavn	1912	10	
Nitridaktieselskap	Tyssedal	1916	20	30
(DNN)				
A/S Norsk	Höyanger, Sögnefjord	1915	13	13
Aluminium Co.				
(Naco)				
Mosjöen Aluminium	Mosjöen	1958	32	20
A/S	Lista			100
(Mosal)				
Ardal og Sunndal	Ardal, Sögnefjord	1946	97	
Verk, A/S	Sunndalsöra,	1954	49	54
(Ardal)	Sunndalsfjord			
	Andalsnes			100
Norsk Hydro	Ora, Karmöy Is.			100
Elektrisk K. A/S				
(Norsk Hydro)				
A/S Elektrokemisk	Lista			100
A/B Svenska	Trondheim			30
Metallverken				
Sör-Norge	Husnes			100
Aluminium, A/S				
	Norway		221	647

TABLE III   *Primary Aluminium Plants – By Countries* (continued)

IIIb. **Western Europe** (continued)

Country Operating Company	Plant Location	Year of Start	Capacity 1961 '000 tons	To be added '000 tons
Greece				
Aluminium de Grêce, S.A.	Matochi, Aspra Spitia			52
Sweden				
A/B Svenska Aluminium-	Mönsbo, Avesta	1934	2	
Kompaniet **(Sako)**	Sundsvall, Kubikenborg	1943	14	15
Switzerland				
Aluminium	Chippis, Valais	1908	35	
Industrie, A.G.	Stegerfeld, Valais			25
(Aiag)				
Usine d'Aluminium de Martigny, S.A. **(Martigny)**	Martigny, Valais	1938	5	
	Switzerland		40	25
EFTA Countries – Total			386	739
France				
Pechiney, Cie de	La Praz, Savoie	1893	4	
Produits Chimique	La Saussaz, Savoie	1905	10	
et Electro-	Chedde, Haute-Savoie	1907	6	
Métallurgiques	St Jean de Maurienne, Savoie	1907	68	
(Pechiney)	L'Argentière, Hautes- Alpes	1910	17	
	Auzat, Ariège	1914	19	
	Rioupéroux, Isère	1926	12	
	Sabart, Ariège	1929	18	
	Noguères, Basses- Pyrénées	1960	89	30
			243	30

TABLE III *Primary Aluminium Plants – By Countries* (continued)

IIIb. **Western Europe** (continued)

Country Operating Company	Plant Location	Year of Start	Capacity 1961 '000 tons	To be added '000 tons
Société d'Electro- Chimie, d'Electro- Métallurgie et des Aciéries Electriques d'Ugine (**Ugine**)	Venthon, Savoie Lannemezan, Hautes- Pyrénées	 1939	16 37	
	France		296	30
West Germany Aluminium-Hütte Rheinfelden GmbH	Rheinfelden, Baden	1897	45	
Vereinigte Aluminium Werke A.G. (**Vaw**)	Erftwerk, Gravenbroich Innswerk, Toeging Lippewerk, Lünen Rheinwerk, Neuss, Düsseldorf	1918 1925 1938	30 54 41	 60
	West Germany		170	60
Italy Settore Alluminio (**Seal**)	Mori, Trentino Bolzano, Trentino	1928 1937	12 49	13 11
Alluminio Sardo, S.p.A. (**Alsa**)	Carbonia, Sardinia			100
Società Alluminio Veneto per Azioni (**Sava**)	Porto Marghera Fusina	1928	26	 20
Alcan Alluminio Italiano, S.p.A.	Borgofranco, Ivrea	1921	6	

TABLE III *Primary Aluminium Plants – By Countries* (continued)

IIIb. **Western Europe** (continued)

Country Operating Company	Plant Location	Year of Start	Capacity 1961 '000 tons	To be added '000 tons
(Kaiser)	Sardinia			N.A.
(Reynolds)	Trieste			N.A.
Italy			93	144
Netherlands N.V. Billiton Maatschappij	Delfzijl			60
(Kaiser)	N.A.			60
(Pechiney)	Delfzijl			60
EEC Countries – Total			559	414
Spain Empresa Nacional del Aluminio, S.A. **(Endasa)**	Valladolid San Balandrán, Avilés	1949 1959	10 17	40
Aluminio Español, S.A. **(Alumespa)**	Sabinañigo, Huesca	1928	7	10
Aluminio de Galicia, S.A. **(Galicia)**	Lagrela, La Corogne	1961	12	42
	Spain		46	92
Yugoslavia (Government)	Lozovac, Dalmatia Kidricewo, Slovenia Razine, Sibenik Mostar, Herzegovina Niksic, Crna Gora	1937 1954 1956	4 30 4	 100 16 N.A. N.A.
	Yugoslavia		38	116
Western Europe – Total			1,029	1,361

TABLE III   *Primary Aluminium Plants – By Countries* (continued)

			Capacity	
Country Operating Company	Plant Location	Year of Start	1961 '000 tons	To be added '000 tons
Cameroun Cie Camerounaise de l'Aluminium **(Alucam)**	Edéa	1957	47	
(Pechiney-Ugine)	Kouala Falls, Sanaga River			50
Angola Aluminio Português **(Angola)**	Dondo, Cuanza River			50
Ghana Volta Aluminum Co., Ltd. **(Valco)**	Tema			200
Congo Aluminium and Electric Inter- national Ltd. **(Alelco)**	Inga Falls, Congo River			N.A.
(Kouilou Project)	Sounds Pass, Kouilou River			250
Guinea Aluminium de Guinée Société Anonyme **(Alugui)**	Souapiti Falls, Konkouré R.			150
(Pechiney-Ugine)	Amaria Falls, Konkouré R.			100

IIIc. **Africa, Asia, Australia**

TABLE III   *Primary Aluminium Plants – By Countries* (continued)

			Capacity	
Country Operating Company	Plant Location	Year of Start	1961 '000 tons	To be added '000 tons
Federation of Rhodesia and Nyasaland				
	South Rhodesia			20
Africa – Total			47	820
India Indian Aluminium Co. Ltd.	Alwaye, Alupuram, Kerala	1943	7	6
(Indalco)	Hirakud, Orissa	1959	20	7
Aluminium Corporation of India, Ltd.	Jaykaynagar, Bengal	1944	3	5
Hindustan Aluminium Corporation Ltd. **(Hindalco)**	Pipri, Rihand Dam, U.P.	1961	20	30
Madras Aluminium Co. Ltd.	Salem, Mettur, Madras			20
Bharat-Reynolds Aluminium Corporation **(Bralco)**	Dandeli, Shravathi, Mysore			30
Koyna Aluminium Co. Ltd.	Koyna, Maharashtra			20
National Industrial Development	Jamnu, Kashmir			20
Corporation **(Nidc)**	Korbe, Madhya Pradesh			25
	India		50	163

TABLE III   *Primary Aluminium Plants – By Countries* (continued)

IIIc. Africa, Asia, Australia (continued)

Country Operating Company	Plant Location	Year of Start	Capacity 1961 '000 tons	Capacity To be added '000 tons
Japan				
Showa Denko K.K.	Omachi, Nagano	1933	12	
	Kitakata, Fukushima	1943	34	
	Goi, Tokyo			59
Sumitomo Kagaku	Kikumoto, Ehime	1936	31	
Kogyo K.K.	Nagoya	1961	14	
	Saki, Osaka			59
Nippon Light Metals	Kambara, Shizuoka	1940	55	16
Co. Ltd.	Niigata, Shinano	1941	29	
(NKK)	River			
	Shimizu, Schizuoka			50
Mitsubishi Chemical	Naoyeta, Niigata			50
Industries Co. Ltd.				
Mitsubishi-Reynolds	Saitama			36
Aluminium Co.				
Yawata Aluminium	Tsurusaka, Kyushu			40
Industrial Co. Ltd.				
	Japan		175	310
Taiwan				
Taiwan Aluminium	Kaosiung, Takao	1935	14	6
Corporation				
Indonesia				
(U.S.S.R.	Sumatra			18
assistance)**	(North or Central)			
Pakistan				
N.A.	West Pakistan			N.A.

I

TABLE III   *Primary Aluminium Plants – By Countries* (continued)

IIIc. **Africa, Asia, Australia** (continued)

Country Operating Company	Plant Location	Year of Start	Capacity 1961 '000 tons	To be added '000 tons
Phillipine Republic (Reynolds)	Iligan, Mindanao			22
Kuwait (Reynolds)	Kuwait			50
Turkey (Reynolds)	Catalazzi (or Hirfanli)			N.A.
Asia – Total			239	569
Australia Comalco Aluminium (Bell Bay) Ltd.	Bell Bay, Tasmania	1955	16	36
Comalco Aluminium Ltd.	Bluff, New Zealand			96
Alcoa of Australia Pty. Ltd.	Geelong, Victoria			40
Australian Aluminium Co. Ltd. (**Australco**)	N.A.			N.A.
Australia – Total			16	172
Africa, Asia, Australia – Total			302	1,561
Western World – Total			4,359	3,922

IIId. **Soviet allied Bloc**

U.S.S.R.				
Soviet Aluminium Trust	Volkhov, Lenningrad	1932	44	
	Zaporozhye, Ukraine	1934	98	
	Kandalakcha, Karelie		25	
	Kamensk-Uralskiy	1939	118	

TABLE III   *Primary Aluminium Plants – By Countries* (continued)

IIId. **Soviet allied Bloc** (continued)

Country Operating Company	Plant Location	Year of Start	Capacity 1961 '000 tons	Capacity To be added '000 tons
	Nowokusnietzk, Kousbas	1943	118	
	Krasno-Tourinsk	1945	123	
	Yerevan, Armenia	1953	25	40
	Sumgait, Azerbaidjan	1953	69	69
	Nadvoitsky, Karelie		20	20
	Walgograd	1959	197	
	Sekhelov, Irkutsk			250
	Pavlodar, Kazakhstan			250
	Krasnoyarsk, Siberia			400
	Myski			N.A.
	U.S.S.R.		837	1,029
Czechoslovakia Ziar Aluminium Works	Svaty Kriz, Hron	1953	49	
East Germany Volkseigener Betrieb Elektrochemische Kombinat (VEB)	Bitterfield		34	16
	Lauta			20
Hungary Magyarsoviet	Felsögalla-Totis	1940	15	
Bauxit Ipar	Ajka	1943	15	
	Inota	1950	30	
Poland Skawinskie Zaklady Metalusgiczne	Skawina, Krakow	1954	45	30
Kombinat Centrozap (Polish State Body)	Moliniec, Konin			94

TABLE III *Primary Aluminium Plants – By Countries* (continued)

IIId. **Soviet allied Bloc** (continued)

Country Operating Company	Plant Location	Year of Start	Capacity 1961 '000 tons	To be added '000 tons
Roumania				
(Government plants)	Taraveni	1955	30	
	Slatina, Olt River			50
China				
(Government plants)	Fushun, Liaoning	1937	90	
	Antung, Yalu River		10	
	Kweiyang, Kweichou			54
	Hofei (Luchow), Anhwei			10
	Sian, Shensi			110
	China		100	174
North Korea[1]				
(Government plants)	Chinnamp'o		3	
	Taedasa-do (Yoshi)		21	
	Hungnam (Konan)		6	
	Wonsam		8	
	Chinnamp'o		50	
	North Korea		88	20
Soviet allied Bloc – Total			1,243	1,433
World – Total			5,602	5,355

1. 1945 figures. United States Bureau of Mines.

I*

TABLE IV *Producers of Primary Aluminium and Alumina – By Companies*

IVa. **Aluminum Company of America** (Alcoa)

Country of Operation	Name of Operating Company	Equity Owned %	by:	Aluminium Capacity		Alumina Capacity	
				1961 '000 tons	To be added '000 tons	1961 '000 tons	To be added '000 tons
U.S.A.	**Alcoa**	100	Alcoa	762	154	1,590	335
Mexico	Aluminio, S.A. de C.V.	35	Alcoa		20		
		55	Mexican interests				
		10	European				
Brazil	Cia Nacional de Aluminios	45	Alcoa		20		
		20	M.A. Hanna Co. (U.S.)				
		35	Byington Co.				
Surinam	Suriname Aluminium Co.	100	Alcoa		50		116
Australia	Alcoa of Australia Pty. Ltd.	51	Alcoa		40		220
		49	Western Aluminium N.L. (Australian)				

TABLE IV *Producers of Primary Aluminium and Alumina – By Companies* (continued)

IVb. Reynolds Metals Company (Reynolds)

Country of Operation	Name of Operating Company	Equity Owned %	Equity Owned by:	Aluminium Capacity 1961 '000 tons	To be added '000 tons	Alumina Capacity 1961 '000 tons	To be added '000 tons
U.S.A.	Reynolds	100	Reynolds	626		1,498	
Canada	Canadian British Aluminium Co. Ltd. (CBA)	60 / 40	Baco (Table IV.f) / Quebec North Shore Paper Co.	80	40		
Mexico	Reynolds Aluminio, S.A.	65 / 35	Reynolds / N.A.		20		
Argentina	(Comodora Rivadavia project)	N.A.	N.A.		23		
Brazil	(Paulo Afonso project)	N.A.	N.A.				90
Colombia	Aluminio de Colombia – Reynolds Santo Domingo S.A.	51 / 49	Reynolds / Santo Domingo		N.A.		
Peru	Aluminio Reynolds del Peru, S.A.	N.A.	N.A.		N.A.		

TABLE IV *Producers of Primary Aluminium and Alumina – By Companies* (continued)

IVb. **Reynolds Metals Company** (continued)

Country of Operation	Name of Operating Company	Equity Owned %	by:	Aluminium Capacity 1961 '000 tons	Aluminium Capacity To be added '000 tons	Alumina Capacity 1961 '000 tons	Alumina Capacity To be added '000 tons
Venezuela	Aluminio del Caroni, S.A. (Alcasa)	50	Reynolds		25		
		50	Corporacion Venezolana de Guyana (Government)[1]				
United Kingdom	British Aluminium Co. Ltd. (Baco)	100	Baco (Table IV.f)	35		105	
Norway	Det Norske Nitridaktie-selskap (DNN)	50	Baco (Table IV.f)	30	30		
		50	Aluminium Ltd.				
Greece	Aluminium de Grèce, S.A.	17	Reynolds		52		100
		50	Pechiney-Ugine (with Compadec)				
		21	Greek Minerals, S.A.				
		12	Government (Industrial Development Corp.)				
Italy	(Trieste project)		Reynolds		N.A.		
			Government (Finmeccanica)				

1. Government of the country of operation.

TABLE IV *Producers of Primary Aluminium and Alumina – By Companies* (continued)

IVb. **Reynolds Metals Company** (continued)

Country of Operation	Name of Operating Company	Equity Owned %	by:	Aluminium Capacity		Alumina Capacity	
				1961 '000 tons	To be added '000 tons	1961 '000 tons	To be added '000 tons
Turkey	(Catalazzi project)		N.A.	N.A.			
Kuwait	N.A.		Reynolds Ruler of Kuwait		50		
India	Bharat-Reynolds Aluminium Corp. (**Bralco**)		Reynolds Mysore Government Indian interests		30		60
Japan	Mitsubishi-Reynolds Aluminum Co.	$33\frac{1}{3}$ $66\frac{2}{3}$	Reynolds Mitsubishi Chemical Industries Ltd.		36		
Phillipine Republic	(Iligan project)		N.A.		22		
Ghana	**Valco** (Table IV.1)	10	Reynolds				
Guinea	**Fria** (Table IV.1)	10	Baco (Table IV.f)				

TABLE IV *Producers of Primary Aluminium and Alumina – By Companies* (continued)

IV.c. Kaiser Aluminum and Chemical Corporation (Kaiser)

Country of Operation	Name of Operating Company	Equity Owned %	by:	Aluminium Capacity 1961 '000 tons	Aluminium Capacity To be added '000 tons	Alumina Capacity 1961 '000 tons	Alumina Capacity To be added '000 tons
U.S.A.	Kaiser	100	Kaiser	544		1,143	
Argentina	Kaiser Aluminio, S.A. (formerly Fadasa)	100	Kaiser		20		
Brazil	Kaiser Mineria de Aluminio		N.A.		N.A.		
Italy	(Sardinia project)		Kaiser Government		N.A.		
Netherlands	N.A.		N.A.		60		
Spain	Aluminio Español, S.A. (Alumespa)	15 / 85	Kaiser / Pechiney (Fr.) and majority Spanish interests	7	10		
	Aluminio de Galicia, S.A. (Galicia)	15 / 15 / 70	Kaiser / Pechiney-Ugine / Spanish interests	12	42		
India	Hindustan Aluminium Corporation Ltd. (Hindalco)	27 / 37 / 36	Kaiser / G.D. Birla (Indian) / Indian public	20	30		40

TABLE IV *Producers of Primary Aluminium and Alumina – By Companies* (continued)

IV.c. Kaiser Aluminum and Chemical Corporation (continued)
(Kaiser)

Country of Operation	Name of Operating Company	Equity Owned %	by:	Aluminium Capacity 1961 '000 tons	To be added '000 tons	Alumina Capacity 1961 '000 tons	To be added '000 tons
Japan	Yawata Aluminium Industrial Co. Ltd.	35	Kaiser		40		
		65	Yawata Iron & Steel Co. Ltd. and other Japanese interests				
Australia	Comalco[1] Aluminium	33⅓	Kaiser	16	36	35	
(Tasmania)	(Bell Bay) Ltd.	33⅓	Conzinc Riotinto of Australia Ltd.				
		33⅓	Tasmanian Government				
(New Zealand)	Comalco Aluminium Ltd.	50	Kaiser		96		
		50	Conzinc				
(Cape York) Peninsula	Comalco Pty. Ltd.	50	Kaiser				360
		50	Conzinc				
Ghana	**Valco** (Table IV.1)	90	Kaiser				

1. **Comalco** (Comalco Industries Pty. Ltd.) is a holding company, owned 50 per cent by Kaiser and 50 per cent by Conzinc Riotinto of Australia Ltd. (this latter being a new company organized by Consolidated Zinc Pty. Ltd., and Rio Tinto Mining).

IVd. Other U.S.A. Companies

Country of Operation	Name of Operating Company	Equity Owned %	Equity Owned by:	Aluminium Capacity 1961 '000 tons	To be added '000 tons	Alumina Capacity 1961 '000 tons	To be added '000 tons
U.S.A.	Anaconda Aluminum Co. (**Anaconda**)	100	Anaconda	58			
U.S.A.	Cerro Corporation (**Cerro**)	100	Cerro		86		
U.S.A.	Harvey Aluminum (Inc.) (**Harvey**)	100	Harvey	72	67		100
Virgin Is. (U.S. Caribbean)	do.	100	Harvey				100
Guinea, Africa	do. (Table IV.1)		N.A.				220
U.S.A.	Ormet Corporation (**Ormet**) (Subsidiary of Olin Metals Division)	50	Olin Matheson Chemical Corp.	161		322	
		50	Revere Copper and Brass Inc.				
Guinea	**Fria** (Table IV.1)	48.5	Olin International				
U.S.A.	Howe Sound Co.	60	Howe Sound Co.		64		
		40	Pechiney Enterprises Inc., N.Y.				
U.S.A.	Consolidated Aluminum Corporation (**Conalco**)		Aiag (Table IV.j)		223		

TABLE IV *Producers of Primary Aluminium and Alumina – By Companies* (continued)

IV.e. **Aluminium Limited**

Country of Operation	Name of Operating Company	Equity Owned %	Owned by:	Aluminium Capacity 1961 '000 tons	Aluminium Capacity To be added '000 tons	Alumina Capacity 1961 '000 tons	Alumina Capacity To be added '000 tons
Canada	Aluminum Co. of Canada Ltd. (**Alcan**)	100	Aluminium Ltd.	704	80	1,140	
Jamaica	Alcan Jamaica Ltd.	100	Aluminium Ltd.			720	
Brazil	Aluminio Minas Gerais, S.A.	100	Aluminium Ltd.	11	28	24	
British Guiana	Demerara Bauxite Co. Ltd. (**Demba**)	100	Aluminium Ltd.			220	
Norway	Det Norske Nitridaktie-selskap (**DNN**)	50	Aluminium Ltd.	30	30		
		50	Baco (Table IV.f)				
	A/S Norsk Aluminium Co. (**Naco**)	50	Aluminium Ltd.	13	13	18	
		50	A/S Höyanger (Norwegian)				
Sweden	A/S Svenska Aluminium-Kompaniet (**Sako**)	21.8	Aluminium Ltd.	16	15	8	20
		78.2	A/B Svenska Metall-verken, and other Swedish interests				
Italy	Alcan Alluminio Italiano, S.p.A) ·AAI)	100	Aluminium Ltd.	6			

IV.e. Aluminium Limited (continued)

Country of Operation	Name of Operating Company	Equity Owned %	Owned by:	Aluminium Capacity 1961 '000 tons	Aluminium Capacity To be added '000 tons	Alumina Capacity 1961 '000 tons	Alumina Capacity To be added '000 tons
India	Indian Aluminium Co. Ltd. (**Indalco**)	59	Aluminium Ltd.	27	13	18	37
		41	Indian shareholders				
Japan	Nippon Light Metals Co. Ltd. (**NKK**)	50	Aluminium Ltd.	84	66	200	
		50	Japanese interests				
Australia	Australian Aluminium Co. Ltd. (**Australco**)		Aluminium Ltd.		N.A.		

IV.f. British Aluminium Co. Ltd. (Baco)

Country of Operation	Name of Operating Company	Equity Owned %	Owned by:	Aluminium Capacity 1961 '000 tons	Aluminium Capacity To be added '000 tons	Alumina Capacity 1961 '000 tons	Alumina Capacity To be added '000 tons
United Kingdom	**Baco**	49.04	Tube Investments Ltd. (U.K.)	35		105	
		4.00	Other British interests				
		46.96	Reynolds (U.S.A.)				
Canada	Canadian British Aluminium Co., Ltd. (**CBA**)	60	Baco (see above)	80	40		
		40	Quebec North Shore Paper Co.				
Norway	Det Norske Nitridaktie-selskap. (**DNN**)	50	Baco	30	30		
		50	Aluminium Ltd.				
Guinea	**Fria** (Table IV.1)	10	Baco				

TABLE IV *Producers of Primary Aluminium and Alumina – By Companies* (continued)

IV.g. **Pechiney, Cie de Produits Chimique et Electrométallurgiques (Pechiney)**

Country of Operation	Name of Operating Company	Equity Owned % by:	Aluminium Capacity		Alumina Capacity	
			1961 '000 tons	To be added '000 tons	1961 '000 tons	To be added '000 tons
France	**Pechiney**	100 Pechiney	243	30	414	98
Netherlands	(Delfzijl project)	N.A.		60		
Spain	Aluminio Español, S.A. (**Alumespa**)	85 Pechiney with majority Spanish interests 15 Kaiser	7	10		
Spain	Aluminio de Galicia, S.A. (**Galicia**)	15 Pechiney-Ugine 15 Kaiser 70 Spanish interests	12	42		
Greece	Aluminium de Grêce, S.A.	50 Pechiney-Ugine (with Compadec) 17 Reynolds 21 Greek Minerals, S.A. 12 Government (Industrial Development Corp.)		52		100
Japan	Mitsubishi Chemical Industries Co. Ltd. (**Mitsubishi**)	Mitsubishi Company concluded contracts with Pechiney and A/S Elektrokemisk of Norway for technical assistance		50		

TABLE IV *Producers of Primary Aluminium and Alumina – By Companies* (continued)

IV.g. Pechiney, Cie de Produits Chimique et Electrométallurgiques (continued) (Pechiney)

Country of Operation	Name of Operating Company	Equity Owned %	Equity Owned by:	Aluminium Capacity 1961 '000 tons	To be added '000 tons	Alumina Capacity 1961 '000 tons	To be added '000 tons
U.S.A.	Howe Sound Co.	60	Howe Sound Co.		64		
		40	Pechiney Enterprises Inc., N.Y.				
Poland	(*see* Table IV.m)						
Africa	(*see* Table IV.l)						

IV.h. Société d'Electrochimie, d'Electrométallurgie et des Aciéries Electriques d'Ugine (Ugine)

Country of Operation	Name of Operating Company	Equity Owned %	Equity Owned by:	Aluminium Capacity 1961 '000 tons	To be added '000 tons	Alumina Capacity 1961 '000 tons	To be added '000 tons
France	Ugine	100	Ugine	53			
Spain	Aluminio de Galicia, S.A. (Galicia)	15	Pechiney-Ugine (*see* Table IV.g.)	12	42	98	40
Greece	Aluminium de Grêce, S.A.	50	Pechiney-Ugine (*see* Table IV.g)		52	100	
Africa	(*see* Table IV.l)						

TABLE IV *Producers of Primary Aluminium and Alumina – By Companies* (continued)

IV.i. Vereinigte Aluminium Werke, A.G. (VAW)

Country of Operation	Name of Operating Company	Equity Owned %	by:	Aluminium Capacity 1961 '000 tons	To be added '000 tons	Alumina Capacity 1961 '000 tons	To be added '000 tons
West Germany	Vereinigte Aluminium Werke A.G. (Vaw)	100	Vaw (West German Government)	125	60	241	43
India	Koyna Aluminium Co. Ltd.		(*see* Table IV.n)				
Guinea	Fria (Table IV.l)	5	Vaw				

IV.j. Aluminium-Industrie-Aktien-Gesellschaft (Aiag)

Country of Operation	Name of Operating Company	Equity Owned %	by:	Aluminium Capacity 1961 '000 tons	To be added '000 tons	Alumina Capacity 1961 '000 tons	To be added '000 tons
Switzerland	Aiag	100	Aiag	35	25		
U.S.A.	Consolidated Aluminum Corporation (Conalco)		Aiag		223		
Austria	Salzburg Aluminium GmbH	100	Aiag	8			

TABLE IV *Producers of Primary Aluminium and Alumina – By Companies* (continued)

IV.j. **Aluminium-Industrie-Aktien-Gesellschaft** (continued)

Country of Operation	Name of Operating Company	Equity Owned %	by:	Aluminium Capacity 1961 '000 tons	To be added '000 tons	Alumina Capacity 1961 '000 tons	To be added '000 tons
Norway	Mosjöen Aluminium A/S (**Mosal**)	$33\frac{1}{3}$ $66\frac{2}{3}$	Aiag A/S Elektrokemisk (Norwegian)	32	120		
	Sør Norge Aluminium, A/S	75 25	Aiag (with Compadec) Norwegian interests		100		
France	Soc. Francaise pour l'Industrie de l'Aluminium	100	Aiag			59	
West Germany	Aluminium-Hütte Rhein-felden GmbH (**Rheinfelden**)	100	Aiag	45			
	Martinswerk GmbH	100	Aiag			153	
Netherlands	N.V. Billiton Maatachappij		Aiag Billiton		60		
Italy	Sà Alluminio Veneto per Azioni (**Sava**)	100	Aiåg	26	20	113	

TABLE IV *Producers of Primary Aluminium and Alumina – By Companies* (continued)

IV.j. Aluminium-Industrie-Aktien-Gesellschaft (continued)

Country of Operation	Name of Operating Company	Equity Owned by:	%	Aluminium Capacity		Alumina Capacity	
				1961 '000 tons	To be added '000 tons	1961 '000 tons	To be added '000 tons
Federation of Rhodesia and Nyasaland	(*see* Table IV.l)						
Guinea	Fria (Table IV.l)	Aiag	10				

IV.k. Montecatini, Soc. Generale per Industria Mineraria e Chimica (Montecatini)

Country of Operation	Name of Operating Company	Equity Owned by:	%	Aluminium Capacity		Alumina Capacity	
				1961 '000 tons	To be added '000 tons	1961 '000 tons	To be added '000 tons
Italy	Settore Alluminio (Seal)	Montecatini	100	61	24		
	Alluminio Sardo, S.p.A.	Montecatini	50		100		
		Italian Government and Sardinian Regional Authorities	50				
	Industria Nazionale Allumino	Montecatini	100			123	25
India	Madras Aluminium Co. Ltd.	Montecatini	27		20		20
		Indian Government Indian interests					

TABLE IV *Producers of Primary Aluminium and Alumina – By Companies* (continued)

IV.1. Companies Operating in Africa

Country of Operation	Name of Operating Company	Equity Owned % by:		Aluminium Capacity		Alumina Capacity	
				1961 '000 tons	To be added '000 tons	1961 '000 tons	To be added '000 tons
Angola	Alumino Português (Angola)	Reported technical and financial assistance from Pechiney			50		
Cameroun	Cie Camerounaise de l'Aluminium (Alucam)	3.0 57.6 14.4 15.0 10.0	Government Pechiney Ugine Caisse Centrale de Co-opération Economique Syndicat Belge de l'Aluminium	47			
	(Kouala Falls project)		Pechiney Ugine		50		
	(Nkonasamba project)		N.A.		N.A.		N.A.
Congo	Aluminium and Electric International Ltd. (Alelco)		(International group)		N.A.		
	(Kouilou project)		N.A.		250		

TABLE IV Producers of Primary Aluminium and Alumina – By Companies (continued)

IV.1. Companies Operating in Africa (continued)

Country of Operation	Name of Operating Company	Equity Owned %	by:	Aluminium Capacity		Alumina Capacity	
				1961 '000 tons	To be added '000 tons	1961 '000 tons	To be added '000 tons
Federation of Rhodesia and Nyasaland	Alumina Development Corp. (Pty.) Ltd.		With technical help of Aiag		20		
Ghana	Volta Aluminum Co. Ltd. (Valco)	90 10	Kaiser Reynolds		200		
Guinea	Cie Internationale pour la Production de l'Alumine (Fria)	48.5 21.2 5.3 10.0 10.0 5.0	Olin International Pechiney Ugine Aiag Baco Vaw			473	
	(Harvey)		N.A.				
	Aluminium de Guinée Société Anonyme (Alugui)		N.A.		150		220
	(Amaria Falls, Konkouré project)		Pechiney Ugine		100		

TABLE IV *Producers of Primary Aluminium and Alumina — By Companies (Continued)*

IV.m. Government-Owned and Government-Participating Companies

Country of Operation	Name of Operating Company	Equity Owned %	by:	Aluminium Capacity 1961 '000 tons	Aluminium Capacity To be added '000 tons	Alumina Capacity 1961 '000 tons	Alumina Capacity To be added '000 tons
Western World							
Dominican Republic	N.A.	N.A.	N.A.	N.A.			
Venezuela	Aluminio del Caroni, S.A. (Alcasa)	50	Government[1] (Corporacion de Venezolana Guyana)		25		
		50	Reynolds				
Austria	Vereinigte Metallwerke, A.G.	100	Government	66			
Greece	Aluminium de Grêce, S.A.	12	Government (Industrial Development Corp.)		52		100
		21	Greek Minerals, S.A.				
		50	Pechiney-Ugine (with Compadec)				
		17	Reynolds				
Norway	Ardal og Sunndal Verk, A.G. (Ardal)	100	Government (with financial aid of Alcoa)	146	154		

1. Government of the country of operation.

TABLE IV Producers of Primary Aluminium and Alumina – By Companies (continued)

IV.m. Government-Owned and Government-Participating Companies (continued)

Country of Operation	Name of Operating Company	Equity Owned %	by:	Aluminium Capacity		Alumina Capacity	
				1961 '000 tons	To be added '000 tons	1961 '000 tons	To be added '000 tons
West Germany	Vereinigte Aluminium Werke, A.G. (Vaw)	100	Government (for Vaw's participation in other companies *see* Table IV.l)	125	60	241	43
Italy	(Trieste project)		Government (Finmeccanica) Reynolds		N.A.		
	(Sardinia project)		Government Kaiser		N.A.		
	Alluminio Sardo, S.p.A.	50 / 50	Italian Government and Sardinian Regional Authorities / Montecatini		100		
Spain	Empresa Nacional del Aluminio, S.A. (Endasa)	27	Government (majority) Spanish companies		40		148

IV.m. Government-Owned and Government-Participating Companies (continued)

Country of Operation	Name of Operating Company	Equity Owned %	Equity Owned by:	Aluminium Capacity 1961 '000 tons	Aluminium Capacity To be added '000 tons	Alumina Capacity 1961 '000 tons	Alumina Capacity To be added '000 tons
Yugoslavia	(State concern)	100	Government	38	116	105	54
	N.A.		Yugoslavian interests Norwegian interests				197
Cameroun	Cie Camerounaise de l'Aluminium (Alucam)	3.0	Government	47			
		57.6	Pechiney				
		14.4	Ugine				
		15.0	Caisse Central de Co-opération Economique				
		10.0	Syndicat Belge de l'Aluminium				
India	Madras Aluminium Co. Ltd.	72	Government and Indian interests		20		20
		28	Montecatini				
	Bharat-Reynolds Aluminium Corp. (Bralco)		Government Indian interests Reynolds		30		60
	National Industrial Development Corp. (Nidc)	100	Government		45		50
Taiwan	Taiwan Aluminium Corp.	100	Government	14	6	29	13

TABLE IV *Producers of Primary Aluminium and Alumina – By Companies* (continued)

IV.m. **Government-Owned and Government-Participating Companies** (continued)

Country of Operation	Name of Operating Company	Equity Owned %	by:	Aluminium Capacity		Alumina Capacity	
				1961 '000 tons	To be added '000 tons	1961 '000 tons	To be added '000 tons
Australia	Comalco Aluminium (Bell Bay) Ltd.	33⅓ 66⅔	Government (Tasmania) Comalco (Table IV.c)	16	36	35	
Soviet allied Bloc							
U.S.S.R.	Soviet Aluminium Trust	100	Government	837	1,029	1,897	1,500
Czechoslovakia	Ziar Aluminium Works	100	Government	49		98	
East Germany	Volkseigener Betrieb Elektrochemisches Kombinat (Veb)	100	Government	34	36	55	
Hungary	(State concerns)	100	Government	60		207	
Poland	Skawina Aluminium Works	100	Government	45	30		
	Kombinat Centrozap (Polish State Body)		Pechiney signed contract with Centrozap to assist in building		94		200
Roumania	(State concerns)	100	Government	30	50		120
China	(State concerns)	100	Government	100	174	190	40
North Korea	(State concerns)	100	Government	88	20	72	100

TABLE IV *Producers of Primary Aluminium and Alumina – By Companies* (continued)

IV.n. Other Companies (not elsewhere listed)

Country of Operation	Name of Operating Company	Equity Owned %	by:	Aluminium Capacity 1961 '000 tons	Aluminium Capacity To be added '000 tons	Alumina Capacity 1961 '000 tons	Alumina Capacity To be added '000 tons
Argentina	Industrias Siderurgicas Grassi, S.A.	100	Argentinian interests		10		N.A.
Brazil	Cia Brasileira de Aluminio, S.A.	80	Brazilian interests: Industrias Votorantim, S.A.	10	10	30	
		20	Other Brazilian interests				
	N.A.		Polish interests		50		
	(Cachoeira da Fumaca project)		N.A.		10		
Norway	Norsk Hydro-Elektrisk	100	Norwegian interests		100		
	A/S Elektrokemisk	100	Norwegian interests (for A/S Elektrokemisk's participation in other companies *see* Table IV.g and Table IV.j)		100		

K

TABLE IV *Producers of Primary Aluminium and Alumina – By Companies* (continued)

IV.n. **Other Companies** (not elsewhere listed) (continued)

Country of Operation	Name of Operating Company	Equity Owned %	by:	Aluminium Capacity 1961 '000 tons	Aluminium Capacity To be added '000 tons	Alumina Capacity 1961 '000 tons	Alumina Capacity To be added '000 tons
	A/B Svenska Metallverken	100	Swedish interests (for A/B Svenska Metallverken's participation in Sweden's A/B Svenska Aluminium-Kompaniet *see* Table IV.e)		30		
Switzerland	Usine d'Aluminium de Martigny, S.A. (**Martigny**)	100	Swiss interests	5			
West Germany	Gebrüder Guilini GmbH (**Guilini**)	100	West German interests			98	
Spain	Alquimia, S.A.	100	Spanish interests				
India	Aluminium Corporation of India Ltd.	100	Indian interests (with technical help of Aiag)	3	5	5	20
	Bombay Mineral Supplies Co. Ltd.	N.A.	N.A.				N.A.

TABLE IV *Producers of Primary Aluminium and Alumina – By Companies* (continued)

IV.n. **Other Companies** (not elsewhere listed) (continued)

Country of Operation	Name of Operating Company	Equity Owned %	by:	Aluminium Capacity 1961 '000 tons	Aluminium Capacity To be added '000 tons	Alumina Capacity 1961 '000 tons	Alumina Capacity To be added '000 tons
	Koyna Aluminium Co. Ltd.		Tendulkar Industries (Private) Ltd. Vaw (or Hungarian) interests		20		40
Japan	Showa Denko, K.K.	100	Japanese interests	46	59	102	
	Sumitomo Kagaku, K.K.	100	Japanese interests	45	59	118	
Indonesia	N.A.		U.S.S.R. assistance		18		70

Appendix C.   Notes on Tables V.9 and V.10

a. TABLE V.9 COLUMN (1) – *Value per Ton Bauxite*

Assumptions made in deriving, from total value per ton Bauxite, the proportions contributed by the several items of cost.

Wages and Salaries: In Table V.4 (Items 1 and 2) the average proportion for years 1957–1958 for Mining, Transport, Drying, Loading is 18.155% of total value; of this 8.062 is allocated to wages and salaries, in the same ratio as in footnote to Table V.4 (i.e., 12.3 as % 27.7 = 44.404%; 44.404% 18.155 = 8.062% total value).

Maintenance: Maintenance allocated out of Items 1 and 2 of Table V.4 (*see* Wages and Salaries above). In the same ratio as in footnote to Table V.4 (i.e., 8.2 as % 27.7 = 29.603%; 29.603% 18.155 = 5.374% total value).

Fuel: Not found possible to separate fuel costs.

Depreciation:

Normal ⎫
Accelerated ⎬ Average proportions for years 1957–1958
(bauxite only) ⎭ (Table V.4, Item 9).

Administration and Research: Average proportion for years 1957–1958 (Table V.4, Item 8).

Cost of Material: Not found possible to separate cost of material.

Transport: Transport allocated out of Items 1 and 2 of Table V.4 (*see* Wages and Salaries above). In same ratio as in footnote to Table V.4 (i.e., 7.2 as % 27.7 = 25.993%; 25.993% 18.155 = 4.719% total value).

Net Cost of Agriculture: Average proportion for years 1957–1958 (Table V.4, Item 3).

Insurance: Average proportion for years 1957–1958 (Table V.4, Item 4).

a. TABLE V.9 COLUMN (1) – *Value per Ton Bauxite* (continued)

Interest: Average proportion for years 1957–1958 (Table V.4, Item 5).

Government Fees: Average proportion for years 1957–1958 (Table V.4, Item 6).

Exploration: Average proportion for years 1957–1958 (Table V.4, Item 7).

Income Tax: 40% 'calculated' profits. 'Calculated' profits derived by averaging the cost items in years 1957–1958 and deducting this average cost from the total nominal cost of Bauxite (Table V.4, Item 14).

Net Profit: Residual.

b. NOTES ON TABLE V.9 COLUMN (3) – *Disbursements in Jamaica*

Assumptions made in deriving, from corresponding items in value per ton Bauxite (Column (1)), the proportions of Disbursement in Jamaica.

Wages and Salaries: In alumina, wages are 59.084% Wages and Salaries (*see* Notes on Table V.10, Column (1)). Assumed proportion of wages in bauxite higher than in alumina, and ratio of 75% instead of 59.084% used (i.e., 75% of 8.062). Assumed all wages and 75% salaries disbursed in Jamaica.

Maintenance: Assumed 56.132% Maintenance is Labour, and disbursed locally.

Material   Remainder of 43.868% Maintenance is Material, and 33% Material assumed disbursed locally.

Fuel: Not found possible to separate fuel costs.

b. Table V.9 Column (3) – *Disbursements in Jamaica* (continued)

Depreciation:	Depreciation assumed on basis that in Bauxite 60% of total assets in Buildings and 40% in Machinery.
Normal	Buildings at 3% depreciation contribute to local disbursements 27.272% Normal Depreciation. Assumed all depreciation on buildings disbursed locally, and on machinery abroad.
Accelerated (bauxite only)	Estimated proportion contributed to depreciation by buildings (12.5%) disbursed locally.
Administration and Research:	Assumed same proportion as for alumina as in Table V.10 (i.e., 4.944 as % 5.816 = 85.007%; 85.007% 9.180 = 7.804% total value), disbursed locally.
Cost of Material: Transport:	Not found possible to separate cost of material. All disbursed locally.
Net Cost of Agriculture:	All disbursed locally.
Insurance:	None disbursed locally.
Interest:	None disbursed locally.
Government Fees:	All disbursed locally.
Exploration:	75% disbursed locally.
Income Tax:	All disbursed locally.
Net Profit:	None disbursed locally.

c. Notes on Table V.10 Column (1) – *Value per Ton Alumina*

Assumptions made in deriving, from total value per ton Alumina, the proportions contributed by the several items of cost.

Wages and Salaries: The proportion used approximates the Krutilla proportion of 5.06 as % 50.56 = 10.008% total value. (*See* Krutilla, John V. *Locational Factors Influencing Recent Aluminum Expansion.*)

c. TABLE V.10 COLUMN (1) – *Value per Ton Alumina* (continued)

Bauxite Wages and Salaries	Derived from Table V.9, Column (2) (Bauxite enterprise).
Alumina Wages	Derived from Table V.5, Item 1, 1956–58. (This is equivalent to 59.084% Alumina wages and salaries).
Alumina Salaries	Residual item on Wages and Salaries. (This is equivalent to 40.916% Alumina wages and salaries).
Maintenance:	A higher proportion than that given in Table V.5, 1956–58, justified on the grounds of higher maintenance costs in the Caribbean. It is assumed that the maintenance cost (Item 3, Table V.5) is as low as it is because some of it is absorbed in the high proportion of alumina cost allocated to Bauxite (Item 4, Table V.5).
Fuel:	Derived from Table V.5, Item 5, 1956–58.
Depreciation: Normal	Estimates include 2.057% on bauxite (derived from Table V.9, Column (2)), and Stern's figure of 14.250% on alumina only.
Accelerated (bauxite only)	Derived from Table V.9, Column (2) (Bauxite enterprise).
Administration and Research:	In alumina, cost of office supplies estimated at 10% Alumina wages and salaries; travelling at 10% Alumina salaries; and rent at 25% Alumina salaries. These together are £0.582 per ton alumina. In the bauxite activity of the Alumina enterprise the amount allocated to administration is £0.595 (derived from Table V.9). £0.582 + £0.595 = £1.177 = 4.454% total value. Add to this 1.360%, being a redistribution from the high notional cost of bauxite. Total 5.816% total value.

c. TABLE V.10 COLUMN (1) – *Value per Ton Alumina* (continued)

Cost of Material: Operating supplies, soda ash, lime and starch are 109.479% Fuel (Krutilla's figures). This proportion of Fuel in Table V.10, is 109.479% 9.420 = 10.313% total value. Add to this 3% for estimated higher cost in Jamaica. Total 13.313% total value.

Transport: Alumina at 4/– per ton, i.e., £0.2, and bauxite at £0.306 (derived from Table V.9). Total £0.506 or 1.915% total value. Add to this 2% as part of the redistribution from the high notional cost of bauxite. Total 3.915% total value.

Net Cost of Agriculture: Derived from Table V.9. (Bauxite enterprise).

Insurance: Based on proportion for Plant Insurance only, as in Krutilla, i.e., 1.366% total value. Add to this 0.5%. Total 1.866%.

Interest: Adjusted on basis of Stern's figure of 8.47% for alumina only, and 0.844% for bauxite (derived from Table V.9). Total 9.314%.

Government Fees: Derived from Table V.9. (Bauxite enterprise).

Exploration: Derived from Table V.9. (Bauxite enterprise).

Miscellaneous: Residual, after cost items available have been deducted from total net cost.

Income Tax: 40% 'calculated' profits. (*See* Notes on Table V.9, Column (1)).

Net Profit: Residual, after net cost and Income Tax have been deducted from total nominal cost.

d. TABLE V.10 COLUMN (4) – *Disbursements in Jamaica*

Assumptions made in deriving, from corresponding items in value per ton Alumina (Column (1)), the proportions of Disbursements in Jamaica.

Wages and Salaries:

Bauxite Wages and Salaries	Same proportion as for bauxite as in Table V.9 (i.e., 7.558 as % 8.062 = 93.748%; 93.748% 1.978 = 1.855% total value), disbursed locally.
Alumina Wages	All wages disbursed locally.
Alumina Salaries	75% salaries disbursed locally.

Maintenance:

Labour	All wages for labour in maintenance disbursed locally.
Material	Approximately 33% (for wood, etc.) disbursed locally.
Fuel:	None disbursed locally.

Depreciation:

Normal	Estimated proportions contributed to depreciation by buildings (13%) disbursed locally.
Accelerated (bauxite only)	Estimated proportions contributed to depreciation by buildings (12.5%) disbursed locally.

Administration:

Office Supplies	75% disbursed locally.
Travelling	80% disbursed locally.
Rent, etc.	All disbursed locally.
Cost of Material:	20% disbursed locally.
Transport:	All disbursed locally.
Net Cost of Agriculture:	All disbursed locally.

a. TABLE V.10 COLUMN (4) – *Disbursements in Jamaica* (continued)

Insurance: None disbursed locally.

Interest: None disbursed locally.

Government Fees: All disbursed locally.

Exploration: 75% disbursed locally.

Miscellaneous: 50% disbursed locally.

Income Tax: All disbursed locally.

Net Profit: None disbursed locally.

Bibliography

AARONSON, Robert L. *'Labour Commitment among Jamaican Bauxite Workers.'* Social and Economic Studies, Vol. 10, No. 2, June, 1961. Institute of Social and Economic Research, U.W.I. Mona, Jamaica.

Allen & Unwin Ltd. *International Organisations.* Ruskin House, London, 1961.

Alcoa. *Annual Report,* 1957. Aluminum Company of America, Pittsburg, United States.

Aluminium Limited. *Annual Report,* 1956; 1961. Montreal, Canada.

BAUDART, G. A. *'L'Aluminium dans le Marché Commun.'* Revue de l'Aluminium, 1961. Paris.

— *'Les Développements de l'Industrie norvegienne de l'Aluminium.'* Revue de l'Aluminium, 1962. Paris.

*— *'L'Industrie Française de l'Aluminium, dans le cadre de la Communauté Economique Européene.'* Revue de l'Aluminium. No. 270. Paris.

*— *'Etude Systématique des Approvisionnements en Alumine dans le Monde en 1960.'* Revue de l'Aluminium, No. 284, 1961. Paris.

BENHAM, F., *et al.* *Report of the Economic Policy Committee.* January, 1945. Government Printer, Jamaica.

BENOIT, Emile. *Europe at Sixes and Sevens.* Columbia U.P., New York, 1961.

BLUE, D. D. *'Raw Materials for Aluminum Production.'* Information Circular 7675, March, 1954. Bureau of Mines, Washington, U.S.A.

*BRACEWELL, Smith. *Bauxite, Alumina and Aluminium.* Overseas Geological Surveys. H.M.S.O., London, 1962.

BROWN, Charles B., SAWKINS, James, G., *et al.* *Report on the Geology of Jamaica.* Longmans Green & Co., London, 1869.

*Bureau of Mines (U.S.). *Material Survey – Bauxite.* Washington 25, D.C., 1953.

— *Mineral Industry Surveys.*

— *Mineral Market Reports.* MMS No. 2683, 1957.

*— *Minerals Yearbook: Metals and Minerals (Except Fuels).* Annual, 1959, 1960, 1961.

CAMPBELL, Ella. '*Industrial Training . . . Methods and Techniques.*' Social and Economic Studies, Vol. 2, No. 1, 1953. Institute of Social and Economic Research, U.W.I., Mona, Jamaica.

Central Planning Unit, Jamaica. *Economic Survey.* Annual, 1960–62. Government Printer, Jamaica.

*Chemical Week. September 15, 1962. '*Aluminum.*' Mc Graw-Hill Publishing Co. Inc., New York.

Colonial Office (U.K.). *Memorandum on Colonial Mining Policy,* Col. No. 206, 1946. H.M.S.O., London.

Daily Gleaner, The. January 7, 1963. Kingston, Jamaica.

*Department of Commerce (U.S.). *Material Survey – Aluminum.* Washington 25, D.C. November, 1956.

Department of Statistics, Jamaica. *National Accounts* (Annual).

— *Trade Reports* (Annual).

— *Surveys of Business Establishments* 1954, 1956, 1960.

*DUMAS, André. '*L'Aluminium et le Progrès Technique.*' Revue de l'Aluminium, No. 282. Paris.

Economist, The. August 4, 1962. London.

Economist Intelligence Unit, The. Notes. (Unpublished).

ENGLE, Nathaniel H., GREGORY, Homer E., and MOSSE, Robert. *Aluminum, An Industrial Marketing Appraisal.* Irwin, Chicago, 1945.

Equity 85–73. Defendants' Exhibit No. 158, p. 24498, U.S. vs. Alcoa *et al.,* District Court of the U.S., Southern District, New York. Consent Order entered on April 23, 1954; reported in 1954 Trade Cases (Commercial Clearing House), Par. 67745.

FRANCIS, O. C. and CLARKE, E. St. A. *Balance of Payments Statistics,* 1962. Department of Statistics, Kingston, Jamaica.

*GINSBERG, Professor Hans. *Die Metallischen Rohstoffe, Aluminium.* Ferdinand Enke Verlag, Stuttgart, Germany, 1962.

Giulini, Ludwigshafen, Germany. *Our Alumina Products.*

HAMER, R. D. (President of Alcan, Zurich S.A.). '*The Future Development of the use of Aluminium in the European Market.*' Fourth International Light Metals Congress, Leoben, Austria, 1961.

Harvey Aluminum (Inc.). *Annual Reports.*

HENIN, L. '*L'Industrie de l'Aluminium en Afrique Nord.*' Academie Royale des Sciences Coloniales, Brussels.

Hearings. Study of Monopoly Power, Aluminium (Serial No. 1, Part 1). Committee on the Judiciary, House of Representatives, 82nd Congress, 1st Session, 1951. (U.S. Government Publication).

HICKS, J. R. and U.K. *Report on Finance and Taxation in Jamaica.* Government Printer, Jamaica, 1955.

HIGBIE, Kenneth B., *et al. Bauxite* 1961, and *Aluminum* 1961. Preprints from Minerals Yearbook, 1961. Bureau of Mines, Washington 25, D.C., U.S.

JOHNSON, A. F. '*Cost Factors in the Utilization of Foreign Bauxite to make Aluminum.*' Mining Engineering, Vol. 6, pp. 598–603, 1954, New York.

Journal du Four Electrique et des Industries Electrochimiques, No. 3, p. 73, 1962, Paris.

Kaiser Aluminum & Chemical Corporation. *Prospectus*, June 26, 1957. Oakland, California, U.S.
Annual Reports.

KITZINGER, U. W. *The Challenge of the Common Market.* Blackwell, Oxford, 1961.

KREINEN, M. E. '*The "Outer Seven" and European Integration.*' American Economic Review. June, 1960, pp. 370–85.

KRUTILLA, John V. '*Aluminum, A Dilemma for Antitrust Aims?*' Reprint from the Southern Economic Journal, Vol. XXII No. 2, October, 1955.

— '*Locational Factors influencing recent Aluminum Expansion.*' Reprint from the Southern Economic Journal, Vol. XXI, No. 3, January, 1955.

KURTZ, H. F. and BLUE, D. D. '*Aluminum and Bauxite.*' Reprint from Mineral Facts and Problems, Bulletin 556, 1955. Bureau of Mines, Washington 25, D.C., U.S.

Legislation:
Jamaica: Regulation No. 21 of November, 1942.
— Minerals Vesting Law, Cap. 38 of 1947.
— Mining Law, Cap. 41 of 1947.
— Bauxite and Alumina Industries Encouragement Law, Cap. 53, 1950.
U.K. The Custom Duties (Dumping and Subsidies) Act, 1957.
U.S. Internal Revenue Code of 1954, Sections 613 (b) (2), 613 (b) (6), 613 (a).
— Public Law 725, 1956.

Light Metals, London. January, December, 1957; January, May, September, 1961; April, May, December, 1962.

MAHOTIERE de la, Stuart. *The Common Market.* Hodder & Stoughton, London, 1962.

MANKTELOW, R., WHITE, H. McD. and MILLS, G. E. *Manktelow Commission Report* 1961–62, *The West Indies Staffing Problems*. Federal House, Trinidad, 1962.

MASON, Edward S. *Controlling World Trade*. Mc Graw-Hill, New York, 1943.

McCURDA, D. B. *The Changing Logistics of the North American Aluminum Industry*. New York.

MEADE, James E. *U.K., Commonwealth and Common Market*. Institute of Economic Affairs, London, 1962.

— *The Theory of Customs Unions*. Amsterdam, 1955.

Metal Bulletin, London. November 12, 1957; June 27, July 25, 1958; July 20, August 10, 1962.

*Metallstatistik. Issues 46–49. Metallgesellschaft A.G., Frankfurt/Main, Germany.

*Metal Statistics, 1962. *American Metal Market*. New York.

MEYER, F. V. *The Seven*. London, 1960.

OECD, Electricity Committee. *The Electricity Supply Industry in Europe*. 12th Enquiry: Achievements 1959–1960, Forecasts 1961–1966. H.M.S.O., London.

*Overseas Geological Surveys. *Statistical Survey of the Mineral Industry*, 1955–1960. H.M.S.O., London, 1962.

Preparatory Commission. *Report on the Volta River Project*. H.M.S.O., London, 1956.

REYNOLDS, R. S., Jr. '*The Aluminum Industry in North and South America.*' Fourth International Light Metals Congress, Leoben, Austria, 1961.

Reynolds Metals Company, Economic Research Department. *Reynolds Jamaica Mines Ltd., its Origin and Development*, 1943–1953. Richmond, Virginia, U.S. *Annual Reports*.

*SALMUTH Von, Curt Freiherr. *Handbuch der Aluminium-Wirtschaft*. Agenor-Verlag, Frankfurt/Main, Germany, 1963.

STERN, Peter M. *The Bauxite Industry in Jamaica*. May, 1956. (Cyclostyled).

Times, The, London. June 12, 1962.

Tube Investments Limited. *Annual General Meeting*, 1957. U.K.

UNDERWOOD, A. J. V. *Report to Secretary of State for the Colonies*. Colonial Office, London.

*VÄTH, A. '*Stand und Entwicklungstendenzen der Aluminium-industrie.*' Metallwirtschaft und Metallmarkt, March 1962, Bonn, Germany.

VINER, Jacob. *The Customs Union Issue.* Carnegie Endowment for International Peace, London, 1950.

VITRY de, Raoul (President of Pechiney). '*Present and Future of the Aluminium Industry in Europe.*' Fourth International Light Metals Congress, Leoben, Austria, 1961.

WALLACE, Donald H. *Market Control in the Aluminum Industry.* Howard University Press, Cambridge, 1937.

White Paper (U.K. Government). Cmd 8702. *The Volta River Aluminium Scheme, Summary of Proposals.* H.M.S.O., London, 1952.

ZANS, V. A. '*Bauxite Resources of Jamaica and their Development.*' Reprint from Colonial Geology and Mineral Resources. Vol. 3, No. 4, 1953. H.M.S.O., London.

---

* Sources marked * are used chiefly in the preparation of Appendix B.

Glossary

AIAG: Aluminium Industrie Aktiengesellschaft (Swiss Aluminium interests).

ALCAN: Aluminum Company of Canada Limited.

ALCOA: Aluminum Company of America.

ALUCAM: Compagnie Camerounaise de l'Aluminium (an international consortium).

ALUMINA: Aluminium oxide (Al_2O_3). For the aluminium industry alumina is obtained primarily from bauxite, and in its refined form it is a white powder. The name alumina (and aluminium) is derived from the Latin word 'alumen' used for substances like alum; the word 'alumine' was suggested by the French chemist de Morveau.

ALUMINIUM: An elemental metal. It is obtained from alumina by a process of reduction or smelting known as electrolysis, and is produced chiefly in the form of ingots, bars, and pigs, with a purity of 99.9 per cent.

AOT: Associate Overseas Territories (preferential status in the EEC).

ARDAL: Ardal og Sunndal Verk Aktieselskap (a Norwegian company).

ANACONDA: Anaconda Aluminum Company, a subsidiary of Anaconda Co. (an American company).

BAUXITE: An amorphous earthy material containing aluminium. It is found mainly in tropical and sub-tropical countries. In colour it varies from white to pink, reddish, yellow, and reddish-brown, depending on its iron content. The word is derived from 'Les Baux' the name of a village in France where the material was first recognized.

BENELUX: Benelux Economical Union, established in 1958 for close economic relations between member countries, Belgium, Luxemburg and the Netherlands, for as much free and internal circulation of goods and capital as possible.

BOOTH: James Booth Aluminium Ltd., Birmingham, England. (Kaiser 50 per cent, Delta Metals Co. Ltd. 50 per cent).

COMMONWEALTH CARIBBEAN: Territories in or bordering on the Caribbean within the British Commonwealth. In the text it refers specifically to the bauxite and alumina producing territories of Jamaica and British Guiana.

CONVERTED: Used in connection with the term 'bauxite' to mean 'changed by processing' of bauxite into alumina.

C.D. & W.: Colonial Development and Welfare (a British organization for financial assistance to British colonial territories).

COBEAL: Compagnie Belge de l'Industrie de l'Aluminium.

COMPADEC: Compagnie pour l'Etude et le Développement des Echanges Commerciaux. This is a French banking group.

CORUNDUM: Contains 52.9 per cent aluminium and 47.1 per cent oxygen, and has the highest known aluminium content of any mineral. It is the second hardest mineral, after diamonds. It can also be obtained from bauxite under high temperature (at about 1000° C) or at a lower temperature (400° C to 500° C) together with high vapour pressure conditions.

CRYOLITE: A mineral (3Na F . AlF$_3$), a double fluoride of sodium and aluminium containing 60 per cent sodium fluoride and 40 per cent aluminium fluoride by weight. It is used in the electrolytic bath in the electrolysis of alumina, i.e. in separating alumina into its components oxygen and aluminium. In its natural state it is mined only in Greenland, but is also produced synthetically for the aluminium industry.

DNN: Det Norske Nitridaktieselskap (a Norwegian company).

EEC: European Economic Community (France, West Germany, Italy, Belgium, Luxemburg and the Netherlands). The Six. Its transitional period started in January 1958.

EFTA: European Free Trade Association (The U.K., Austria, Denmark, Portugal, Norway, Sweden and Switzerland). The Seven. It was organized in November 1959, and came into force a year after. Its aims were directed towards the removal of trade barriers and the promotion of closer economic co-operation between members of the OEEC.

ENELCAM: Energie Electrique de Cameroun, a government-owned power plant with which Alucam has a long-term contract.

GATT: General Agreement on Tariffs and Trade. An international agreement drafted in 1947 (with substantial revisions in 1958), directed towards the reduction of tariffs and other barriers to trade, and towards the elimination of discriminatory treatment in international commerce. It was accepted fully by thirty-seven countries, with a further six taking part in the work. The Secretariat is in Geneva.

HAGUE CONVENTION: Organized for the pacific settlement of international disputes. It was signed on October 18, 1907 by forty-four nations, and came into force on February 28, 1910.

HARVEY: Harvey Aluminum (Inc.) (an American company).

I.C.I.: Imperial Chemical Industries.

KAISER: Kaiser Aluminum and Chemical Corporation (an American company).

KWh: Kilowatt hour.

LAFTA: Latin-American Free Trade Association. It was set up in 1960, with the signing of the Montevideo Treaty. It aims at an eventual South American common market. Its member countries are Argentina, Colombia, Brazil, Chili, Ecuador, Mexico, Paraguay, Peru, Uraguay.

MOSAL: Mosjöen Aluminium Aktieselskap (a Norwegian company).

NACO: Norsk Aluminium Company (a Norwegian company).

OECD: Organization for Economic Co-operation and Development. It was set up in September 1961. It took the place of the OEEC, with full membership status given to the United States and Canada, and with the additional task of Development Aid to third countries. Yugoslavia, Finland and Japan have 'special status' relationship.

OEEC: Organization for European Economic Co-operation. It was established in January 1948 by the Conference of European Economic Recovery (CEER) which met in July to September 1947. The OEEC worked together with the American Administrative Agency, the ECA (Economic Co-operation Administration), to promote co-operation of the Western European countries which received aid from the United States under the Marshall Aid programme. The United States and Canada had only Associate membership status, and Yugoslavia had 'special status' relationship.

ORMET: Ormet Corporation (an American company, and subsidiary of Olin Metals Division).

OLIN: Olin Mathieson Chemical Corporation (American interests). The Olin International and the Olin Metals are two of its divisions.

PVC: Polyvinyl chloride, used extensively in plastics.

PECHINEY: Pechiney, Compagnie de Produits Chimiques et Electro-métallurgiques (a French company).

REYNOLDS: Reynolds Metals Company (an American company).

THE SEVEN: *See* EFTA.

THE SIX: *See* EEC.

UGINE: Société d'Electro-Chimie d'Electro-Métallurgie et des Aciéries Electriques d'Ugine (a French company).

VAW: Vereinigte Aluminium Werke Aktiengesellschaft (a West German Government-owned company).

£: Symbol for Pound Sterling, the British monetary unit. The pound is subdivided into 20 shillings (20/–).

$: Symbol for United States Dollar.

sfr: Symbol for Swiss Franc, the Swiss monetary unit (metric). *See* Table IV.4 of Text.

1 long ton = 2,240 lb. (British measure)
        =   1.12 short tons (American measure)
        =   1.016047 metric tons (chiefly European)

Special conversion units used in the Text:
2.8 tons bauxite (Jamaica) produced 1 ton alumina, in 1954–55
2.47 tons bauxite (Jamaica) produced 1 ton alumina, in 1956–61
1.91 tons alumina (Jamaica) produced 1 ton aluminium.

Index

General

Names of Places

Names of Companies